DIRECTIONS IN HOUSING POLICY
Towards Sustainable Housing Policies for the UK

DIRECTIONS IN HOUSING POLICY

Towards Sustainable Housing Policies for the UK

edited by
Peter Williams

P·C·P

Paul Chapman
Publishing Ltd

Paul Chapman Publishing Ltd
144 Liverpool Road
London
N1 1LA

British Library Cataloguing-in-Publication Data

Directions in housing policy: towards sustainable housing
    policies for the UK
    1. Housing policy – Great Britain
    I. Williams, Peter
363.5'0941

ISBN 1 85396 303 8

Typeset by Dorwyn Ltd, Rowlands Castle, Hants
Printed and bound in Great Britain

B C D E F G H   9 8

CONTENTS

NOTES ON CONTRIBUTORS

Richard Best
Director of the Joseph Rowntree Foundation since 1988 and Director of the Joseph Rowntree Housing Trust. Between 1973 and 1988 he was Director, National Federation of Housing Associations. In 1989 he was appointed a Commissioner of the Rural Development Commission and is Chairman of the UK National Council for the United Nations Conference on Human Settlements (The City Summit) 1996. He was Secretary to the Duke of Edinburgh's Inquiry into British Housing 1984–91, Member of the Social Policy Committee, Church of England Board for Social Responsibility 1986–91, Member of the Executive Committee, Association of Charitable Foundations 1989–92 and is Vice-President – ACRE (Action with Communities in Rural England). In 1993 he was a special adviser to the House of Commons Environment Committee.

Mark Boléat
Director General, Association of British Insurers. Before taking on this position in 1993, he was Director General – The Building Societies Association and the Council of Mortgage Lenders. He served on the Housing Corporation Board from 1988 to 1993. His publications include *The Building Society Industry* (George Allen and Unwin 1982 and 1986), *National Housing Finance Systems, A Comparative Study* (Croom Helm 1985), *Housing in Britain* (Council of Mortgage Lenders 1993), and *Trade Association Strategy and Management* (Association of British Insurers 1996). He has undertaken consultancy work on housing for the OECD, the United Nations, the World Bank, The Canada Housing and Mortgage Corporation and the Government of Jersey.

Ray Forrest
Professor of Urban Studies in the School for Policy Studies, University of Bristol. His research and teaching interests include housing policy, the sociology of housing, the interaction of housing and labour markets and the political economy of urban change. Publications include *Home Ownership: Differentiation and Fragmentation* (with A Murie and P. Williams) *Selling the Welfare State: The Privatisation of Public Housing* (with A Murie) and *Housing and Family Wealth* (with A Murie). He is currently undertaking research on the future of home ownership and social change on council estates.

Barry Goodchild

Reader in Housing and Urban Planning at Sheffield Hallam University (previously Sheffield City Polytechnic). His main interests in housing are housing design, housing development and related aspects of urban renewal and urban planning. He has undertaken research in these fields for *Le Plan, Construction et Architecture* in France, for the Department of Environment, the Housing Corporation and the Joseph Rowntree Foundation. He has also written articles in the main scientific journals, including *Les Annales de la Recherche Urbaine* (France), *The Town Planning Review and Housing Studies*.

Alan Holmans

Halifax Senior Research Fellow in the Property Research Unit, Department of Land Economy, Cambridge University. Before retirement in 1994, Chief Housing Economist, Department of the Environment. Recent publications include: *British Housing Policy: a History* (Croom Helm 1987); *House Property and Inheritance in the UK* (with M Frosztega, HMSO 1994); *Estimating the First Time Buyer Population* (Council of Mortgage Lenders 1995); *Housing demand and need in England to 2011* (Joseph Rowntree Foundation 1995). Current research interests include: housing demand, including demographic aspects; the housing market and house prices; housing need; tenure patterns and housing markets in other countries compared with Britain.

Valerie Karn

Professor of Housing Studies in the School of Social Policy at the University of Manchester since April 1994. Before that, she was Professor of Environmental Health and Housing at the University of Salford and Senior Lecturer in Urban Studies at the University of Birmingham. Valerie is currently doing research on a number of housing issues, including: the role of ethnic minority housing associations, tenants' complaints, renewal of older housing and the control and promotion of quality of new housing. She is also active in British and international housing organisations, such as the Peabody Trust, the Chartered Institute of Housing, the Housing Association Tenants' Ombudsman Service and the Coordinating Committee of the European Network for Housing Research. Her recent publications include *New Homes in the 1990s* (with L Sheridan); *Comparing Housing Systems* (with H Wolman) (OUP); and *Tenants' Complaints and the Reform of Housing Management* (with O Hughes and R Lickiss) (Dartmouth).

Peter Kemp

Professor of Housing and Urban Studies in the Centre for Housing Research and Urban Studies at the University of Glasgow and from 1 August 1996, Director of the Centre. He was previously Joseph Rowntree Professor of Housing Policy and Director of the Centre for Housing Policy at the University of York. His main research interests are on the relationship between housing and social security and on private rental housing. He has also done research on homelessness, housing management and the history of housing. His publications on the privately rented sector include *The Private Provision of Rented Housing* (1988), *Tax Incentives and the Revival of Private Renting* (1991), *Private Landlords in Scotland* (1994), *The Lower End of the Private Rented Sector: A Glasgow Case Study* (1994), and *The Supply of Privately Rented Homes* (1995).

Philip Leather
Professor of Housing at South Bank University in London. He was previously a Senior Research Fellow at the School for Advanced Urban Studies, Bristol University. His research interests span issues relating to housing conditions and policies towards the renewal of the older housing stock, the housing implications of the ageing of the population, housing policies and community care, and the future of home ownership. In relation to housing renewal he is co-author of *Maintaining home ownership: the agency approach* (Longman IOH 1992), and *The Future of housing renewal* (The Policy Press 1994). He is currently working on *An introduction to housing renewal* (to be published by UCL Press), and is co-editor of *Housing Renewal Policies in Europe* (to be published by The Policy Press).

Sheila Mackintosh
Visiting Research Fellow at South Bank University in London. She was previously a Research Fellow at the late lamented School for Advanced Urban Studies at Bristol University. Her research interests cover housing renewal policy, housing and older people, housing for people with disabilities, and home improvement agencies. With Philip Leather she is co-author of *Maintaining home ownership: the agency approach* (Longman IOH 1992), and *The Future of housing renewal* (The Policy Press, 1994).

Duncan Maclennan
Ian Mactaggart Professor of Land Economics and Finance and Director of the ESRC 'Cities' Programme. Previously he was a lecturer at the University of Aberdeen and then Professor of Applied Economics at Glasgow (1985–1990). He has been Sussman Professor (visiting) of Real Estate Finance at the Wharton Business School (1988) Regent's Professor at the University of California at Berkeley (1996) and Director of the Centre for Housing Research and Urban Studies (1981–1996). Professor Maclennan was previously Principal Consultant to OECD (Paris) on housing issues, Chairman of the National Advisory Committee for Care and Repair in Scotland from 1988–1993. He is Chairman of the Joseph Rowntree Programme on Area Regeneration. He is a Member of the Board of Scottish Homes, since its inception, and in 1996 was made a Member of HM Treasury's Panel of Advisers on micro-economic issues.

Alan Murie
Professor of Urban and Regional Studies and Director of the Centre for Urban and Regional Studies at the University of Birmingham. He was previously Professor of Planning and Housing at Heriot-Watt University and has held posts at the University of Bristol and the University of Ulster. He is Editor of the journal *Housing Studies* and joint author of a number of major housing books including: *Housing Policy and Practice*, (4 editions), Macmillan (with P Malpass); *Selling the Welfare State*, Routledge (2 editions), (with R Forrest); *Home Ownership; Differentiation and Fragmentation*, Unwin Hyman, (with R Forrest and P Williams); *Housing Inequality and Deprivation* (Heinemann).

Christine Whitehead
Reader in Housing Economics in the Department of Economics, London School of Economics, Director of the Property Research Unit in the Department of Land Economy, University of Cambridge and Visiting Professor at Glasgow University. Her research interests include housing economics, finance and policy. Her latest

work relates to the impact of private finance on Housing Associations, the role of the private rented sector, and estimating housing needs, on which subject she was specialist adviser to the Environment Select Committee in 1995/6. Her latest publications include, as well as articles in refereed journals, *Rents and Risks* (1995) published by the Joseph Rowntree Foundation, *The Private Rental Market* (1995) published by the Council of Mortgage Lenders.

Peter Williams
Head of Research and External Affairs, Building Societies Association and Council of Mortgage Lenders and Visiting Professor, University of Bristol. Peter Williams joined the BSA/CML in January 1994. He has been responsible for the CML Social Housing Panel and is major contributor to BSA/CML inputs into housing policy issues. Previously he was Professor of Housing Management at the University of Wales, Cardiff and Director of the Centre for Housing Management and Development. After a PhD at Reading University, he worked at the Centre for Urban and Regional Studies, University of Birmingham and the Urban Research Unit, Australian National University on housing and related research areas. He then became Assistant and then Deputy Director at the Institute of Housing with responsibility for education, training and research. In 1988 he joined the University of Wales. He was Chairman of the Secretary of State's Housing Management Advisory Panel and was a Board member of Housing for Wales from 1989–1994. In late 1995, he was appointed a Board Member of the Housing Corporation. He is Policy Review editor of *Housing Studies* and is in the editorial board of *Roof*. He has an extensive publication list, mainly in the fields of housing and urban studies. Books include *Safe as Houses, Housing Inheritance in Britain* (with C Hamnett and M Harmer) and *Home Ownership; Differentiation and Fragmentation* (with A Murie and R Forrest).

PREFACE

This book has been prepared as a tribute to Alan Holmans, the former Department of the Environment Chief Housing Economist and now Halifax Senior Research Fellow at Cambridge University. All of the contributors would wish to ackowledge the great debt they owe Alan both personally and professionally for his enormous contributions to scholarship and fellowship in the field of housing studies. In a policy arena characterised by the short term, Alan has been a beacon of light, guiding thoughts and works towards the long term and the significant. Our thanks to him for all he has done (and continues to do).

ACKNOWLEDGEMENTS

I am grateful to the authors for their contributions and their patience. The pace of housing policy change in the UK has had a direct impact upon the speed with which this volume was brought to completion. I am grateful to them and to the publishers for the patience they have shown. My thanks also to Cindy Sheppard, Bronny Wigram and Mary Dervish for their help in preparing the manuscripts and to my employer the Building Societies Association (BSA) for allowing this work to be concluded. Neither the BSA or the Council of Mortgage Lenders should be held responsible for any of the views expressed.

Peter Williams

CHAPTER 1

Introduction: Directions in Housing Policy

PETER WILLIAMS

For the last seventy years or more the UK has been struggling to identify and put into practice a coherent set of housing policies (and housing practices) which might be effective and sustained through the life of governments of different political persuasions and a range of social and economic conditions. At times there has been consensus around a narrow set of objectives, most notably in the immediate post-war period when an increase in supply was of primary importance, but typically the housing debate (and housing policy) has been characterised by major changes of emphasis upon the election of new governments or during periods of high inflation, and of course these two factors can be closely related.

It is this search for 'the long term' concerns which might itself inform a set of housing policies sustainable through successive governments and economic cycles which is the focus of this book. Our concern is not with trying to depoliticise housing and to extricate it from the very legitimate and inevitable pressures for change or challenge which the democratic process engenders. Nor is it concerned with sustainability in the environmental sense, albeit that this should be one of the fundamental issues around which all party agreement could be secured.

Interestingly, it is the Government itself which has recently begun to use the term sustainable with respect to housing policy. In the 1995 Department of the Environment Annual Report and then in the Housing White Paper, the Government refers to 'sustainable home ownership', signalling very clearly that in the light of the major market recession of the late 1980s (in which the Government itself played a significant part) it was now important to find a new stable position for the tenure with, one presumes, much lower levels of government assistance.

The purpose of the book is therefore to examine and debate both contemporary housing policy and the housing situation and to think more radically and openly about the policies and practices which might be. Policy of any kind and housing policy in particular is typically dominated by the short term and yet many housing issues are both of long term importance and can only be tackled with that timescale in mind. Moreover, since housing policy is about homes and lives and people live over a span of many years, policy needs to be sensitive to that. While housing needs and demands change over the life cycle the fundamental requirement for safe, comfortable and affordable homes remains throughout.

We are not aiming to set down what might be seen as a radical and perhaps unrealistic agenda but rather to search for policies which might be sustained in the longer term and thus contribute to tackling big and difficult issues such as the renewal or replacement of the housing stock.

Short termism?

The frequency of policy changes and additions is a product not simply of fluctuating ideologies and new governments but also of the evident lack of knowledge of the actual impacts policies might have. While it is true to say that we have significantly increased our knowledge of the housing system over that time we still do not fully understand the interactions between different elements or the ways these combine in different ways in different settings. As a result policy, however well conceived, can have major unintended consequences, worsening the position and forcing yet more policy interventions.

Although we can point to individual elements of policy which are effective within their narrow and specific objectives, it is typically the case that, collectively, policies are in conflict and produce contradictory effects. Moreover the complexity of the system is such that policy effects take time to work through and thus their negative (or positive) effects are not known immediately. In part, this is because central government policy might be the starting point for change but in reality policy is actually implemented by a range of organisations (typically providers, e.g., local authorities and housing associations, lenders, builders) and through the actions of individual consumers.

What we have discovered is that all these relationships are complex and changing reflecting structural and behavioural shifts. The British housing system has undergone profound change in the last seventy years (as has the polity, economy and society) as it has moved from one dominated by private renting to one based around home owning (and even then important regional and local variations remain). It has also become increasingly dependent upon loan finance at market rates.

Inadequate policy because it is based upon an inadequate understanding of the situation is one issue we have had to contend with. Given the complexities alluded to above it is, however, unlikely we will ever have the full understanding that might completely eradicate this problem. A problem of a different order is that policy (and the analyses underlying it) is typically framed for the short term. In other words it frequently fails to anticipate change because it does not look ahead and its goals are set around shorter term concerns and are often highly focused on questions of political advantage. As Sir John Garlick, Permanent Secretary at the DoE 1978–81, has remarked about that period, 'decisions were not based on long term study and overt concern for the long term consequences of policy change' (cited in McQuail, 1995, p 17).

Short termism is endemic in all government policy making, reflecting as it does the cycle of elections and the need to secure re-election. However, housing is built for the long term and requires a considerable degree of forward planning and commitment. It also requires a longer term view when corrective action is planned and put into place. In Alan Holman's important discussion of the 1977 Housing Policy Review (Holmans, 1991) he points to the Review's failure to anticipate major shifts in employment (the rise in unemployment) and in interest rates (to record high levels) and thus to consider the growing need for income related assistance. He also points to the unanticipated high take up of the Right to Buy, the rise of home ownership as a tenure and the 'fall' of public housing with the consequent growing polarisation between owners and tenants.

The work for the Housing Policy Review was undertaken in 1974 and before the International Monetary Fund intervention which resulted in the substantial cut in public expenditure and fundamental policy shifts. In that sense the Review was written in a fundamentally different climate from that which actually followed. While the Review might reasonably have failed to anticipate subsequent developments (although it could perhaps have 'tested' different scenarios given that policy change/government change would always be likely) it must be said that there were a number of commentaries subsequently which argued that the policies adopted would have important negative effects not least on the public housing sector. Here it seems there is an example of how a policy has had cumulative and major longer term negative effects in ways governments have not been prepared to consider when such policies offer shorter term political advantage.

Holmans argues that we need to 'assess what lies at the other side of the hill' and to look at longer term returns. The book aims to offer a longer term view of housing issues in the UK and the policies which might sustain and support them. In so doing it does not seek to argue that there is a single rational way forward nor does it pretend that incremental and opportunistic housing policy making will or can disappear.

At the same time it is evident that simply to accept contemporary policy agendas is to severely limit our frame of reference for discussing and analysing housing issues. It is quite plain from some of the analyses which follow that major issues of long term importance are not even on the agenda and that the UK is simply storing up problems which will ultimately have to be addressed, not least at great expense.

The contributions to this volume are framed within the context of a search for the longer term policies which might conceivably be sustainable across parties and between governments. Certainly those policies will be hotly debated (and rightly so given that housing policy has major social and economic effects) but the aim is to set out the major housing issues of today and tomorrow and to think out loud about the kinds of policies which might be put into place to address them.

This might be dismissed as a luxury we cannot afford and realistically can never be approached. However, unless we have identified the longer term goals and the barriers to achieving them we are even less likely to be able to construct the medium to longer term programmes which might address them. We are thus condemned to live in a world of short termism where policies are most likely to be incremental and contradictory and where we can only bemoan the failure to anticipate and plan for the future.

Long term change

Part of the aim of the book is to focus on what might be seen as the neglected issues. Mention has already been made of long term needs such as the condition of the stock which is easily overlooked in the concern to deal with pressing issues of the moment. The same is true of housing standards. It is relatively easy to set low standards because the most serious costs of such decisions are probably borne over the long term. We might also ask how has the UK housing system changed over the last seventy years? Has it changed for the better? What are the successes and failures? What lessons might we learn? Again such matters are rarely considered (though see Maclennan, 1995a). A brief consideration of the past reveals a fundamental transformation in terms of housing tenure, from renting to owning; a substantial improvement in housing conditions and standards, much of it due to the contribution of the public sector; wider housing access for a greater proportion of the population through both market and non market processes but a substantial narrowing for a significant minority; greater influence by consumers, including tenants; a reduction in overall resources devoted to housing and a fundamental redistribution of government assistance, albeit that McCrone and Stephens (1995) suggest the UK remains high in the European range in terms of assistance given; over the long term a general improvement in security of tenure but more recently heightened risk and exposure to market forces; and finally a redistribution of power in terms of the capacities to direct resources with a move from local government to central government and from central government to quangos.

Maclennan (1995) concludes that over the last quarter century there have been 'major successes for UK housing policies'. However, he notes that 'there are deepening problems for those on the margins of society and the economy' and that 'policies have reinforced these margins'. He also comments that 'by international standards, UK housing policy goals are expensive, in PES terms, to attain'. He argues for an integrated and strategic approach, a much stronger supply side dimension and for flexibility. He concludes:

> Looking back over the last 25 years it is clear that successive cohorts of DoE ministers have spent much of their effort in dealing with the adverse consequences of policies promoted by their predecessors. The 1980s were spent 'undoing' the municipal sector and the 1990s coping with ownership growth. These tasks derived not just from shifting ideologies but from a persistent failure to create a housing system responsive to quickening change (ibid, p 33).

The study of long term change is bedevilled by the absence of data, consistent or otherwise. It is striking for example that housing tenure was not a component of the Census until 1961 and only recently has a regular annual survey of housing been introduced and then only in England. The inspiration for the study of the long term in the housing sector has been the work of Alan Holmans to whom this volume has been dedicated. A brief survey of Alan's contributions as both an academic and as a policy analyst within the Department of the Environment is given below but there can be no doubt that both through his own work and the generous encouragement he has given others we are at last beginning to develop a longer term view and it is against this we can then measure the success and failure of both housing policy and housing politics.

Alan Holmans

Alan Holmans had a long and distinguished career as Senior Economic Adviser and then Chief Housing Economist within the Department of Environment (and its successor the Ministry of Housing and Local Government) before retiring in 1994 and taking up his new position as Halifax Senior Research Fellow at Cambridge. Alan began his career at the University of Glasgow and from 1959 to 1967 he was successively Assistant, Lecturer and then Reader in Political Economy. He was a consultant to the Department of Economic Affairs in 1965 and to the Treasury (1965–1967). He was made a Companion of the British Empire (CBE) in 1989.

His first publication *United States Fiscal Policy 1945–59: Its Contribution to Economic Stability* (Oxford University Press, 1961) was a developed version of his Ph.D which he had completed at Nuffield College, Oxford in 1959. A sequence of economic and industrial development papers was then published in the 1960s before his first housing publication 'A forecast of effective demand for housing in Great Britain,' was published in *Social Trends* in 1970. Twenty-five years later, forecasting housing need and demand remained central to his work. In 1987, Alan published his first major book on housing, *Housing Policy in Britain: A History*. This was a typically exhaustive account of housing policy up to 1979. Wisely as a career civil servant he felt unable to comment on the current administration.

Along with books and articles, Alan Holmans is author of a number of major Government Economic Service Working papers, HMSO published reports and chapters. These include *House Property and Inheritance in the UK* (with M Frosztega, HMSO, 1994), *House Prices: Changes Through Time at National and Sub-National Level* (DoE 1990) and *Estimates of Housing Equity Withdrawal by Owner Occupiers in the United Kingdom 1970 to 1990* (DoE, 1991). The 2 Technical Volumes to the 1977 Housing Policy Review, the last major published government review of housing, owe much to his hand although no author is acknowledged. All are seminal contributions, characterised by scrupulous scholarship, precise and well based assumptions and estimates and the ability to extend and enhance existing understanding and debate.

The stream of work continues undiminished. A recently completed analysis of first time buyers in the 1980s and 1990s for the Council of Mortgage Lenders has been followed by major Rowntree Foundation reports on *Housing Demand and Need in England, 1991 to 2011* and *Housing Need and Demand in Wales to 2011*. As both of these underline, he has sustained his interest in the long term and in being willing to project and forecast, based upon best information and estimates. The impact of work such as this is very considerable. First, it provides the basis for innumerable other pieces of work with the estimates providing the basis for other studies, e.g., for policy debate and analysis. Second, his work provokes questions and challenges those who use statistics uncritically or with insufficient attention to detail.

The Rowntree Foundation commissioned Holman's work on housing need and this was published in October. This was timed to coincide with the start of the Inquiry into Housing Need initiated by the House of Commons Environment Committee. Both are part of a major upsurge in activity in this area and renewed pressure on the Department to engage in and publish estimates of housing need. In May 1995, the DoE's *Memorandum on Provision for Social Housing* was published by the Environment Committee. This has then led into submissions to the Inquiry and to the commissioning of a feasibility study of an economic model of the future demand and need for social housing. As the DoE tender document states (DoE,1995):

neither the household formation projections nor the projections of the demands and supply of owner occupied and private rented housing are modelled explicitly as functions of economic variables such as income, house prices, mortgage costs and rents – they are simply based on extrapolations of past trends.

In his work, Alan Holmans has put considerable emphasis upon demographic pressures and changes and this has done much to awaken policy makers and analysts to the importance of these forces alongside the economic and policy context. Inevitably there will always be disagreements about the relative importance of these different effects. However, as a senior civil servant Holmans, like others in his position, was fully aware of the difficulties of analysing and publishing evidence in relation to the impact of policy or the management of the economy. Demographic change both reflects and reinforces those other dynamics and it has provided powerful insights into the ways in which the UK was being shaped and changed.

Through his own scrupulously detailed research and analysis Alan has set a high standard for others to follow and housing studies in the UK are much stronger as a consequence. Through his own work and through the exceptional support and encouragement he has offered to others, Alan Holmans is very deserving of the high reputation and regard in which he is held.

This volume has been prepared as a small mark of gratitude to Alan Holmans for his work in the housing field. All of the contributors would acknowledge the importance of his contributions in general and the value of his work to their own research. Moreover, many would point to Alan's generous support and guidance for their own work. This volume hopefully goes some way to acknowledging the debt we all owe him.

The book takes up themes common to Alan's own work. That is a concern with the longer term, with the unanticipated consequences of policy and with the range of forces working their way through the housing system. None of the contributions matches his own for the detail of the empirical analysis but all strive to draw the threads together, make connections and speculate on the future. It is through such processes we hope we might make better progress towards the goal of efficient and effective housing policy and the creation of a truly sustainable housing system which delivers good affordable homes to the population of the United Kingdom.

CHAPTER 2

Changing Needs, Changing Incentives: Trends in the UK Housing System

CHRISTINE M E WHITEHEAD

It is always difficult to identify long term trends and to separate these trends from the shorter term, often volatile interests of commentators and policy makers. This is especially true at the present time because so many of the immediate housing problems in Britain arise from the process of transition from a heavily protected and regulated system to one which is directly affected by fundamental economic pressures, particularly those associated with the globalisation of the finance market on the one hand and the growing need for governments to control public expenditure on the other. One outcome of this more open system is that these problems of adjustment, arising in particular from changes in employment opportunities, the reduced rate of inflation and greater targeting of housing assistance, have affected the housing circumstances of a far higher proportion of households than in the past. As a result it is easy to forget how much improvement there has been in housing conditions since the Second World War and equally how rapidly our housing aspirations have expanded to include many other attributes in addition to adequate shelter.

Political attitudes to housing

It is in the context of rising aspirations, rising standards and rising costs, that we must understand the structural changes that are occurring both in political attitudes to housing and in the way the housing market is operating. In the political context an important question is why housing has fallen right down the agenda at a time when large numbers of owner-occupiers are facing problems that they did not predict, many tenants are having to pay rents which have been rising much faster than inflation, there are continuing high levels of homelessness and difficulties of access to suitable accommodation, and the electorate itself still sees housing as a priority area for additional spending.

Arguably, these difficulties, however important for the individuals affected, are more a matter of adjustment than fundamental shortage. As basic shelter needs are satisfied for the majority of households the political emphasis has moved away from regarding housing as a social good, providing the necessities of life which society thinks should be available to all, towards an approach which sees

housing as more of a private good, emphasising individual choice and responsibility and which recognises that each dwelling is a complex set of attributes
which will provide very different levels of satisfaction for different households.
This change in attitudes is linked with policy change – away from new building to
improving the existing stock, away from bricks and mortar subsidies towards
income related benefits and away from social provision towards a more market
oriented approach. These policies are often seen as being an outcome of Conservative ideology. Yet equivalent policies, shifting housing out of the administrative
domain and reducing government spending, would probably have been introduced whatever government had been in power.

In evaluating these fundamental shifts in policy it is important to look at the
trends in provision, allocation and indeed satisfaction which lie behind the country's success, or lack of it, in ensuring a decent home for every family at a price
within their means. In this chapter I want to examine three aspects of how the
housing system and housing policy have evolved, generating both changing needs
and changing incentives:

i)   the shift away from new building, particularly in the public sector towards
     both market provision and a greater emphasis on the more effective use of the
     existing stock;
ii) the restructuring of tenure in response to changing attitudes to housing and
     policies of privatisation; and
iii) the shift in methods of government intervention away, at least in principle,
     from directly addressing physical needs to assisting individuals to pay for
     acceptable standards of housing.

The chapter also examines the ways in which these problems are analysed have
similarly changed. In this context Alan Holmans has played a pivotal role, both
through his own research and by helping others, notably government but also
almost all other housing researchers in the country, better to understand the
operation of the housing system in Britain.

The numbers game

A fundamental housing question is how many dwellings must be provided in
order to ensure that households can be adequately housed. A second, related,
question is whether those units can be generated through private development,
which will occur only if developers can make a reasonable rate of return on their
investment, or must entail some form of social sector incentive or provision. The
starting point for any estimate is the number of households that require accommodation compared with the number of units currently available – at its simplest
a crude balance between households and dwellings. More complex estimates take
into account the need for vacancies to allow the housing system to operate effectively and the suitability of the existing stock as well as different categories of
households that might be regarded as in need of separate accommodation.

Until the late 1960s housing policy was in many respects simply a numbers
game – which government could help to provide the largest number of units –
anywhere and of any type. This was not surprising as in 1951 there were some
6.5% more households than dwellings, while around 75% of all households were

living in substandard or overcrowded conditions or having to share with other households (Department of Environment, 1977a). Given these shortages, which affected households right up the income scale, it is not surprising that all political parties stressed the importance of their building programmes – with the Conservatives under Macmillan promising half a million units per year and actually achieving 425,000 units in 1968. In these conditions any detailed analysis of future demands and needs could be regarded as almost irrelevant.

Estimating housing requirements

It was only in the early 1970s, when the census suggested that there were perhaps 700,000 more dwellings than households in Great Britain overall (although this figure was subsequently revised downwards) and that there were crude surpluses in most localities, that the argument became more sophisticated at the political level, and questions about what types of unit should be provided, and where, became part of the debate. Yet, in terms of analysis, Holmans had already, in the late 1960s, developed a framework for more detailed assessment of housing needs. This relied on a medium term forecast which attempted to clarify both the extent to which the market would meet these needs through the owner-occupied sector and the extent of public sector investment necessary to ensure that remaining needs recognised by government would be met (Holmans, 1970).

By 1976, the number of dwellings exceeded the number of households by over 3.5%, although only two regions, North and West Midlands, still had a surplus once involuntary sharing and concealed households, together with a vacancy level adequate to achieve a reasonably operating housing system, were taken into account (Whitehead, 1977). It was in this context, of a crude surplus but an obvious continuing need for large-scale investment, that Holmans produced an updated version of his forecast for the Housing Policy Review. This looked at the requirement for additional publicly provided units, if needs were to continue to be alleviated at a rate consistent with existing government policy (Department of Environment, 1977a). The definition of need included in the estimate was consistent with government criteria, taking into account concealed married couple households, sharing and overcrowding, as well as unfitness and lack of amenity, but not single people or couples without children.

The projection (it was not a forecast as it consciously assumed that the future would be like the past, as compared with trying to predict actual outcomes) was based on an examination of the numbers of households who could be expected to be suitably housed in the owner-occupied sector, given the existing stock, transfers of units from the rented sector into owner-occupation and the level of new private sector building which might be generated by this demand. Projected private sector output, together with an estimate of the number of households that could be expected to be adequately housed in the existing rented stock, in turn generated an estimate of the numbers of additional units required in the public sector if the number of households living in unacceptable housing conditions were to be reduced at the rate that was expected to be achieved during the period 1972–1979. These units were expected to be provided almost entirely by the local authority sector. This approach, called the gross flows approach, modelled the entry points through which households could expect to gain access to housing and how they might move through the system, as well as the tenure distribution of both existing and new dwelling units. The projection suggested that production in England would need to be of the order of 300,000 units per annum over the following decade, with public sector output running at well over 100,000 units per annum, if there were to be continuing progress in meeting housing need. However, it also suggested that if this output were to occur, the crude surplus of dwellings over households would be over 1.3 million units, generating a 'vacancy' rate of around 6.5%, by the mid-1980s (Department of Environment, 1977a).

When the Conservative government came to power in 1979 such forecasts were ruled out of order on the grounds that there was the largest crude surplus ever, and what was important was more how the private system responded to demand, rather than an automatic assumption that needs should be met through the public sector (House of Commons, 1981b). Thereafter estimates of need played a very different role, partly in informing housing pressure groups which favoured social provision as a means of reducing housing problems and partly in assisting private sector organisations to plan their strategies. As such they were undertaken outside government, were generally far more simplistic than the original Department of Environment estimates, and concentrated mainly on net stock comparisons (i.e. comparing the stock of households, classified by different types of need with the stock of dwellings of acceptable standard) without necessarily analysing how the required units might be produced (Whitehead and Kleinman, 1992).

Some of these estimates (e.g. those by the National Housing Forum (1989) and by the London Research Centre (1991) for needs in the London area) took account of much wider definitions of needs than those accepted by government policy. In particular they included potential households who prefer to live separately, among whom were included many one person households. They also took account not only of the suitability of the stock in terms of fitness and amenity but also the match between households and that stock including problems of crowding, suitability for disabled households and for households with children. This generates very large numbers of households in need, although by no means all of these needs require additional building if they are to be met. These estimates suggest that the backlog of existing needs, which cannot be expected to be met by the market, is still very significant. That estimates of the backlog of need are not provided by government points to the fact that in the current political and economic environment it is unlikely that resources will be made available to provide significant numbers of additional social sector units. Instead the emphasis is now on helping households in the social sector who can afford it, or can afford it with some additional grant, to transfer into owner-occupation leaving vacancies in the social sector stock to be filled by more needy groups. The needs of those not recognised as being in priority groups must be met either through the private rented sector or within existing households.

The main element of any medium term needs estimate, in addition to measuring backlog, is the projection of demands and needs into the future mostly on the basis of new household formation. These figures are generated by the Department using population forecasts and trends in headship rates. The predicted numbers vary considerably from one estimate to another as additional evidence becomes available. For instance the new 1992 based figures (Department of Environment, 1995) suggest that there will be almost one million more households by 2011 than the number predicted by the 1989 based projections. Falling birth rates are now coming through into lower levels of new household formation. On the other hand life expectancy is rising rapidly, generating additional needs from older households, while net immigration is expected to increase (mainly as a result of fewer households leaving the country). The net effect is that there are likely to be many more older and single households than in the past. What is less clear is, on the one hand, whether economic recession and changes in the structure of the labour market have reduced household formation among younger households and, on the other, how government policy on social security and pensions will affect older households' capacity to pay for separate housing.

Later needs assessments using the medium term forecast approach no longer assumed that needs would be met by direct provision, but rather estimated the numbers of households in need of assistance additional to that currently being provided. This involves estimating, as in the original models, the numbers likely to be adequately housed in the owner-occupied sector, the numbers of units available in the social sector and the likely role of the private rented sector. It can also involve constraining the expected vacancy rate – reflecting the extent to which the existing stock can be reorganised to meet certain of these needs. Using government definitions of households in need these projections suggested, on the basis of 1989-based estimates, that about 100,000 additional households per annum require assistance to obtain adequate housing, although by no means all of these need additional new units (Kleinman, Morrison and Whitehead, 1994).

In 1995, the government finally reversed its position with respect to publishing estimates of need – with a document which projected the numbers of households that would require additional social assistance with housing until 2001 (House of Commons, 1995). This in turn led the Environment Committee to set up an Inquiry into the wider question of housing need (House of Commons, 1996). An important input to that Inquiry was a report by Alan Holmans prepared after he left the Department which included both a far more detailed projection than that provided by the Department covering the period to 2011 and based on the net stock approach and an estimate of the backlog of unmet need (Holmans, 1995b). This work has now been extended to Wales (Holmans, 1996).

The Inquiry generated an active debate on methodology as well as projections. The main areas of difference between the government and most of the other organisations giving evidence related not only to the numbers of households requiring social housing, but also whether these could be provided effectively by the private rented sector rather than directly through additional provision in the social sector. The fact that the numbers the government regarded as in need, at about 60,000 per annum, were far smaller than the estimates by other researchers (notably Holmans) was perhaps unsurprising (Department of Environment, 1996). The most important outcome of the debate into the longer term was rather the acceptance by government that projections were a valuable policy tool and that resources should follow these estimates. Another important recommendation concentrated on the need for more research into the behavioural factors affecting household formation as well as demand and need.

While there are clear benefits to modelling the process rather than simply assessing outcomes, there are also considerable limitations relating both to the large number of assumptions necessary about how the system operates and the extensive data requirements. In particular, because the estimated figure is the residual from other very large flows, small changes in the totals generate large changes in required net output. On the other hand the approach does provide projections that can be checked against outcomes. In the case of the projections in the Housing Policy Review, actual output levels during the ten year forecast period fell short of the projected levels by some 40,000 units per annum. At the same time numbers of households were higher than predicted. The result has undoubtedly generated shortages and problems of the type which would have been predicted by the analysis undertaken for the Review (Holmans, 1991).

Although projections of housing needs are only accepted to a limited extent by the government in the context of housing policy they still play a role, in a simplified form, in determining land use planning policy in that needs assessments are used to assist local authorities to determine the quantity of land to make available to ensure adequate levels of new building. Under the current land use planning system regional groupings of authorities use information on household formation and migration to determine the levels of demand that they project must be accommodated in each local area and the extent to which this is to be accomplished through new building. On the basis of these estimates local authorities must identify suitable sites to allow the required levels of building to take place and should ensure that a five year supply of suitable land is always available. In the current environment, which emphasises protecting the rural environment, urban regeneration and sustainable urban development as well as limiting additional supply of greenfield sites, this approach is seen by many as being too simplistic (Joseph Rowntree Foundation, 1994b). Once again the emphasis is moving away from mechanistic projections towards greater understanding of the way in which local housing markets operate.

Incentives to build

This discussion of approaches to estimating the demand for new units in the private sector and the need for social provision is not simply methodological. They reflect important underlying changes in government policy as well as in the way the housing system operates. With respect to the first, they reflect the shift away from direct public provision towards providing market incentives. With respect to actual requirements they reflect the fact that the overall need for additional, as distinct from replacement, units to meet the needs of existing households has declined significantly as the backlog of needs has been addressed. Moreover, in the future the rate of growth of new households may not generate the same requirement for additional units as was the case in the 1960s and 1970s, when the growth in households was concentrated among family households.

Two particular areas of uncertainty about how the housing system is now working concern the number of households entering owner-occupation and the extent and sustainability of the revival of the private rented sector. The two questions are of course interrelated and both affect the numbers of additional units likely to be provided. With respect to new entrants into the owner-occupied market, the number of first-time buyers has fallen from a high of nearly 550,000 in 1988, following five years of around 450,000–475,000 per annum, to less than 400,000 per annum in every year thereafter (Holmans, 1995b). This in turn impacts on the numbers of additional dwellings that will be built in order to meet this demand and therefore the extent to which needs can be met through private provision. The fall in the number of first time buyers is in part a result of shifts in the timing of purchases, arising both from the late 1980s boom and the subsequent slump, and from changing tax benefits. However, a far larger proportion of the fall can be directly associated with declining demographic pressures, which had been clearly signalled in the forecasts and which can be expected to continue to exert downward pressure on demand over the next decade (Kleinman and Whitehead, 1988). What is less clear is how much of the fall arises from a structural decline in young households' desire to enter owner-occupation, as some of the benefits of entering owner-occupation are eroded and the opportunities for obtaining privately rented accommodation increase.

The complementary question is how and whether the private rented sector will expand to meet such demands. Until the late 1980s it was reasonable to assume that the private rental sector would continue to decline. As a result of changes in legislation, notably the deregulation of rents on new lettings in 1988, changes in the extent of tax benefits to owner-occupiers and the introduction, if initially on a short-term basis, of subsidies to private rental provision, as well as an economic environment which has made owner-occupation less desirable, the incentives to let and to rent have been significantly modified. The government estimates that as a result over 300,000 units have been added to the sector in the first five years of the new regulatory regime (Down et al., 1994) .

How much difference does this type of change make to the likely output of new units? First, the assumption that owner-occupiers have the financial capacity to generate new investment may not apply equally when that demand is instead generated from the rental sector. If so there could be a structural shift in the relationship between household formation and new building. Landlords may well be more likely to buy property on the existing market, but does private renting reduce the number of vacancies in the stock? Historically, much of the evidence would suggest the opposite: vacancy rates are usually higher in areas where private renting is concentrated, implying that a larger stock would be necessary to house a given number of households. Similarly, demand for private renting is unlikely to be concentrated in areas where overall demand is low, so allowing the vacancy rate to be reduced. Finally, there is little evidence that the numbers of households that wish to live in non-self-contained accommodation will grow – so if the existing stock is to be better utilised there will need to be additional conversions. The most likely outcome is therefore that rental demand will simply substitute for owner-occupier demand, in which case, while the immediate effect of a shift to private renting may be less demand for new units, the overall effect on the market would be to put more pressure on the owner-occupied sector and therefore to increase the demand for new units in that sector. The alternative would be that prices would rise without generating additional new investment, in such a way as to reduce the numbers of new households coming on to the housing market and so induce greater utilisation of the stock through larger households.

The same type of analysis applies to the effect of government intervention. The role of local authorities is no longer to invest directly but instead is to enable the private and independent sectors to provide accommodation more effectively, either through new building or by better use of the existing stock. The net effect is to shift production to the private sector, but not necessarily to reduce overall output, unless subsidies are reduced. At the same time, this more market approach inherently entails less control over actual outcomes – so the extent to which identified needs will actually be met by a given level of investment is less certain.

Models of demand and need have consistently pointed to a declining role for new building to meet both the backlog in housing needs and future requirements based on demographic pressures, even though each estimate is revised upwards as household formation continues to exceed expectations. Public policy has ensured that what is provided is mainly at the behest of the private sector and is therefore directly affected by economic variables, notably incomes, interest rates and the general buoyancy of the economy. The evidence of the last decades bears out these predictions. New housebuilding in 1994 was running at about 180,000 units per annum as compared with over 350,000 in 1971; 80% of these units were provided by the private sector, as compared to a split of 55:45 in 1971; and volatility around these lower building levels has been greater than in earlier decades.

These trends in building rates are set to continue as demographic factors tend to dampen the demand for additional units, governments of whatever colour limit their involvement in provision and the pressures to generate sustainable development tend to concentrate investment within existing built up areas. Nothing in the way either the market or public policy is operating suggests that there will be much incentive for new building to replace obsolete existing units. Indeed, unless national income rises rapidly enough to remove the demand for the worst quality housing, all the tensions point the other way: i.e. towards greater use of the existing stock. If, as we hope, housing standards continue to rise over the next twenty years in the way that they have in the last, the majority of that increase in investment is likely to be achieved through improving the existing stock. Even so, it is unlikely that the resultant standards will be high enough to satisfy the continuing growth in aspirations.

Tenure restructuring

Trends in owner-occupation

The most obvious housing trend over the last twenty years has been the growth of owner-occupation. In 1971 just half of all households were owner-occupiers, as against 30% local authority tenants and nearly 20% renting from private landlords. By 1993 two thirds of households in Great Britain were owner-occupiers, 20% were local authority tenants, and less than 10% rented from the private landlords – with a further 4% renting from housing associations. An important question is whether these trends will continue or whether, as many now argue, owner-occupation has reached its limit and the emphasis should be on restructuring the rented sector to provide greater choice of rented accommodation for all types of household.

The growth of owner-occupation has clearly reflected the aspirations of most households, given the tax and subsidy system, the other housing opportunities available, and the large proportion of houses in the dwelling stock. In 1975 for instance 69% of individuals over the age of sixteen wanted to be owner-occupiers within the next two years, although only 62% actually expected to be owners within ten years. By 1993 69% of the sample had achieved that tenure – but by then the proportion wanting to become owner-occupiers had risen to 81%

and that proportion had hardly faltered in response to a five year recession, significant declines in subsidy and expectations of a far riskier future (Coles and Taylor, 1993).

The sale of council houses was one important factor allowing households to achieve their aspirations. The policy could be regarded as generating a sort of equity, between those who had been able to overcome financial constraints to become owner-occupiers and so obtain the benefits of borrowing at generous rates in the 1960s and 70s, and those who had been excluded from these benefits. One could also argue that the policy tended to reduce spatial polarisation, as otherwise those who were able to become owner-occupiers would have moved out of the social sector and been replaced by those in the greatest need. Instead, because of the Right to Buy, the second generation, who purchase these properties when they come on the market, will have attributes similar to those who sell (House of Commons, 1981a; Whitehead, 1993).

While the Right to Buy was a useful mechanism to generate change, it could not have been effective without the deregulation of housing finance within a liberalised general finance market, which itself enabled large numbers of households to enter owner-occupation directly (Kleinman and Whitehead, 1988). There have been obvious costs to individuals to this liberalisation, especially in the face of lower inflation and recession, because many households have taken on borrowing commitments which they cannot meet. Yet it can be argued that these are necessary costs of transition, as both lenders and borrowers learn the true nature of the risks involved. Ultimately, what is required is the correct pricing of risk and finance (including tax neutrality between borrowing and own financing) in order that the benefits of deregulation can be fully achieved (Lea, 1994).

One factor working against the growth of owner-occupation (and indeed of investment in the private housing stock) is changes in the tax and benefit structure, especially in the current recessionary economic environment. Over the last few years the range of investment options open to individuals has increased significantly, while at the same time the value of tax benefits to owner-occupation has declined, both through the reduction in the availability of mortgage tax relief and because of real reductions in capital values. In addition the safety net, by which mortgage interest costs are paid by government when mortgagors lose their jobs, has been and is continuing to be eroded. More fundamentally, demographic factors, both in terms of the numbers of households coming into the market and the numbers of older households, and dissolving households, such as divorcees, who may wish to realise their assets mean that there are significant pressures for disinvestment in the market (Miles, 1992). All of these factors mean that net demands are unlikely to increase rapidly even when the economy recovers. There is therefore less expectation of large capital gains, which in itself further reduces demand. The short-term problem may well be one of overshooting in the late 1980s when people overestimated the relative benefits of increasing their investment in owner-occupied housing, together with the difficulties in turning round a downward spiral in a low inflation economy. The longer term position is undoubtedly less strong than in the past, although once incomes rise, real demand for housing will once again increase (Meen, 1994b).

Given normal cohort effects the proportion of owner-occupiers would undoubtedly tend towards 70% in the country as a whole, and perhaps even exceed it. The relative decline in the investment benefits of owner-occupation is unlikely to offset this trend significantly, except to the extent that people may enter owner-occupation somewhat later. Owner-occupation remains the best choice for a very wide range of households – and will continue to do so at least until what is on offer in the rented sector is radically improved. On the other hand it is reasonable to argue that in a low inflation environment, but one in which people expect to have to change jobs and to experience periods of unemployment more often than in the past, many of the benefits of owner-occupation for younger and poorer households will be lower in the 1990s than in the 1980s. In the past many of these benefits arose from constraints elsewhere, which meant that tenants could not achieve the access to borrowing and other related benefits or the type of housing that they wanted as compared with the choices available to those who could gain entry to the owner-occupied sector (Whitehead, 1979). On the other hand the more fundamental benefits, relating to the underlying distribution of income and wealth and the contractual failures normally associated with the landlord and tenant relationship, still remain important when people are making their tenure choices and still tend to favour owner-occupation.

Rental prospects

Any significant increase in the size of the rented sector, at least in the current political environment, must come from private renting. It is here that changes in political attitudes have been most obvious. In the 1960s and 1970s there was a strong, and in many ways bi-partisan, view that private renting was inherently an inferior product, not only for ideological reasons but also because the costs of organising the landlord and tenant relationship were seen to be lower in both owner-occupation and social renting than in the private rented sector (House of Commons, 1982). Now the pressures are all the other way: private renting is seen as necessary in order to generate flexibility in the labour market and indeed the macro-economy, while private landlords can be expected to find it worthwhile to house many younger and more mobile households (Maclennan, 1994).

The reductions in tax benefits to owner-occupation have helped to make private renting more desirable, in that landlords receive relief on their mortgage interest and other costs of letting against rental income, although they remain subject to capital gains and income tax. While they are still at a disadvantage in tax and subsidy terms against owner-occupiers, and even more in comparison with social renting, the extent of that disadvantage has declined considerably (Kleinman & Whitehead, 1996). Yet landlords, if they are to remain in business, must cover their costs of letting and make an adequate return on rents and the now limited, or indeed negative, capital gains. There are few reasons to expect landlords' costs of letting, and therefore the rent they have to charge, to be lower than the costs of owner-occupation. So if a household finds buying difficult they are likely to find renting similarly difficult. The main reason to choose renting is that it may be easier for the tenant to adjust expenditure in the light of changing circumstances and tenants are eligible for housing benefit based on their current income levels.

Thus, while the relative benefits of owner-occupation have undoubtedly declined, there seems little reason to expect the vast majority of owners and potential owners to change their choice of tenure, except among the young, the mobile and those with insecure incomes. For those with adequate incomes private renting is a viable, although by no means a cheap, alternative. Among those with low and uncertain incomes choices are limited by the nature of the subsidy system and access to finance. At the present time, it is only because of the existence of generous housing benefit that landlords are prepared to provide for this group. The prospects for a significantly larger private rented sector thus still depend on the extent of government assistance (Whitehead, 1994).

The increasing importance of affordability

A third fundamental trend has been growing concern about affordability. Historically, financial rationing in the owner-occupied sector, rent controls, and heavily subsidised rents in the social sector had meant that the vast majority of those who were housed in the major tenures were able to afford the housing they consumed. Liberalisation of the finance markets, deregulation of rents in the private sector and rapidly reducing subsidies to social suppliers have changed this position, so that many of those who have been able to obtain suitable accommodation are now finding it difficult to pay the bills. At the policy level discussion now tends to emphasise the costs of housing to the consumer and the extent to which this cost generates affordability problems rather than simply the need for acceptable housing. There are two distinct areas of concern. The first relates to the capacity of owner-occupiers to enter and remain in the market. The second relates to affordability in the rented sector and the capacity of lower income households to afford adequate quality housing.

Affordability in owner-occupation

Within the owner-occupied sector the extension of homeownership to over two-thirds of all households has brought into the sector many people whose incomes have proved insecure and who have few resources to support any changes in their circumstances. Liberalisation of finance markets has made it easier for more people to borrow a higher proportion of both the value of the dwelling and the household's income, while on the other hand, unemployment and greater casualisation of labour markets have made many of these incomes far more uncertain. At the same time government has removed, or at least limited, some of the tax benefits which used to go with owner-occupation as compared with other investments. These factors, together with the volatility in the macro-economy experienced in the late 1980s and the structural reduction in the rate of inflation, have led to something of a crisis of affordability in the owner-occupied market.

The form of this affordability crisis is very different to that experienced in earlier economic cycles. Historically the problem has been one of incapacity to afford the first year payments, in part because high inflation made initial payments unaffordable, resulting in the exclusion from the owner-occupied market of many who could have afforded to pay over the lifetime of the mortgage. In the current cycle the costs of entry are probably lower than anyone can remember: prices have fallen, as have interest rates, while the incomes of those in work have continued to rise in real terms. So for those who enter the sector in the early 1990s and whose circumstances do not change, it is easier to afford the outgoings than at any time over the last two decades. The problem is not entry, as it has been so often in the past, it is exit – i.e. the difficulties of selling, or otherwise adjusting payments, if household circumstances change, and with this the fear of such changes – which means that people may not be prepared to take the risk in the first place. One result has been that many households who rushed into owner-occupation in the late 1980s, in part because there were few other housing options, in part because they thought it was a good investment and in part because lenders were happy to finance them, have found themselves both with a lower valued asset, often leaving them with negative equity, and very little capacity to trade down or out of the sector in order to get out of trouble. This has resulted in a very significant affordability problem for many households, manifested in arrears and possessions on a scale never observed before. Another result has been far fewer new entrants into owner-occupation in the early 1990s than had been expected and, more generally, an environment has been created in which owner-occupation is seen as much more risky than in the past – and therefore more costly.

Affordability in the rented sectors

In the rented sector, the current government's policy is to target assistance towards those in the greatest need and more fundamentally to move towards a market based system, where rents reflect the cost of production. The mechanism is that of reducing subsidies to providers, deregulating markets and subsidising households who cannot afford the resultant price. In the private sector this has meant deregulating rents and finance markets but also the provision of housing benefit to cover market rents. For social rental housing it has led to reducing subsidies so that rents increase more rapidly than inflation and again to greater emphasis on housing benefit. The outcome is seen by many again to be a crisis of affordability.

Affordability implies not only that people can obtain the minimum acceptable level of housing but also that they can then afford to purchase the other necessities of life (Whitehead, 1991; Hancock, 1993; Hulchanski, 1995). Two basic measures of affordability are used when setting social sector rents and subsidies in the UK: the *ratio* measure used by the National Federation of Housing Associations and most commentators in the area, and the *residual income* measure implicitly used by government when determining the package of income related subsidies.

Ratio measures simply compare rents with incomes. Traditionally 20% of income was regarded as a reasonable maximum for lower income households. Now it is usually argued that gross rents, including service charges, should not be greater than 25% of net income for working households entering the sector, while the Housing Corporation applies an implicit benchmark of the order of 33%–35% when negotiating suitable grant rates. In the USA figures as high as 40% are often quoted, but these include property taxes, heating and other housing related charges (Maclennan and Williams, 1990).

The second, residual income, measure is embedded in the social security and housing benefit systems. Under this approach housing is affordable as long as, once housing costs have been paid, the household has enough other income to purchase the necessities of life. That is, in principle, exactly how the benefit system works: the whole rent is payable through benefit whenever a household's income falls below the income required to buy the basket of goods deemed necessary for that household, given its composition and any special circumstances. Above that level of income 65% of each additional £ is withdrawn, until the full housing cost is paid by the tenant.

This approach has obvious implications: first, as long as all those eligible actually claim, no household on benefit has an affordability problem, measured in the government's own terms. Moreover eligible households are fully protected from any changes in rents. This does of course assume that the residual income is correctly determined, enabling adequate standards actually to be achieved and that the costs of buying these goods is constant across households and areas – both of which assumptions are debatable.

Second, the income taper, the proportion of each additional £ that must be used to pay the rent as benefit is withdrawn, at 65%, is steep. Because other benefits are withdrawn at the same time, households may only keep a few pence in the £ of any increase in income. Moreover, the higher the rent the larger the income must be before the tenant obtains any significant increase in spending power. This potentially generates a major disincentive to work. And, while those on full housing benefit pay no rent, for those with incomes above that level, the proportion of income spent on housing can go on rising without any limit except that arising from ensuring that the residual income plus the few pence per additional £ of income is maintained. Thus the more government increases dwelling rents, by reducing subsidies to suppliers, the greater the problem.

Finally, like the ratio measure, the residual income measure is applied to actual housing expenditure. It therefore does not directly ensure that standards are achieved. On the other hand as households in receipt of benefit pay no increases in rent, if tenants are able to choose their own accommodation there is a problem of 'upmarketing' (tenants choosing higher quality with no incentive to negotiate the minimum rent), which increases subsidy costs. This has already been reflected in growing concern about the way housing benefit is operating in the private rented sector (Crook et al., 1995).

A number of obvious points can be drawn from this discussion. First, the system of assistance still assumes that those who cannot afford adequate housing for themselves will be accommodated in the rental sector. Assistance in the owner-occupied sector is limited to addressing sudden changes in circumstances – and even this is, at least under the present government, likely to be dealt with more and more through the private insurance market (Douetil, 1994). Within the rented sector the trend is undoubtedly still away from regulation and bricks and mortar subsidy towards targeted income related subsidies. This has within it, in principle, the capacity to adjust prices to real resource costs – a necessary condition for effective market provision of a private good (Whitehead, 1989). But it also generates very considerable practical problems. The most important of these at the present time are, within the social sector, the concentration of disadvantaged households and the associated costs of increasing polarisation and, in the private sector, the non-sustainability of a system which provides no incentive for either landlord or tenant to negotiate the least cost rent. Finally, the very high implicit tax rates facing those on housing benefit are both inequitable and inefficient. It is these aspects of the move to a more market approach which have still to be effectively addressed.

Conclusions: a sustainable system?

In this chapter three longer term trends have been discussed, as well as the ways in which they have been analysed. These trends are first, the apparent continuing decline in investment in new building; second, the growth of private ownership, notably through owner-occupation, but latterly including private landlordism; and third, the increasing emphasis on affordability rather than need as prices and rents more closely reflect the real costs of providing housing. All these trends are linked to a fundamental shift in attitudes, as housing standards rise, away from regarding housing as a social good, to be provided within a regulated and/or administered system, towards seeing it as a private good which can be better allocated by the market.

These trends may not, however, generate a stable and well-operating housing system. First, levels of housebuilding are not high enough to ensure reasonable access for all. Over the 1980s some elements of the stock have been used more effectively, but problems of access have also become more obvious. Greater longevity means that there will not be so many social sector units coming free to house those in need than had been predicted when determining current government policies. The additional million households now projected for the year 2011 have to be accommodated, although not necessarily wholly in additional units. It is not clear that the market will generate the demand necessary to provide the incentive for significant additional investment in private sector new building. The shift away from housing subsidies, together with the growth in other investment opportunities and the reduced likelihood of capital gains in housing, and as importantly the numbers of older households who may wish to disinvest, all tend to suggest that housebuilding levels will not increase greatly over the next decade. It is therefore difficult to see how adequate housing for lower income households can be made available except through direct social investment or subsidies to suppliers.

A second question, currently much under discussion, is whether the existing levels of owner-occupation are sustainable. The obvious answer is that there is no reason why they should not be, although one would not perhaps expect the proportion to go much above 70%. There are good reasons to think that those whose housing circumstances are likely to change rapidly would be better off renting. But there are also few reasons to expect the cost of renting in a reasonably operating market to be less than those of owner-occupation. The nature of the UK stock generally favours owner-occupation, and prices can adjust to demand. Any significant decline would involve older households shifting into renting. The mechanisms by which this might occur are certainly not yet in place.

It is less clear that a large scale expansion of the private rented sector in its current form is sustainable, simply because of the nature of demand. What is more likely is that the social sector will be restructured to include more private finance and management and so generate a larger independent rented sector from within the existing stock, providing longer term accommodation. Some of this might ultimately be provided for profit. This would bring the UK more in line with the rest of Europe, giving easier access to the whole rented sector, rather than only to a narrowly defined, commercially provided, sector as is the case at the present time.

Even this extent of restructuring depends on developing a better system of income-related benefits. The housing benefit system cannot, and should not, be sustained in its current form. It must be replaced by one which gives tenants the incentive to choose the level of housing commensurate with both their needs and their resources, and landlords the incentive to provide that level at a reasonable cost. We are a long way from that position at the present time, let alone one where people have true tenure choice. As a result it will not be possible to achieve a well-operating rented sector simply by raising rents to market levels and allowing landlords to respond to those incentives. Such a well-operating system may well not be obtainable at all unless (and until) there is greater efficiency in production generating lower costs; income growth, so that housing, in the sense of its basic attributes, takes up a smaller proportion of income and so is less of a burden on the household budget; and a more even distribution of that income so that everyone can afford at least the basic necessities of life.

CHAPTER 3

The UK Housing Market: Up, Down and Where Next?

DUNCAN MACLENNAN

Recovery: The Curate's Egg

Confusing signals?

The British economy, in the wake of a typical, but pronounced, seven year period of boom and bust, has been expanding since early 1992. Since then, GDP has grown by 2 to 3% per annum and, since 1993, unemployment has fallen by more than a million. There is, of course, nothing atypical, in relation to the UK's postwar economic evolution, in that broad pattern.

However, the sectoral components of growth and recovery have been rather atypical in their roles and sequencing. The recovery has been led by export growth, but with sterling devalued, after 1993, by 15–20% against major European currencies in the EMS this is also unremarkable. Investment and profits, at least until 1996, recovered more significantly than consumer expenditure and earnings. Indeed, with changing wage/profit shares and increases in household taxation the real disposable income of UK households did not begin to rise until mid-1995. Four years into the recovery inflation has remained low and within the government's target range of 2–4%.

Continuing global economic competition, the Maastricht convergence process (which has induced even more sluggish recovery in the rest of the European Union) and the government's determination to minimise inflation all have a role to play in explaining the relatively good economic performance of the 1992–1996 period. However a sense of recovery has not, at least until the summer of 1996, permeated measures of consumer confidence and spending. This sense of recession hangover has been particularly evident in the UK housing market.

In previous postwar cycles general economic recovery has been led, statistically, by rapid increases in private sector housing starts which then continue to expand until just before the cyclical downturn, see Figure 1. Sales of existing homes follow a broadly similar pattern. And typically, in the recovery phase, increases in nominal house prices rise above the retail price index and continue to do so until the end of a boom period, see Figure 2. Housing starts, transactions level and nominal prices,

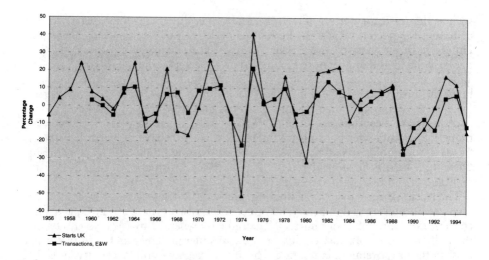

Figure 1   Percentage changes in new private starts and housing transactions 1956–95

Source: Central Statistical Office and Board of Inland Revenue

albeit with marked regional variations, have all increased since 1991. But they have done so to a less marked extent and with a more fluctuating pattern than in previous recoveries. Indeed it was only by the summer of 1996 that there were signs of sustained increases in housing lending, prices and market activity.

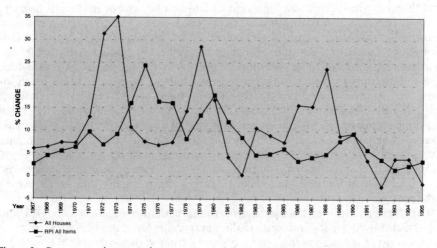

Figure 2   Percentage changes in house prices and the retail price index (RPI) 1967–95

Source: Central Statistical Office and Department of Environment DoE non mix adjusted house prices, at mortgage completion stage

The sluggish performance of the UK housing market has prompted a number of ad hoc explanations, most accompanied by calls to reflate the housing market. Some have emphasised 'hangover' factors from the housing market recession, such as the depressing effect of negative and lost equity on trading-up activity and of reduced expectations about the real capital gains to be achieved in housing. Others have emphasised more long term structural change explanations, particularly the likelihood of more flexible labour markets reducing income certainty and, in turn, the demand for home-ownership. Many of these explanations have, however, neglected or de-emphasised two more obvious and important factors. First, rising disposable incomes are a critical factor in housing market recovery and they have been missing until 1996. Secondly, inflation rates have been extremely low and lower house price inflation is likely to have reduced the urgency for new households to enter the sector and of existing home-owners to trade-up. Once these factors are considered the 1992–1996 performance of the UK housing market can still be regarded as different but hardly mysterious.

The recent performance of the housing, market, though welcomed by some economic commentators as dampening inflationary impulses, is now raising considerable concern from a number of quarters. The million owners with negative equity, and the millions more with lost equity, are clearly suffering stress as house prices rise close to the low, overall inflation rate. The map of negative and lost equity in the UK correlates very closely and positively with percentage shares of Conservative votes and with an election in prospect, back-benchers are manifesting an acute interest in housing market trends. Finally, and reinforcing the concerns of owner/voters and their representatives, there is a continuing wave of Jeremiah-like pundits forecasting continuing recession in UK housing markets for as long as 30 years ahead, though their views have had less credibility as 1996 has progressed.

Structuring an explanation

This chapter, whilst reflecting on recent boom-bust behaviour in the UK housing market, seeks to explore how and why the behaviour of the market has changed and whether this is likely to be a permanent shift. Three broad avenues of explanation are investigated. First, the severity of the 1989–1992 housing market downturn has created adverse household circumstances for particular groups which have still not unwound and, at the same time, changed more general expectations about the riskiness of and returns to housing investment. Secondly, there is the possibility that long-term structural shifts in the labour market, driven by global economic competition, are now more evident and are layered upon the lingering effects of housing recession. Thirdly, broad economic and housing policy changes have played a key role in restraining the housing market. That is, in seeking competitive, low inflationary growth there is a deliberate policy strategy to avoid boom and bust in housing, and other, markets and to secure long term growth with lower inflation.

Whilst it is a convenient simplification to discuss change factors as being cyclical, structural or policy-induced, reality may be more complex. Structural or secular shifts, for instance the growing share of home-ownership in the national tenure pattern, may impact on the timing and extent of instabilities. The nature of past instabilities may also shift the growth path of the economy; witness, for example, the Chancellor's avowed intent to avoid boom and bust possibilities as the rationale for current UK interest rates. And policy shifts arise from past experience as well as hopes and fears for the future.

This chapter is not a hard econometric analysis of the evolution of the UK housing market (cf. Miles, 1994) though it does draw upon the results of empirical studies and models. This emphasis is not just a reflection of the technical limitations of the author but also arises because current models and data gathering for the UK housing market seldom include all of the key driving linkages which flow back and forth between the economy and the housing market. All too often important operational features of housing markets are assumed away in reductionist overall modelling; for instance, the inevitable and critical regional dimension of housing markets. Indeed it may be misleading, for both housing and economic policy purposes to conceive of a 'national' housing market.

The next section takes an expanded view of major interactions between housing and the economy. In subsequent sections specific key links in relation to housing demand, housing investment, housing turnover and housing prices are examined. Policy shifts are then outlined and some future directions for housing market policy probed. Finally, the chapter then offers a brief conclusion.

Housing in the Economy

Obvious interactions

The importance of housing in national economic magnitudes is indisputable. On average residential construction accounts for a fifth of gross fixed capital formation; paying for housing typically absorbs between a quarter and a third of the incomes of relatively new buyers; housing assets now comprise a third of net household wealth and housing loans are the largest element of personal sector debts (Glass, 1994). It is also well established that the UK housing market has a strongly cyclical pattern. There have been three major cycles in prices and output since the early 1970s, see Figure 1, and UK instability lies towards the top end of European Union experience (along with Finland and Sweden), see Stephens (1995). Housing cycles have an amplitude markedly greater than the economy as a whole.

Until the late 1980s housing-economy connections were primarily seen as comprising two key sets of linkages, see Figure 3. First, it was widely recognised that rising household formation, disposable income growth and falling interest rates increased the demand for home-ownership. Rising demand promoted an increase in housing investment which induced higher demands for construction employment, building materials and so on. Income and profits earned in these sectors then raised aggregate demand. Subsequently an inflation effect was likely both directly from rising house prices and indirectly from the multiplier effects of construction activity.

In this view of the economy, the driving force was the growth and change in macro-magnitudes, particularly income and interest rates, with relatively simple reinforcing feedbacks on employment and inflation. Empirical evidence (see Meen, 1995) confirms that such influences are of considerable significance and weight in econometric analysis of the economy and the housing market and have remained so in the 1992–95 period. However, it is a theoretical and empirical approach which attributes little to the nature of the housing sector and its role in transforming macro changes into specific price and output effects. A more subtle analysis is required.

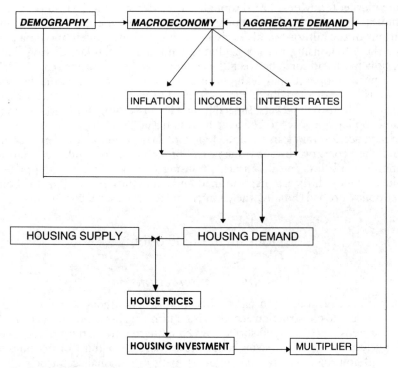

Figure 3   Key housing–economy links: old view

Emerging connections

The 1980s boom and 1990s bust have drawn attention to previously unconsidered influences (Ermisch, 1990). Firstly, it was recognised that demand side expansion, and contraction, impacted not only upon new housing investment but also had major effects on household mobility. There is clear empirical evidence that house price increases and the volume of transactions are strongly positively correlated in the UK, see Figures 1 and 2. Movement involves transaction costs and professional service employment (surveyors, lawyers, estate agents etc) as well as expenditure on consumer durables and the possibility of equity extraction. Prior to the 1990s the consequences of market activity levels for consumption had largely been ignored.

The second major omission was even more surprising. From the 1950s onwards UK citizens and politicians had been widely aware of real long run gains in holding housing assets. The growing, until 1989, housing wealth of UK homeowners and its impacts on consumption were only recognised in economic analysis just about when they had stopped occurring (Muellbauer, 1990). With 1980s house prices increasing ahead of rapidly growing consumer borrowing, housing came to form 45% of personal sector wealth by 1988. This wealth also represented a gross net equity in housing of around £800 billion. Falls and rises in this total no doubt had a direct effect on household well-being and consumption, even without housing equity withdrawal. However equity withdrawal, see Figure 4, rose significantly in the boom in turn fuelling consumer spending (Muellbauer 1990; Westaway 1994).

These two additional mechanisms of 'turnover' and 'housing wealth' imply more complex feedback effects from housing to the economy. Further as housing starts, price increases, turnover and wealth gains are all positively correlated it is readily apparent why housing sector feedback effects have a strongly pro-cyclical effect on the economy. And these effects have been growing in scale over time as real housing values have increased and the home-ownership sector has expanded both in absolute terms and as a share of dwelling stock.

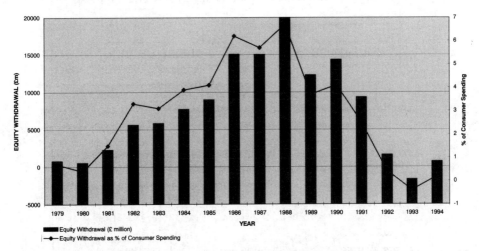

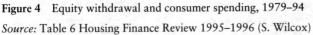

Figure 4   Equity withdrawal and consumer spending, 1979–94

Source: Table 6 Housing Finance Review 1995–1996 (S. Wilcox)

Recognition of this suite of cyclical effects calls for more attention to the role of housing in the economy. The traditional view of the housing market as a simple receptor and reinforcer of macro-change could still be maintained, even if more and subtle linkages have to be embraced. This may now be the prevalent view amongst mainstream UK economists (Miles, 1994) and the Treasury; it was most clearly articulated by the Chief Economist at DoE in the autumn of 1994 (Glass, 1994).

But is it enough? Is there not a more worrying concern that the price and output performance of the UK housing market affect real economic magnitudes which shape the growth path of the economy and worsen the growth-inflation trade-off? Are there imperfect housing or credit market features or imperfect policy arrangements which have negative consequences for the economy in the longer term?

Micro-economics research does not conclude that the housing market can be viewed as a competitive, unitary system. Credit markets are also segmented and incomplete. Aside from the obvious spatial dimension, there are well established supply inelasticities which are not solely the product of restrictive land zoning (Malpezzi and Maclennan, 1994). When housing prices rise they affect wage claims and efficiency wages. Research evidence suggests that both sharply rising (Bover et al., 1988) and sharply falling (Maclennan, 1994) house prices may hamper labour mobility. And with major regional differences in economic

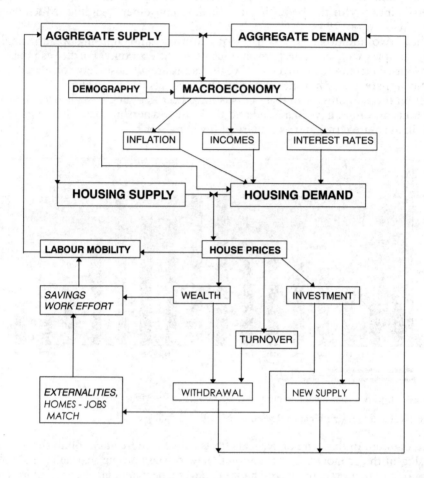

Figure 5   Key housing–economy links: emerging view

growth, house prices and house price changes it is doubtful if policy control via mortgage rate increases is either fair or efficient. At the same time housing invest-ment may have important long term 'externality' effects on family wellbeing, health and crime rates, all of which ultimately impact the aggregate supply capa-city of an economy. There is room, therefore, for the view that there is a diversity of important ways in which housing markets operate can influence the growth-inflation trade-off, or the non-accelerating inflation rate of unemployment. Links from the housing sector to the supply-side of the UK economy are only now, for the first time, being explored.

The research of the last decade suggests that the appropriate 'wiring diagram' of linkages, back and forward, between the economy and the housing market is considerably more complex than implied in Figure 3. A possible framework for examining the relevant connections is summarised in Figure 5. With this chart in mind we can begin to explain the present and contemplate the future in a broad supply-demand framework.

Prices and quantities of houses sold in the owner-occupied market reflect, broadly, the demand for and supply of homes. In assessing how housing markets are changing it is useful to unravel demand and supply side changes.

Key Linkages, Changing Demand

Housing and tenure choices

The demand for owner-occupation essentially reflects two household decisions. First, it can be argued, the consumer chooses between housing and other goods and services and, secondly, chooses between housing tenure alternatives. UK evidence, in line with other advanced economies, suggests that the income inelasticity of demand for housing lies between one and two, that is housing spending rises at least as fast as income. Past, but only cross-section, studies indicate that the price elasticity of demand is around –0.5, that is demand rises (falls) relatively little as prices fall (rise). However, for quite sustained periods of time optimistic price expectations may result in rising prices and rising demand.

The manifestation of these demands, however, within a particular tenure sector depends on a plethora of other factors, and these can be grouped into three key influences – preferences, the user cost of capital and non-price constraints. And, of course, in moving from individual to market demand change in the number of households is a critical influence. To understand the cyclical nature of the housing market and recent experience these myriad influences have to be considered in more depth.

Demographics

The housing market is impacted by the changing age structure of the existing stock of owners, but it is new household formation and its impact on the number of first-time buyers which has the most significant role.

Fluctuations in birth rates tend to be reflected, 20 to 25 years later, in demands for independent living. Holmans has established (1995) the size of the 23–25 age group rose from 2.3 million at the start of the 1980s to 2.9 million in 1993 and is likely to fall to a low point of 2 million in the year 2001.

These calculations suggest that the longer population cycle reinforced housing demands otherwise arising in the long economic boom of the 1980s and have then turned down at much the same time as the general economic cycle. However, Holmans has produced two important supplementary pieces of evidence. First, age of entry to the housing market varies with the economic cycle. That is, the boom period 1984–88 witnessed a tendency for home-ownership entrants from a given age group to accelerate their purchase dates. This effect, which supports the notion of a 'frenzy' factor when households assume that prices will continue to rise, probably led to 86,000 households advancing purchases into the boom period, thereby depressing demand in the subsequent 1989–1993 period. This highlights an important self-reinforcing effect of house price changes.

Holmans also notes, however, that this forward shift only explains about a fifth of the extent to which the actual flow of first-time buyers in the 1989–93 period fell short of expected new entry levels given current age structures and past age-specific entry rates. Age-specific home-ownership entry rates rose in the 1983–1988 period, adding a quarter of a million 'additional' entrants in that period. However, between 1989 and 1993, age-specific entry rates behaved very differently. It is clear that these rates fell most for younger entrants, and overall there were some 440,000 new entrants less than anticipated in the 1989–93 period. The JRF household surveys of Luton, Bristol and Glasgow in 1993, see Maclennan (1994), produced micro-evidence which indicated that a third of home-buyers in the 1989–93 period, had postponed purchases, and 9% delayed entry to independent living, as house prices were falling and incomes were uncertain. These effects were almost absent in Glasgow where nominal house prices continued to rise.

In the sections which follow the economic influences which shaped such decisions are considered in more detail. At this point however it is useful to review three possible interpretations of the Holmans figures. First, it is clear that, *ceteris paribus*, demographic pressures on the market will reduce towards 2001 but household formation rates will still be positive. This does not mean that house prices will have to fall; rather it means that equilibrium levels of additional housing output will be smaller than in the 1980s, as will the market for first-time buyer loans. Secondly, it could be argued that the 'lost' first-time buyers are postponing entry until the economy and housing market further strengthen, and this may accelerate rapidly any upswing which does now occur especially if age-specific entry rates return to 1980s levels. A final, and more likely, interpretation is that 'postponed' purchasers will gradually re-enter the market but with age-specific entry rates for the under 25s remaining lower than in the 1980s.

More education, less housing

Such a change would represent an important structural shift in young persons' housing demands and it has implications for rental sector provision, government policy and the cyclical stability of the housing market. It is also noteworthy that in two countries with home-ownership shares similar to the UK, the USA and Australia, age-specific home-ownership rates have been falling for the under 30s since the early 1980s. Linneman and Gyurko (1995) suggest that in the USA, where reductions are spreading up the age distribution, they reflect changes in education and in the structure of employment and incomes as economic policy has sought a better trained and more flexible labour. Is there any evidence to suggest similar shifts in the UK? In Sweden, with a recent market experience similar to the UK, age-specific ownership rates are also falling sharply.

Before turning, in the next section, to changes in incomes, it is important to note a recent and significant shift in the behaviour of young people in Britain which has not been discussed in the housing market debate. The proportion of UK school leavers progressing to full time education has jumped sharply since 1988. In England alone the numbers increased from 567,000 to 897,000 (1994).

This growth will have diverted some demand (18–21 year olds) from owning to renting as more young people study rather then enter employment. But there are wider and long term implications as parents and students now pay an increasing proportion of student living costs. Students now commonly leave courses with debts, often in the range £3,000–£4,000. By 1995 only £20 million of the £751 million lent since 1990 under the Student Loans Scheme had been repaid. This overhang of educational debt, and with increased parental support likely to reduce gifts for deposits on homes, will undoubtedly postpone entry to home-ownership. The importance of these factors will grow as both major political parties wish to see higher education grow and parents take increasing responsibility for fees.

There is a real issue here. Future economic competitiveness, the Government argues, requires greater flexibility (less certainty of incomes) and higher skill levels (implying more personal sector 'educational' debt). But both trends will delay entry to ownership. Alan Holmans 'missing first-time buyers' may increasingly be already debt encumbered former students seeking to establish their real career chances and renting for the meantime. It would be no surprise if age-specific purchase rates remained depressed (by historic standards) for the under 25s but recovered for the 25–35 age range.

Incomes and employment

Slow Income Growth?

As noted above, income is a key shaper of housing spending and prices. Rising GDP per capita usually boosts the demand for home-ownership both by increasing incomes and by reducing the fear of increases in unemployment. That is, home-ownership growth is associated with greater incomes and increased security for potential buyers. Why is the owner occupied housing market not now recovering? GDP growth ran at a rate of almost 4% in 1994 and has been increasing for almost three years. Unemployment has also fallen, significantly, from 11.5 to 8%. So what has changed?

First, as noted above, it is personal, disposable income per capita, and not GDP, which drives housing demand. During the 1990s recovery personal, disposable income has been growing much less rapidly than GDP; it rose by 1.3% in 1993 and by even less, 0.8%, in 1994. These rates are well below the 2.4% per annum achieved in the 1980s. They reflect the fact that in the early recovery phase profits recovered much more rapidly than wage rates. And, of course, the three budgets from 1992–94 created a steady increase in the average household tax burden. Even by mid 1995 average pay settlements (3.5%) were barely above the headline inflation rate.

A key change, therefore, from earlier recovery periods is that economic policies and labour market conditions have meant that households have captured a smaller share of upswing growth in income. As disposable household income is a major driving force in the housing market it is hardly surprising that the overall market remained sluggish and that the regions with now recovering house prices are those where incomes and employment have risen most rapidly over the last year.

Changing employment and 'flexibility'

These observations would suggest that the relationship between GDP growth and disposable household income has changed. In part, at least, this is due to changes in the labour market which have shifted patterns of income, employment and bargaining power since the start of the 1980s (see Gibb, 1994). However, these same changes may also affect the certainty of home-owners, and others, about current incomes and future jobs. If so, they will then also alter the relationship between current disposable incomes and the demand for home-ownership. Income certainty positively affects ownership demand and, of course, the willingness of lenders to provide home loans. What, then, are the relevant changes in UK labour markets?

The large stock of low-cost, unskilled labour in newly emerging countries and labour saving technological progress at home have resulted in downward pressure on the wage rates of unskilled workers in advanced economies and/or reduced employment prospects (see Maclennan, 1994). At the same time more skilled workers have faced a different context of rising real earnings but reduced job and income certainty. For instance, organisational changes within firms, with a new emphasis on out-sourcing reducing the core size of organisations, has generated both higher redundancy rates and more flexible employment contracts for managers. Similar forces have impacted on the public sector from Her Majesty's Treasury to local refuse collection services.

Part-time employment has grown steadily since 1974 (from 14 to 20% of the workforce). Self-employment has doubled (up from 6 to 12%) and temporary employment risen from 2 to 5%. Further trends have been the growth in employment for women and reductions in the male activity rate. Even for those with jobs 'pay' certainty in the medium term has been reduced by the growth of performance related pay.

In brief over the last 20 years more skilled women have displaced unskilled men in the workforce and the certainty of future incomes and where and how they will be earned has been reduced. Further, whilst earnings for those already in work have been increasing, wages for new entrants have been steadily falling (Wadsworth, 1995a). These trends have not developed suddenly, they have mostly been apparent for the last two decades.

The issues are now recognised to be important in the housing market for two reasons. First, the downturn in the economy in 1989 really exposed the downside effects of 'flexibility'; in growth periods 'flexibility' has beneficial effects but in the downswing it is likely to mean faster and more sectorally/socially spread unemployment. Secondly, the rapid growth in home-ownership from 1978–88 was partly driven by a policy intent to spread home-ownership to all socio-economic groups, including those with lower and less certain incomes.

Some commentators have argued that 1980s labour market deregulation has resulted in a more 'flexible' labour market (Minford and Riley, 1994); others believe that the labour market is no more efficient than in the past even if the earnings dispersion has increased and households feel less certain (Gregg and Machin, 1994).

To be useful, the notion of 'flexibility' does need to be explored and explained. In essence, the notion implies that markets are adjusting more in line with price signals. That is, if labour demand falls there are effects on both wage rates and employment as respondents make their own labour supply decisions. Equally, if labour demand expands then price signals will encourage workers to retrain, relocate etc. In this context, it is reasonable to distinguish between 'downward flexibility', i.e. when firms wish to lay off labour, as opposed to 'upward flexibility' when specific demands are rising. Prior to 1994 most of the UK 'testing' of flexibility notions had been in the context of deindustrialisation (i.e. downward flexibility impacts on the unskilled), i.e. 'downward' shifts. Flexibility in the upswing is only now being tested.

Downward Flexibility and Tenure

The findings from national surveys and local research make it clear that 'downward flexibility' for semi and unskilled labour in the UK largely impacted, until 1990, on the rental sectors and especially in the council housing sector. This reflected a number of different processes, particularly:

- council housing had been expanded in the period 1955–75 to house the labour market groups who subsequently became unemployment prone in the post-oil shock era
- the declining physical quality of vacancies in the sector and, after 1978, the shift of subsidies towards means tested rental subsidies and away from renting to owning meant that home-ownership became increasingly attractive for households with jobs
- Right-to-buy policies, after 1980, encouraged tenants with modest incomes and less skilled jobs to purchase their previously rented homes.

In consequence, by the end of the 1980s fewer than one household in three in the council sector was connected to the labour market and cross-tenure income differences grew. Conversely, home ownership had grown in the 1980s boom to embrace less-skilled households who were always likely to be unemployment prone in the downswing. By 1991, for example, some two-fifths of semi-skilled manual workers were owners with a mortgage and a quarter of the unskilled had a mortgage. This pattern, importantly, varied from region to region. The 1989 JRF surveys (see Maclennan et al., 1991) indicated that the social housing sectors in northern regions (and London) housed almost double the proportion of partly-skilled and unskilled workers similarly housed in the south.

Home-Owners in Trouble

When the late 1980s downswing ensued the owner-occupied sector was therefore exposed to a much higher risk of job loss, and income loss, than in past recessions. First, 'downward flexibility' spread job loss further up the job skill/income distribution. Secondly, the sector (and especially in the south) contained higher proportions of traditionally unemployment prone skill groups.

That said, owner-occupation, both at the end of the 1980s and at the start of the recovery, was a 'job rich' housing tenure. Both the 1989 and 1993 JRF surveys give a flavour of the broad patterns. These surveys revealed that

- some 56% of all adults have full-time jobs, and 11% part-time employment
- in households of working age there is an average of 1.5 jobs, with a third of homes containing full-time workers, 55% two jobs (full or part-time) and only 13% (usually retired) no jobs
- women workers had a strong life-cycle pattern of employment.

Cross section studies reveal a low rate of unemployment for adults in home-ownership, of the order of 3 to 4%. This is less than half the national average.

More detailed analysis of the 1993 JRF surveys indicated that this rate varied in significant ways:

- it was substantially higher in Bristol and Luton than in Glasgow (reflecting past regional tenure specialisation)
- it was higher for men than women
- it was significantly higher for men in the age groups 16–20 and 51–64 (averaging 10%).

These figures, however serious, nevertheless mask the real extent of job and income loss for home-owners. The 1993 survey contained only those households then 'surviving' in ownership. Unemployment can lead to relatively fast home repossession (within a year). Ford and Kimpson (1995) have recently argued that the impact of the 'flexible labour market' on home-owners is also clear. Only a third of households that lost their homes were headed by someone in a full-time permanent job. Two out of ten were self-employed and one in 20 had a temporary job'. It is difficult to move from a 'stock' of repossession cases to a 'flow' rate of unemployment. As other studies, (e.g. SRS, 1995) also report unemployment and income loss as responsible for half to two-thirds of home repossessions then, with some 4% of UK homes repossessed since 1989, the Ford and Kimpson conclusion appears to be justified.

A further consideration is that households dropping out of the labour force do not always enter the 'unemployed' category; this applies to women reporting themselves as 'housewife' and men and women taking 'early-retirement'. The 1993 JRF survey reported 14% of 51–60 year old men as retired and a rise in the reported share of 'housewife' respondents in the same age group.

The 1993 JRF survey probed the economic experience of home-owner adults over the 1989–1993 period. That analysis suggested a more pervasive role for labour market flexibility, see Table 1. A quarter of adults in Luton and a fifth in Bristol had lost their jobs, and a fifth more suffered a significant loss in income. In Glasgow, fewer lost jobs, fewer lost incomes and a higher proportion of those made unemployed were re-employed. As the average unemployment rate in Glasgow (at nearly 20%) was double that of the other regions involved these figures primarily reflect the mis-matching of lower skilled jobs and housing tenures in the southern areas. In the south, job loss rates were lower for professional and skilled owners than for less skilled mortgage owners. The Social Class As and Bs suffered less than the C1s and C2s.

Table 1 Regional differences

	Percent of Adults Losing Jobs	Proportion of Job Losers Re-employed	Percent Keeping Jobs But Losing Incomes
Glasgow	14.2	94	10
Bristol	19.5	88	17
Luton	25.7	89	21

Source: 1993 JRF Survey

The survey, see Table 2, also revealed that two-thirds of those men losing jobs were re-employed, but only 30% of women. Some 7% of job losers who were men became 'early retired' whilst 43% of women left the labour force, at least temporarily. There was also evidence that for a given age and socio-economic group, those losing jobs then re-employed had annual incomes 10 to 15% below those of equivalent categories not losing jobs. This suggests that mortgage debt commitments encourage wage flexibility when owners become unemployed.

Table 2 Current status of those who lost jobs in the 1989–93 period (per cent)

	Men	Women
Full-Time Work	64	29
Part-Time Work	5	14
Unemployed	24	14
Other	7	43
n	140	96

Source: 1993 JRF Survey

There are two important conclusions from this analysis. First, changing labour market and housing tenure patterns inter-meshed throughout the 1980s to form a more cyclically unstable nexus in the housing market. Secondly, a fifth of southern owners faced a 'moment of truth' in the job market and survived as owners. Those that did were acutely aware of the 6% who did not. Clearly a large segment of owners will have revised their expectations about the ease of sustaining home-ownership in a downswing and this unease is still evident in saving/consumer spending patterns, housing market behaviour (can we really afford to trade-up?) and political opinion polls.

Interest Rates and User Costs

Changes in jobs and incomes are not the only uncertainties facing home-owners with mortgages. Mortgage rates are another key influence on both housing demand and discretionary disposable income for households.

Variable rate mortgages

Prior to 1989 fewer than 7% of UK home owners used fixed rate mortgages, a stark contrast to European patterns where fixed rates were the norm. After the high mortgage rates of 1989 and 1990 more than half of new mortgages had fixed rate arrangements. The JRF sample in 1993, by no means intended as a national sample, indicated that few of these mortgages had an average fixed-rate duration of more than four years. In the mid 1990s, fixed rate loans comprised around a third of new loans to former-owners and first-time buyers.

There has been no UK research on why some households take fixed rate loans and others do not. Nor has there been much discussion of the long-term implications of changing the mix. The present UK approach with mainly variable loans and short-fixed rates means that UK purchasers are still more exposed to interest rate changes than European competitors. In consequence short term changes in interest rates are still likely to see stronger links between the housing sector and the economy than say, France and Germany. On the other hand, fixed rate systems often have more pronounced quantity cycles – purchases fall sharply when fixed rates are rising and rise when they fall. Variable rates ameliorate such influences.

The key issue for the future is whether in a world of globally determined interest rates, even without monetary union, the UK can afford to have markedly different housing loan instruments from major competitors. But for the present, although Britain remains confused about its choice of instruments, there is no evidence that the mix available is, in any way, depressing housing market demand.

Interest rates and user cost of capital

Rising mortgage rates in 1989 and 1990 did much to curtail the boom and, throughout the 1990s, there have been recurrent calls to reduce or restrain interest rates to 'encourage' the housing market. And there has been some surprise that with interest rates at low levels that demand did not rise more rapidly in the period 1993 to 1995. Arguably, with the deregulation of mortgage markets and the introduction of market clearing mortgage rates it could have been expected that housing demand, via mortgage rates, would have become more and not less synchronised with the evolution of macro-variables.

The reason that such a relationship is not more evident is that the prevailing rate of interest on a loan is only one of several components of the real cost of using capital to purchase a home (this is labelled, in technical economic circles as 'the user cost of capital', see Miles (1994)). If an individual rents a home, then the cost of their housing services is the rent paid. If they own, however, a range of factors influences their real costs of using capital in housing. Obviously higher mortgage rates, management and maintenance costs increase user cost. However, there are at least two key other factors, inflation and taxation.

The impact of inflation on the UK housing market has been rather neglected in past discussions, but it is crucial to understanding the economics of mortgage based ownership growth. There are three relevant considerations. First, mortgage debt is fixed in current (or nominal) values. After the value of debt is fixed, when a home is bought, inflation may then raise household nominal incomes, thereby eroding repayment to income ratios and reducing pressure on the household budgets of borrowers. Only if nominal mortgage rates are adjusted (on variable rate debt) to fully reflect inflation does the real debt to income relationship remain unchanged. In general, UK mortgage rates have not made such compensating adjustments (implying that savers have subsidised borrowers).

The second influence has been that house price inflation rates and the general inflation rate have generally been positively correlated. From 1968 to 1989, real UK house price gains ran at an average of 2 to 3% per annum, albeit that the pattern was strongly cyclical. Thirdly, it could be argued that inflation facilitated a smooth, if distorted, operation of the housing market. The direct prospect of mortgage arrears or default was reduced by falling real repayments and rising real values. Movement was easier when past 'gains' were available to pay transaction costs and movement costs.

Taxation, in the context of the UK, meant that MIRAS reduced the real user cost. However, both in relation to taxation and inflation the mid 1990s are very different world from a decade ago. Over time inflation and policy change have reduced the share of mortgage interest financed by tax expenditures from 40% in the mid-1970s, through 20% in the mid-1980s to 8% at the present time. The 1995 reductions in income support payments for mortgage interest (ISMI), see further below, have also added to the real user cost of capital. In relation to inflation, current policy imperatives to maintain low rates through interest rate changes mean that inflation is unlikely to erode real user costs in the foreseeable future.

When all of these influences on the real costs of financing home-ownership are taken into account, it is clear that not only have real user costs been historically high and positive in the 1990s (at plus 10%, see Miles 1994), contrasting with negative values in the previous two upswings) but they are also likely to continue to be so as long as 'competitive disinflation' is the key thrust of national economic policy. And if British jobs are to survive and be created then low inflation rates will be a necessity.

Arguably, the UK housing market is adapting to a major shift towards real economic fundamentals rather than inflationary expectations, shaping housing market evolution. Households will have to pay for housing in real terms with reduced subsidies, and in that context they will be increasingly sensitive to expectations about interest rates and incomes. It is, then, hardly surprising that the UK housing market is behaving differently in the upswing of the 1990s. Before reviewing present experience and looking forwards it is now pertinent to examine key supply side linkages running between housing and the economy.

Key Linkages: Shifting Supply and Turnover

New construction

There is no great mystery about the current behaviour of the residential construction sector in the UK. After increasing levels of output in 1993 and for much of 1994, new housing starts declined in the first quarter of 1995 before rising again into 1996. This is a predictable reflection of slow and uncertain housing demand growth.

Econometric research (see Meen, 1995) indicates that private residential construction responds with a lag to increases in consumer income and house prices. It is also clear that rising interest rates are quickly reflected in reduced starts, not just because of their demand side implications but also because construction activity is largely financed from bank borrowing. Clearly a recovery in new construction will only follow a sustained recovery in incomes and house price stability.

There are, however, two important aspects of the construction sector which are noteworthy in relation to the changing nature of UK cycles. Overall housing construction appears to have become more pro-cyclical during the last decade. There are three factors contributing to this shift. Public new construction, which was generally less cyclical than the market sector, has fallen sharply as a share of output. Secondly, there has been a post 1980 tendency for public housing investment to become pro rather than anti-cyclical. Prior to the 1980s governments often raised or maintained public starts as an anti-recession measure. With the abandonment of Keynesian orthodoxy the more recent practice has been to reduce public spending as the Government deficit rises in recession – 1992 was a major exception. At the same time new construction has fallen as a share of private housing output whilst repair and improvement have increased. As will be shown in the next section, rising housing equity for existing owners is an important determinant of owner occupier repair behaviour. In consequence the market sector has also become more cyclical.

The second important question, looking forward, is whether the residential construction sector has now formed new expectations about the market, or whether 'old cycles' still dominate expectations. In 1991 and 1992 the recession generated reductions in the building cost index and in land prices, and this may have helped the recovery in market volume in 1993 and 1994. But the cost indices are now rising, especially materials such as glass and cement, and land prices for housing have risen in most parts of the UK since 1993. This raises a fundamental point. If these costs and prices were based on 'old' expectations about housing market recovery then they are likely to be disappointed and the current recovery in building industry profits halted.

On the other hand, the UK housing supply industry has displayed notoriously low supply price elasticities. Recession in the housing industry disrupts and destroys firms and leads to the closure, sometimes permanently, of building material supply capacity. Land zoning may remain tight in many locations. That is, the non-inflationary capacity limit of the industry may have been seriously dented by the deep recession from 1989–1992. Indeed, it is likely to be these supply side factors which have under-pinned the 1994 and 1996 house price rises ahead of the inflation rate in growth regions such as East Anglia and the East Midlands.

The long-term issue here is that there may now be a fundamental shift occurring in consumer perceptions of the housing market which has not been matched by restructuring of housing provision cost structures. If that is the case, then housing output is unlikely to rise significantly in the short-term, indeed until demand pressures grow. New construction costs may provide a 'floor' to UK housing prices.

Turnover

At any point in time the flow of vacancies in the housing market comprises not just newly completed units but also sales of existing units. Some of these vacancies arise from household deaths, emigration and switches into the rental sector by existing owners. The vast bulk of second-hand vacancies arise from moving owners, who are both buying and selling homes. In the introduction it was noted that the broader economic consequences of this flow had largely been ignored until the late 1980s. This was an important omission in understanding cyclical behaviour.

The volume of housing market transactions in England since 1982 is indicated in Figure 1. Transactions for Northern Ireland and Scotland are available separately, and they indicate much greater stability over the 1988–1993 period. The regional pattern also differs sharply within England. In general, from 1988–93, the percentage reduction in the volume of transactions in the northern regions was significantly higher than in southern areas; that is, northern regions had a greater degree of endogeneity which was reflected in lower downward price pressures in the recession. For whatever reason, southern markets appear to have lower levels of discretion about when housing moves are made. Further, the sharp, post 1990 rise in the ultimate forced move, repossession, has meant that a significant proportion (ranging from 5 to 10% in southern regions) of transactions in recent years have been in falling markets.

Reduced volumes of new construction and turnover in the existing stock reflect rational supply side reactions, in the main, to 1990s economic conditions. As noted above, with present demand side patterns, and their likely persistence, the volume of new housing output in owner occupation is likely to remain low unless construction costs and land costs fall further in real terms. As these markets have their own ratchets, or inflexibilities, then such reductions may take some time as low nominal inflation rates eat slowly into real costs. Equally, lower inflation is likely to reduce the speed and frequency of local trading-up with households facing smaller 'cushions' of past capital gains.

In this chapter, so far, there has been an emphasis on how the economy impacts the housing sector. And it has been argued that housing market behaviour has been predictable given new economic realities and policies. However, it was argued in the introduction that the housing sector interacts with and mediates current macro-economic forces to feed back on or shape subsequent change. Hence the widespread belief that 'housing held back' the upswing. The next section of the chapter addresses these 'feedback' effects occurring when demand and supply interact.

Feedback Effects from Housing Output, Turnover and Prices

It is apparent, from what is written above and by others, that the housing market does not have a neutral, linear dynamic within the economy. This is not to claim that the housing sector can drive permanent economic growth or change, far from it. Rather, it is a complex sector which shapes broader macro-economic change into price, output and incentive effects which fashion the national economic structure left to confront the next wave of change. Hydrologists who wish to explain floods and flows have to know not just the physics of river systems but the characteristics of channels through which waters flow. Housing channels shape the macro-economies flows and to claim otherwise is absurd reductionism.

Housing activity and construction employment

There is a long recognised linkage from housing demand, through supply, to construction sector employment and profits. Some estimates (see Maclennan, 1994) suggest that a third of the jobs lost in the downswing were in the construction sector. In general the investment of £1 million in housing results in 20 to 25 construction jobs (for a year). With combined private sector and housing association starts declining then residential construction employment is now falling as is domestic demand for building materials (though exports increased by 14% in 1994). Builders reported profits rose in 1994, as did the share values of material producers, but both are likely to slip back in 1995. As noted in the previous section, there is no reason to believe that they will increase significantly in the few years ahead until supply side prices adjust.

Turnover, Consumption and Employment

Nor is there any surge in the volume of transaction volumes on the horizon. As noted above, static or falling house prices induces withdrawal from the market. The 1993 JRF surveys probed some of these dimensions of mover discretion, contrasting the sharply contracting markets of Luton and Bristol with modest decline in Glasgow. In the southern cities some 35% of the non-moving owners had removed their properties from the market place or subsequently deferred market search. Further as markets weakened there was a high proportion of 'forced' movers within the group that had moved (in contrast to Glasgow, or earlier boom-period studies of English regions).

This 'endogenous' withdrawal, which has contributed in the past to a 'ratchet' effect on nominal house prices, reflects rational consumer re-timing of primarily local moves. In the downturn, selling time (costs) rise, higher interest rates discourage up-market moves to larger loans and homes and, of course, selling prices may shade. Questions arise, see below, as to whether this is a fully rational response for all households, but it is, regardless, what the majority do.

In consequence when prices in the market begin to rise less rapidly, or fall, the volume of transactions also falls (in contrast to most goods markets). This matters to employment and consumption. In the UK 2–3% of sales values pay for professional fees – estate agents, surveyors and solicitors. Issuing new loans also involves a fee and employs financial sector personnel. Moving home, another 1% on the average house value, adds to the demand for removal services. And then there are the new carpets, curtains, furniture, white goods, garden gnomes, plants and so on. These are the sectors of 'high street' sales in which volumes and margins remained depressed, into the mid-1990s.

There are few precise numbers on how moving home either boosts or shifts (in time) the demand for household durables. Moving provides an opportunity for households to extract housing equity. Arguably such funds could have entered other forms of assets/savings, particularly for older households, but younger households used the vast bulk of withdrawn equity to pay transaction costs and buy durables for the new home. If all moving equity withdrawn had been spent in the boom years, this would have added 3 to 4% to consumption expenditure. Glass (1994), on the basis of Treasury estimates, does suggest that housing moves do contribute to fluctuations in spending on consumer durables.

Although the precise magnitudes are not known it is clear that housing moves are pro-cyclical and that they boost consumption in the upswing and depress it in the downswing. Clearly a less cyclical pattern of housing market activity would help to stabilise consumption.

The presently sluggish volume of transactions, with the number of moving owners running just above half the level of 1988, has restrained consumer spending. But existing households, other than the minority who previously traded-up to 'over-consume' housing for asset gain purposes, cannot stay put forever. The number of moving owners is presently similar to that prevailing in the 1975–81 period, although the UK stock of home-owners has subsequently risen from 11.5 to 15.5 million. This suggests that mobility rates, for the last four years, have lain a third below (crudely) expected levels. In turn, this implies that there are 10–15% of owners who are frustrated movers. This is broadly consistent within the JRF 1993 survey which suggested a higher rate of almost a fifth.

At a maximum there are 1.5 to 2 million home-owners in the UK who would like to move. Why do they not do so? Some, but not all of these households, have negative equity (see below). Others are awaiting income increases and others may be waiting for prices to recover. The rationality of this latter group is questionable. In general, in the 1993 JRF case studies, price falls were proportionately greater for higher value homes. There has been little recognition by those holding lower value homes that they could wipe out their net housing capital losses by moving up-market. Perhaps their selling costs are exceptionally high as first-time buyers have disappeared, or they may have resolved to invest less in housing. Whatever the cause, it is likely that any increase in first-time buyers in the market would trigger extensive chains of market movement in the present context of 'frustrated' owners. The abiding concern of government must be how to unwind owner frustration without triggering inflationary house price increases.

Housing Wealth and Consumption

The last key connection is the asset role of housing in the economy. There are periods over which Britons have become habituated, perhaps addicted to, real house price increases. *Real* house prices in Britain increased every year from 1959 to 1973, and from 1958 to 1993 real house prices have only fallen in 10 years. More recently, in the period 1982–89, real house prices rose for seven successive years. Taking the period 1968 to 1988, real house prices increased at an average rate of 2%.

Of course, gains made by particular consumers have varied sharply depending on periods of purchase and resale. For instance purchasers in 1971, assuming they held their homes until the present, have never encountered a period of real negative equity. However, those purchasing in late 1972 and early 1973 did not see the real (as opposed to nominal) value of their purchases rise until after the mid-1980s.

Averages may be misleading, but there is little doubting the growing gap between housing asset and mortgage debt totals in the UK in the 1980s. Even though UK personal sector borrowing, particularly for housing, rose spectacularly until 1988 (by other advanced economy standards), housing asset values rose even more. Even after recent price falls the gap remains at £700 billion. Net housing wealth is therefore of a major magnitude and the extent and timing of the liquidation of that wealth could clearly have a major impact on the trajectory of the economy. In proportional terms, net housing wealth in the UK ran at around 35% of household net wealth for much of the 1980s before rising sharply to 42% in 1988/89 before falling back to 33% in 1993/94 (Glass, 1994).

Again, however, averages are a little misleading given the skewed nature of the distribution of total wealth in the UK. Housing is the most widely held asset in the UK economy and for the majority of households it is the largest single asset. Further, unlike the second most widely held asset, pension funds, its value is regularly well known to households and is more liquid (if less liquid than most financial assets).

Some economists, most notably and skilfully David Miles (1994), have de-emphasised the role of housing wealth and rising house prices in influencing aggregate consumption. The Miles position is that housing wealth will have a modest, if any, impact on consumption because a rise in wealth for home-owners means a fall in wealth for someone else. That is, if Miles is correct, house price changes redistribute wealth rather than fundamentally reshape the total.

There is, however, a serious weakness in this argument. Consider an instance where the demand for starter homes exceeds supply. Supply inelasticities mean that prices will rise. Miles is, of course, correct in that the equity gain of the seller (raising wealth and consumption) will be largely or entirely offset by increased purchase debt (and reduced consumption) by the first-time buyer. But this is not the end of the story. Non-trading home-owners will take the market trading signal that their wealth has increased. Half a million current first-time buyers may feel worse off but 15 million existing owners perceive a wealth gain and, with equity withdrawal routes, they do not have to trade to either feel wealthier or spend the gain.

But who, in effect, supports this perceived wealth gain? If prices are to be sustained then it is the future flow of first time buyers. Arguably they could perceive rising prices as a signal to save more, for ownership entry, and consume less. But with key entry ages in the 23–25 age range, at most only four years or so of the future flow will be living independently. The majority will be residing in households perceiving a wealth gain. To assume a neutral effect imparts a long-sightedness and inter-generational altruism for which there is little evidence. In effect the main impact of house price gains is to shift wealth from future to present households with future households largely unable to adjust to the change. Now, static housing prices are shifting that balance and existing owners are recognising that they are significantly less wealthy than they had imagined.

David Miles has also argued that rising incomes are the key source of rising consumer spending, and house price rises follow income growth. This view has much substance, at least in 'normal' recovery phases. It is more open to doubt in the chaotic signals and processes of a boom and a recovery with structural change. But even in a recovery phase it is too general. There are almost a third of UK home-owners who have no mortgage to pay. The vast majority are over 55, and three quarters (in the 1989 JRF survey) had no labour market incomes. The distribution of net housing wealth in the UK therefore varies little in relation to household incomes and the highest net wealth holdings are held by those who have both the highest and the lowest labour market incomes.

In consequence, there is a significant minority of older households, divorced from the labour market, who find a scenario of relatively low deposit rates and static or falling house prices a worrying scenario. There is, therefore, an a priori case that shifts in housing wealth matter in determining the current level of consumer expenditure, and the JRF studies of 1989 and 1993 provide micro evidence to support this position.

Maclennan and Yong Tu (1995a) have indicated that for non-moving home owners equity withdrawal rose sharply after 1986. The largest withdrawals were in the regions with faster house price appreciation rates. Analysis of mortgage careers indicated that successive five year cohorts of owners, from 1968 to 1988, borrowed at increasingly earlier stages in their mortgage. Financial deregulation appeared to have accelerated that process, especially for post 1983 purchasers. By 1988, some 40% of the 1983–88 cohort of purchasers had already borrowed against the equity in their homes. In the 1986–89 period, the largest loans were extracted by households who were relatively recent purchasers, i.e. who had the least built-up equity. This greatly enhanced their exposure in the downturn. The micro-evidence suggests that at least half of the additional borrowing directly entered consumption rather than home improvement.

The 1993 JRF surveys revealed a changed pattern in contrast to 1988. In the southern regions, households had lost 30–40% of their housing wealth, on average, but not at all in Scotland. A quarter of existing owners had been discouraged from taking additional loans, and the extra-loan rate in the south ran at a quarter of the boom period rates (though they had fallen little in Glasgow where they had been historically lower). Further, 80 to 90% of loans were now matched to home repair and improvement.

The cross-sample variation in housing wealth losses and gains was, along with other factors such as changes in household incomes and demographic circumstances, related (via logit models) to household assessments of changes in durable and non-durable consumption. After controlling for other factors, see Maclennan and Yong Tu (1995b), changes in housing wealth were seen to have a clear statistical impact on selected components of household spending on consumer durables. Consistent results have been produced at the regional scale (Muellbauer and Murphy, 1994). National estimates, with multi-co-linearities inherent in system change, may be ambiguous. The local evidence is, however, clear that housing wealth acts as an accelerator and decelerator to consumption in booms and busts respectively.

This is not, emphatically, an argument to encourage a looser Treasury stance on house prices to facilitate the sluggish consumption upswing. The soundest consumption recovery, for the long-term, would be based on income growth and not rising house prices. It should be based on raising current incomes rather than an expected capturing of the incomes of future first-time buyers.

In the downswing process, in contrast to the sharp positive equity gains of early boom purchasers, households who had purchased after 1987 quickly entered negative equity. This was predominantly younger households and first-time buyers, but not exclusively so. The number of households in negative equity, most commonly to an extent of £3000–£5000 per case, peaked at 1.8 million in early 1995 and currently runs at around 1 million households. The pattern of negative equity is not static, nor the population involved a constant one. Since the second half of 1994, southern UK regions have continued to experience nominal house price growth. But northern regions have experienced a new, if small scale, wave of price falls. It is likely that in 1993 negative equity rose in, for instance, Scotland, the North and Yorkshire and Humberside.

Forrest and Leather (1994) have established that the vast majority of households experiencing negative equity have developed coping strategies to sustain home-ownership. Further price falls won't help these strategies and 1989–93 experience is likely to have generated a fear factor. For many households negative equity is likely to be encouraging higher, non-housing forms of savings. Higher savings will slow consumption growth, the recovery and, with savage irony, house price recovery. A false boom would help this group, but at great cost to the economy. It is a harsh reality that the households affected will have to earn and save their way out of their earlier, and then government lauded, unwise speculation. Forbearance by financial institutions is critical to unwinding this problem. And this forbearance is likely to be maintained as long as price falls do not recommence. A growing worry is whether the negative equity of the late 1980s will be fully unwound before the next cyclical downturn in the economy and the housing market, let alone more imminent elections.

Thankfully, housing loan arrears rates have been falling since 1992 as employment has recovered, but at the end of 1995 there were still close to 85,000 owners with in excess of a year's arrears, and 127,000 with 6–12 months' arrears. Repossession rates, with 49,000 homes taken into possession in 1995, are still uncomfortably high. Now there are concerns that they may begin to rise again as income support rules for mortgage interest change.

No wonder the present recovery is different in the housing market. New household formation rates are falling, as are early age-specific home-ownership rates. There are historically high rates of frustrated non-moving owners, perhaps as many as a quarter of owner-occupied households. Just under one in ten owners has negative equity and one in 25 an arrears problem. Repossession, outwith the 1991–1993 peak period, is still at historically high levels. Recoveries in output and transactions volumes remain muted. For 1995, UK house prices were still falling in real terms, and nominal falls were recorded in five of the 12 economic planning regions. Who mentioned 'feel good factor'?

But yet, if the Government can keep the lid on house prices there will be gains for the competitiveness of the economy and the economic recovery will, eventually, resolve many of the problems of the housing market. From the academic standpoint government policy makes sense, but can it wait for consumer/voters to change the established housing market perceptions of the last 30 years, which have done so much to foster its own power. What can policy achieve now?

Changing Policies and the Housing Market

There has, in both Government and Whitehall, been an increasing recognition of the role that housing plays in the economy. Although a sharp increase in house prices and turnover might now boost consumer spending and the Government's standing in the polls it is now understood that the longer term consequences will be higher inflation, eroded competitiveness and lost jobs. At the same time the budget deficit has left little scope for tax cuts, let alone a return to universally higher rates of MIRAS. To their credit, policy-makers appear to have placed long term national interest ahead of the sectional interests of the housing industries and home-owners.

This new, post 1992, emphasis is reflected both in the conduct of macroeconomic policy and continuing changes in subsidy policies favouring home-owners. At the macroeconomic level anticipatory increases in interest rates have been applied since mid-1994 to keep the inflation rate within the target range as output recovers. This strategy, given global interest rate changes, offers little prospect of general interest rate reductions after early 1996. By 1995 mortgage rate margins over LIBOR had doubled since 1989 but the competitive pressures to restore this relativity has to reflect the new, higher and explicit riskiness of UK mortgage business. There is unlikely to be any sudden 'macro' induced support for the housing market.

This then leads to the question of what policy for home-ownership should do in the new housing market? After 1985 the Danish Government deliberately reduced home-owner tax concessions to reduce the impacts of house price inflation

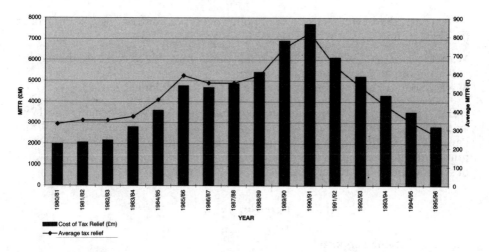

Figure 6 Mortgage interest tax relief, 1980–95

Source: Housing Finance Review 1995–96 (S. Wilcox), Tables 95 and 99

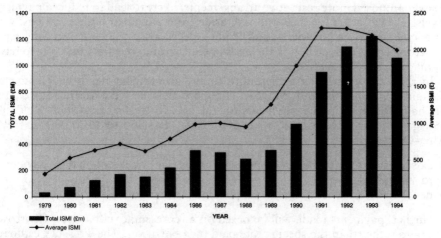

Figure 7 Income support for mortgage interest (ISMI), 1979–94

Source: Housing Finance Review 1995–96 (S. Wilcox), Tables 99

on economic growth. There, real house prices have fallen by a fifth over the last decade, but this has been managed without falling nominal house prices. The great pity is that the inefficient and inegalitarian system of UK MIRAS was not removed before the 1980s boom. The resultant dilemma for the UK Government is that real house prices have had to fall and more rational tax arrangements put in place not only in a recession but when low inflation became the essential objective of economic policies in the advanced economies. In consequence new, necessary, long term policies appear to exacerbate the difficulties of 1990s housing market losers, at least into the medium term.

There are, then, two, related sets of policy questions confronting government at the present time:

- are there changes in policy which can be made now which will help the market with minimal macroeconomic damage?
- what should housing market policy look like for the longer term?

Both sets of questions are being actively addressed with back-benchers, in 1995 and 1996, lobbying for a market boost and the Government publishing a White Paper (HMSO, 1995) on the future of housing policies. The discussion which follows divides, perhaps artificially, the policy debate into specific measures proposed and the longer term concerns of the White Paper.

Current Issues

Reducing Income Support

Housing policy support has, since 1990, moved sharply against owner occupation. MIRAS has been significantly reduced, see Figure 6. And Figure 7 indicates the growing importance, until 1993, of income support payments for mortgage interest payments (ISMI), generally paid to unemployed home-owners. The 1994 Budget proposed more restrictive arrangements, likely to lead to reduced payment levels. The rationale for this proposal, aside from intending budget savings, was to encourage wiser borrowing and lending decisions. As such it is a long-term structural changes issue but, in the current climate of uncertainty, is likely to have significant short-term effects.

In the face of growing expenditure totals, government has been seeking to contain ISMI since the mid 1980s. In 1986, beneficiaries were restricted to claiming half of their mortgage payments for the first 16 weeks of assistance; eligible mortgage limits were reduced to £150,000 in 1993 and to £100,000 in 1994. After October 1995,

- existing borrowers will receive no support for eight weeks and half of payments for the next 16 weeks
- new borrowers will receive no support for the first 36 weeks.

Further, payments made will be based on a representative 'basket' of borrowing rates rather than the specific rate paid by a borrower. The Treasury estimate that the new arrangements will save (annually) public expenditure of £200 million, aside from more 'efficient' lending and borrowing decisions. But is this gain worth the apparent enhanced 'fear factor', and might not other spending headings have to increase?

The Government is assuming that private 'creditor' insurance will grow, and efficiently, to replace government support. This may be likely, in the main, but there are also reasons to believe that it will reduce home-ownership levels at the margin. Industry estimates suggest that, presently, around a fifth of buyers have relevant personal cover but with more than half of lenders having less than a 10% penetration of such schemes amongst their borrowers. Most such policies have a 90 day qualifying period and replace income for up to a year with exclusion clauses for those deemed responsible for their own loss of income (e.g. dismissal, sports injuries etc.). Policies, in 1995, cost around £7 per month for every £100 of monthly mortgage payment, implying a total cost of around £35 per month for the average loan. This is equivalent to a 1% increase on mortgage rates.

An increase in 'user cost' of this kind will clearly reduce the demand for home-ownership. However, the extent to which demand is reduced will not just reflect costs; the extent to which the events causing income loss can be insured against is also an important consideration. Lenders and insurers recognise that insurance schemes can have both moral hazard and adverse selection problems.

Academic and industry research indicates that a range of factors, which differ by life-cycle stage and socio-economic status, can induce the income loss which leads to mortgage payment problems. As noted above, job loss and reduced pay prevail in at least half of cases. Divorce/separation, death in a household, disablement for work, and the arrival of a child are also important factors. There is little evidence that moral hazard in relation to mortgage support induces any of these behaviours. It is difficult to envisage how efficient insurance schemes can be devised to deal with separation/divorce or the arrival of children (though mortgages with 'holidays' may ease difficulties).

Adverse selection may be a real difficulty in relation to job and income certainty. Borrowers who are likely to face problems will be most inclined to conceal their true prospects. In order to make schemes effective, lenders will have to make precise appraisals of the likely income careers of borrowers in the context of local labour markets. And, as noted above, they will have to do this in the context of more flexible labour markets. Thus, even if all lenders introduce block coverage for all borrowers, they are also likely to refuse loans to borrowers with more volatile labour market prospects, notwithstanding borrower willingness to pay the premium.

If all lenders react by taking block creditor policies for all borrowers and add premiums to the mortgage rate charged then there will be less exclusion. Interestingly, however, if it is included in mortgage rates DSS will, with its 'basket of rates', end up paying for insurance for those who default and, thereby, lose around half of the budget savings! If block insurance is not pursued, lenders may have a propensity for 'cherry-picking'. That is, they may only lend to 'safe' cases or, alternatively, charge higher premiums to riskier cases. Of course, these riskier cases are likely to have lower incomes and be on the margin of home-ownership.

If marginal owners are rationed out of owning and into renting it is difficult to see the budget gains of £200 million remaining intact. They may enter social renting, involving public capital expenditures, or private rental housing. If they do so then, under present rules, income or job loss will result in Housing Benefit payments. At present rent and benefit levels it would only require 130,000 'displaced' owners to remove the £200 million gain to the Treasury (leaving aside any element of capital subsidy).

The proposed changes to ISMI may well be economically efficient but they are not consistent with either the short-term stabilisation of house prices or sustaining, let alone expanding, the national home-ownership rate. The insurance industry can be ingenious, but it cannot make bricks out of straw. In consequence reductions in MIRAS and private provision of repayment insurance will both boost the demand for rental housing provision.

In a world of free-functioning rental housing markets we could perhaps stop worrying at this point and, unless obsessed by tenure, forget Holman's 'missing' first-time buyers. As noted earlier, once in independent living, households have to live somewhere. Reducing home-owner demand merely raises rental demand. In turn, landlords require properties to let if the sector is to expand. Their demand for property will surely put new pressures on prices for willing sellers. In this scenario the market adjusts by switching homes as well as clients from owning to renting. And such a transformation may be desirable. Housing market recovery will be driven by rental as well as owner demands. Although the UK rental market has grown from 1.7 to 2 million units since 1988, the penultimate section of this chapter raises doubts about rental sector supply efficiency.

The likely effect of ISMI, boosting rental demand, does not, however, sit entirely consistently with the second area of current policy initiatives. There are growing calls for a package of measures to boost the market and remove negative equity.

It is widely argued that negative and lost equity are now still putting downward pressure on housing sales volumes, mobility and consumer confidence. From 1993 onwards government did try to ease these difficulties by encouraging lenders to allow owners to transport up to £30,000 of negative equity to the next home. Should something more be done to help this group out of negative equity?

Glass, using end 1993 figures, has indicated how a 10–15% increase in house prices is likely to reduce the scale of the negative equity group to a small number, with minimal effects on the economy. However, a 10–15% increase in prices (nominal) may take until the end of the millennium to occur in some regions. There is, of course, no case for deliberately relaxing monetary policy to engineer such an increase as the wider economic damage is likely to be significant.

Can measures to help then be targeted on the negative equity group, who were predominantly young, below average income first-time buyers in 1987 to 1989? Many, considering mobility data from earlier periods, are coming closer to the expected average duration in a first home, i.e. about seven years, and may be susceptible to movement related incentives. One approach would be to grant those in negative equity tax relief on £30,000 of a new mortgage plus any sum of negative equity de facto revealed by a sale. Indeed with around two-thirds in negative equity having less than £5,000 of such debt the fiscal cost of such assistance would be modest, reaching £½ billion or so if all owners with negative equity moved (and prices did not rise in the process).

A more radical, and expensive, move would be to allow those with negative equity to write off their position over say a five year period against tax obligations. If prices rose at 3% nominal per annum, then assuming a £5,000 negative equity on an average £50,000 house such a measure would, very roughly, cost the Exchequer £1.6 billion over a three to four year period (and if prices rose faster then this amount would fall). There are two particular problems with such an approach. First, the fiscal bill would be much greater if prices did not rise. Secondly, there would have to be an agreed measure of negative equity for non-moving owners.

The general problem of targeting the owner in negative equity is that it particularly rewards those borrowers who made rash, over-stretched purchases in southern England during 1987–1989 period or northern buyers in the period 1992–1994 who misjudged the rate of recovery in the housing market. Similar households who purchased with larger deposits (having saved harder in the past) may have incurred the same equity loss as the high loan to value buyer but still have a small positive stock of housing equity.

What if government decided to help all those who were first-time home buyers in the period 1987–1990, i.e. those most caught in the boom-bust trap? This involves around two million purchasers via building societies and just under half a million buyers using bank loans. The costs involved in directly assisting all of this group would be prohibitive (about two to three times that of assisting only those in negative equity).

One relatively costless strategy would be better advice to those in negative equity. This would involve two steps. First the Treasury should be encouraged to form and publish an authoritative statement on expected house price inflation, with appropriate caveats, over three and five year periods. Removing fear may be the key to removing mobility blockages. Secondly, there should be wider publicity given to how moving can help to unwind negative equity positions.

Direct measures to help those with negative equity have design and fairness difficulties, in addition to creating potentially perverse long term signals to home buyers, i.e. that the Government will bail them out. It may be more appropriate, therefore, to pursue measures with indirect support. For instance, either re-running a modified version of the Housing Market Rescue Package or stimulating private rental or directly assisting first time home buyers – that is any measure which raises the demand for housing will stabilise, even raise, house prices. These measures should reflect long term policy priorities.

Are there single instrument national level policy levers to pull, assuming that the policy objective for owner occupation is to help unwind present difficulties, and keep the owner occupied sector at much its present scale?

Few countries provide no support for home-owners, though Australia and Canada are near the bottom of the league of explicit fiscal support. In Canada, government support for lower income households in owner occupation primarily arises from the pooling of loan insurance costs. The transfers between better-off and poorer borrowers in the loan pool are significant, and similar arrangements exist in the USA. If market based loan insurance emerging in the UK unbundles all pooling, there may be a case for looking at assistance with loan insurance costs for low income borrowers. However, this is a policy approach which requires some time to develop and is, therefore, unlikely to be a priority before the 1997 election.

A second alternative, if the Government seeks to maximise the scale of the owner occupied sector, would be to re-target assistance towards first time buyers. Assisting this group makes most sense, not least as it is first-time buyer and new sales markets where prices have been least resilient. There have been first-time buyer support policies previously in the UK, indeed they have ranged from small ineffectual schemes (overtaken by high inflation rates) to the whole thrust of mid-1980s policies which sucked households with labour market incomes into 'ownership' as successfully and crudely as 'Klondykers' trawl Britain's shores. But surely now the issue is 'which' potential owners the Government wishes to attract and how fine the mesh of support should be.

The Government should resist the temptation to boost ownership by inducing upward shifts in age-specific ownership rates for the youngest households. It should not facilitate 'entry' for a significant volume of households who are unlikely to be able to permanently sustain home-ownership. Ideally it should be targeting rental households who are at the long term permanent margin of home-ownership but who have a period of established labour market performance and, indeed, experience as savers. French and German housing finance systems achieve such objectives through contract savings systems. However, contract savings schemes, with a tax bonus, have system inefficiencies which the UK does not need. The UK approach should be to develop forms of assistance which delays market entry until households are at least 25 years old, perhaps marginally older.

This assistance could take the form of a time limited tax concession and the measure should be inversely related to head of household income. This is not the place for more detailed discussion, but such a scheme could be financed by further reduction in current MIRAS rates. Alternatively, a less depressing effect on existing owner activity would be to begin to curtail MIRAS on the basis of the length of time for which it has already been received. Long time mortgage holders are not only likely to be inactive market participants but are also likely to have little of their net incomes contributed by MIRAS relief. At the time of writing, summer 1996, the government have resisted all calls for special measures and it appears that they are relying on general economic recovery to remove, slowly but surely, the hangover from 1990–93 difficulties.

Longer Horizons, Wider Visions

Looking to the future, what strategic purpose or vision should home-ownership policies have in the new reality?

It is likely that the general economic pressures towards a more competitively configured economy will sustain pressures to improve the efficiency of the housing system and to reduce housing subsidy claims on the public budget. In that view of the world there is little room for an imposed government view about housing tenure targets. Individuals are best left to assess their own housing market opportunities and make their own choices with a sense of responsibility instilled by realistic lending policies. That is, government should continue to level the playing field for renting and owning. Ultimately, pushing mass ownership down the income distributions has had neither obvious political gains for the government, nor economic benefits for the nation. Within the rental sectors, equally, there should be 'investor neutral' competition for the capital subsidies which are now re-recognised as being essential to adequately house the poor without deepening poverty traps. That is, the central concerns of housing policy should be the efficiency of the system. The emphasis should be on remedying market failures by improving consumer information and advice and in removing the obvious supply side blockages and driving down costs. This approach could be broadly labelled a 'housing market policy'.

Since 1945 Britain has never had a housing market policy. It has had waves of anti-private renting, pro-council, pro-association, pro-ownership, anti-council policies. But it has never had an articulated housing market policy. Price instability is not the only evidence for such an omission, repair quality in ownership and supply price inelasticity are other major symptoms. For almost two decades we have embraced the market but without thinking about market operations, efficiencies and failures. Addressing these issues is essential for the future.

The 1995 White Paper (DoE, 1995d) explicitly recognised some of the weaknesses of past approaches and advocated an emphasis on 'sustainable' owner occupation. The paper recognised, correctly, the importance of further expanding the rental housing market in the UK. Although private rental housing has expanded from 1.7 to 2 million units since deregulation it would be rather stretching experience to claim that all of Britain has an expanding, free-functioning rental market closely integrated with home-ownership.

The White Paper, in proposing to introduce Authorised Housing Investment Trusts, has eased one of the key differences in the inter-sectoral costs of investment funds. However a number of problems remain which reduce returns and increase risks in renting *vis-à-vis* owning. Owners still receive MIRAS at 15%, and renters nothing (other than benefit). Landlords pay tax on incomes and capital gains; owners do not. The owner-renter yield gap (or user cost of capital) may be narrowing but the playing field is not level. Even more importantly, in the year before an election landlords must be acutely aware of the political risks in investment; the clear political alternatives to the present government have articulated no firm policy scenario for renting beyond 1997.

There are also second-order problems. In making rental and owner choices households do not choose identical dwellings. For instance, younger households frequently live in multiple occupation properties rather than single household dwellings. Young couples may seek rental homes similar to those which first-time sellers wish to sell, but young singles (a quarter of current FTBs) may choose spaces in larger homes. Expanding rental demand may help owners wishing to sell but not necessarily in a bottom up sequence. If, at least until 1997, rental investment grows slowly (as it is at present), then rising rents arising from sticky supply will divert demand to either home-ownership (with risky outcomes and rising user costs) or to social sector waiting lists.

The White Paper does not discuss approaches to clearing up the mess from the unsustainable expansion of 1980s ownership. Rather, it is committed to further expansion of the sector. Two issues are of concern in this. First, there does not seem to be any recognition of the extent to which responsible actions of consumers in their 20s may actually reduce home-ownership rates (for the kinds of reasons noted above). Such a reduction may offset growth in the chosen expansion routes. Secondly, do the preferred expansion routes make sense, are they safe and effective?

The White Paper on Housing Policy, ensuing legislation, and the 1994 and 1995 Budgets looked, essentially, to the housing association sector for new owners. Within existing programmes, the reducing real Housing Corporation budget is increasingly to be switched away from rental housing provision to home-ownership initiatives. Now housing association tenants also have a 'Right to Buy'.

These changes raise a number of concerns. First, where measures do not release to an association property to let or capital to construct a new unit, then tenure change is being put ahead of meeting housing need. With social sector lettings running below needs estimates such shifts are clearly inequitable. The Tenants Incentive Scheme (TIS) and the new right to buy will provide, respectively, units and capital. However, TIS will encourage thriving tenants to leave particular streets or neighbourhoods thus reducing the income 'mix' of communities. The Right to Buy avoids this difficulty, and if construction and land costs remain flat then sensible pricing of units for sale need not lead to any major difficulties.

Reducing Income Support

The key question is whether purchasing tenants will be able to sustain their mortgage payments. Will a new vulnerable group be created? There is an impression that former council tenants purchasing with Right-to-Buy sowed the seeds of the deep downswing of the 1990s. There is no solid empirical evidence for such a view, indeed the 1993 JRF samples, though small in number, suggested the opposite. Former council tenants were only marginally more prone to job and income loss than other 1980s buyers in the C1 and C2 groups. They were less likely to have mortgage arrears, as discounts had halved their mortgage outgoings. Moreover, they were all in positive equity as deep discounts greatly exceeded local price falls. Selling homes to association tenants would have similar implications. To put sustainability ahead of expansion as an objective, however, it is imperative that such loans must be entirely provided by market lenders and not 'guaranteed' by public funding. That said, the association sector is nationally small in scale so the net addition to home-ownership rates is unlikely to be greater than 1% (as almost two-thirds of association tenants receive some Housing Benefit assistance).

TIS and the Right-to-Buy are both essentially demand side subsidies, and they both suffer from unclear additionality factors (would tenants using the schemes have bought in the market anyway)? TIS boosts market demand and this will help the recovery in the housing market. Shared equity schemes increase choice, though flexing 'down' as well as 'up' would be desirable to promote sustainability. However, the rationale of other forms of low-cost home-ownership initiative, unless they are addressing market failures, seems rather weak in a sluggish housing market. Why should the state be subsidising reduced price ownership when former first-time buyers are struggling to sell homes on which they have made equity losses? This is precisely the kind of perverse policy action which arises in the absence of a housing market policy.

A housing market policy should emphasise the consumer interest. For instance, in England there should be some concern to radically alter a sales system which is twice as slow as Scotland under any market conditions. In the same vein, homes should have credible energy and quality ratings before they are sold; multiple, repeat, superficial house surveys should be replaced by a serious single survey if housing quality and energy efficiency objectives are to be secured via market means. Consumers should have access to skilled advisers to draw up personal housing plans and to help new buyers understand some of the responsibilities as well as opportunities of home-ownership.

At the geographic scale of local housing systems, which is often at a supra-municipal scale, there should be an informed view on local housing markets (both owning and renting). This is essential if local planning policies, private investment and public grant aid are to effectively support local housing change. Markets should be monitored. A coherent local housing system analysis, identifying demands, needs and supply side restrictions is then required and an agreed local housing strategy pursued.

This is not an argument for neat, theoretical perfection in housing planning. It is merely an observation that housing consumers, producers and bureaucracies are generally poorly informed of what is happening in local housing systems. The notion that one can change the UK housing market from Whitehall now seems absurd. Change in the future will be led from a more localised scale.

Some municipalities plan well and others abysmally. There may be some merit in strengthening the regional/metropolitan information and strategy roles of the Housing Corporation. Good strategic information should, in any case, be already guiding the regional allocation of the Corporations Budget rather than old-fashioned 'needs' indicators (how many of these indicators say anything useful about local market systems?). And local splits between for-rent, TIS and other low cost, ownership initiatives should be driven by local, informed strategies. In many regards the argument here is that a key to good future policy is good housing market practice.

The future implementation of such policies, if they are to constitute housing market policies, may require re-thinking within the DOE and the Housing Corporation. First, the implementing agency will require to develop market intervention skills. This will necessitate not only re-orientation of staff skills but the development of local housing market indicators for top-level resource allocation as well as local implementation. The absence of such skills and indicators merely reinforces the previous argument that the UK has never had a housing market policy. At the same time, either the Corporation or the DOE should be simultaneously monitoring private provision of rented homes.

Conclusions

There is little doubt that a fundamental shift is occurring in housing market careers for the UK young. Market hangover effects, new job patterns and shifts in economic and housing policies have all depressed the demand for ownership in the mid-1990s. Arguably, in the absence of policy action, rental demands may stabilise prices. There is little sign that nominal UK house prices will be allowed to rise significantly ahead of the general price level. The housing market, by past standards, may have played a lagging role in the recovery but equally it is now unlikely, unless policies are reversed, to accelerate the upswing to the peak of the cycle.

If the UK is to have a sustainable home ownership sector it can get there by two routes, whilst adhering to broad macro policy goals. It can carry on as in the first half of the 1990s and ultimately risk margins for lenders and insurers will drive down the home-ownership rate. At the same time, without rental sector action, the rental sectors will tighten with investment constrained either by political preferences (social renting) or political risk (private renting). Ownership will be 'protected' but lower income groups will suffer in the process. Alternatively, the Government can address the appropriate owning/rental mix for the likely economic future of the nation and its households. In the market sector, depending on the 'desired' ownership rate, it will have to pursue appropriate local mixes of market rental and ownership policies.

What the Government cannot have is a 'quick fix' for housing market discontent without medium term inflationary consequences and a future 'exposed' tranche of marginal owners. It is essential to develop a 'real housing psychology' if Britain is to compete in the world. Home-owners will have to see ownership as an investment with some risk which they really have to pay for. Government will also have to confront the reality that those households who cannot compete effectively will require their continuing support if an uncivil society is not to permanently permeate the nation.

Acknowledgement

This paper brings together research sponsored, separately, by the Economic and Social Research Council and the Joseph Rowntree Foundation. I am grateful for their support.

CHAPTER 4

The Politics of Home Ownership

MARK BOLÉAT

A feature of Government housing policy since 1970 has been the encouragement of home ownership. This policy has been particularly pronounced since the Conservative Party came to power in 1979, but was also apparent in the policies of the Labour Government between 1974 and 1979. Policy has been influenced by both political and more practical issues. More recently, as a result of a combination of circumstances largely unrelated to housing, the attractiveness of home ownership has declined and there is now a very different housing market in operation. This chapter analyses the development of policy and practice over the last 20 years, largely from a public policy angle, albeit tinged with a modest element of economic analysis.

The Underlying Market

For most of the 1970s and 1980s the market for owner occupied housing was very healthy. This resulted from a combination of factors, some resulting from housing policy and others being a consequence of a range of Government policies and macroeconomic conditions.

An important underlying factor was the combination of rising living standards and there being no satisfactory alternatives to home ownership. The private rented market had been declining since the imposition of rent controls during the First World War. As tenancies came to an end, so properties were sold rather than put back on the rented market. The increase in local authority rented accommodation provided an alternative but only for those households who met the eligibility requirements. Local authority housing also gave people no choice as to how much housing they consumed or where their housing was. As people's incomes increased, so young people in particular were less willing to continue to live at home when they wanted their independence, or to rent rooms in what little housing was available on the rented market. Accordingly, for those with the financial means to purchase a house, this was not only something that was possible but actually was virtually a necessity. The huge desire for home ownership therefore represented little more than a recognition that there were no satisfactory alternatives. As real incomes increased so the desire was transformed into effective demand.

Housing was also favourably treated by the tax system. Owner occupied housing was exempt from capital gains tax, and mortgage interest qualified for tax relief at the borrower's highest marginal tax rate with there being no corresponding tax on imputed rental income. There is scope for a lengthy academic debate (and, indeed, there have been many such debates) about the correct tax régime for owner occupied housing. This debate has been quite separate from public perceptions and political realities. A tax on imputed rental income is a concept that does not strike chords either with the public or with politicians. Tax relief on mortgage interest is more tangible even if its effects, including increasing house prices, may work to the disadvantage of housebuyers. What people could see was that if the mortgage rate was 10% and the tax rate was 35% then they were paying only 6.5% on their mortgage loan while they could probably obtain a higher rate of interest on their savings. For higher rate tax payers the calculation was even even simpler. Somebody borrowing, say, £100,000 on a 60% tax rate would be paying only 4% interest, yet they could easily obtain a better return through investing in national savings certificates, low coupon gilts or other tax-favoured instruments. Accordingly, it made sense for people to borrow to purchase a house even if they had the necessary savings because of the opportunity to arbitrage the tax system.

The third factor encouraging the growth of home ownership was inflation. For much of the 1970s and 1980s inflation was at a relatively high level. Indeed, interest rates were frequently negative in real terms. House prices also tended to outperform inflation. Even in years of relative housing recession, such as 1974 and 1975 when real house prices fell by over 20% a year, nominal house prices continued to rise.

Given this combination of circumstances, it is hardly surprising that owner occupation proved a good investment and was very popular. The public were able to borrow money at a rate of interest that was artificially low because of tax relief and was negative in real terms to purchase an asset that was free of all tax and was appreciating in real terms. Furthermore, those people in a position to purchase a house effectively had little choice but to do so because they were denied access to the other sectors of housing.

The Development of Policy

For much of the 1970s and early 1980s housing was one of the major political battlegrounds. In many ways it was a natural battleground because the two principal parties came from opposite directions. The Conservative Party has seen itself as being the party of home ownership, in line with the Conservative philosophies of private ownership of capital and personal self reliance. Labour has been more naturally allied with the local authority rented sector, seeing a major role for the public sector in providing good quality housing for those unable to provide for themselves. This situation was given force, if somewhat spuriously, by analyses which showed a correlation between voting intentions and housing tenure. There is a close relationship between the proportion of home ownership in an area and the Conservative vote. The Conservatives became associated with the suburbs and rural areas while the Labour strongholds were in the inner cities and new towns. At the micro level, this concept was given some support through local authority policies which aimed to change the housing tenure of a particular marginal ward or parliamentary seat. Herbert Morrison is widely regarded as having followed such a policy with the London County Council in the post-war years, while more recently Westminster City Council has been under the spotlight with accusations that its policy on sales has been more geared to short-term political considerations than giving opportunities for individual tenants to buy their homes.

In practice, the relationship between housing tenure and voting intention is more complex and less direct than the simplistic views of the 1970s suggested. While it may be true that home owners are more likely to vote Conservative than are council tenants, it does not follow that transforming someone from a council tenant to a home owner makes him likely to switch his vote from Labour to Conservative. If this was the case then the combination of an increase in home ownership from 50% in 1979 to 67% in 1992, together with a fall in a proportion of local authority housing from over 30% to 20% over the same period, should have led to the ending of the Labour Party as a political force with the Conservatives being overwhelmingly the most popular party. In the event, there has been comparatively little change in the balance between the Conservative and Labour Parties over the past 20 years.

The Labour Government of 1974–79 had an ambivalent attitude towards home ownership. It recognised that this was a preferred tenure of the majority of the population, although instinctively it still believed in the concept of municipal housing and facilitated a high level of house building by local authorities. Policy towards council house sales was neutral to restrictive.

The 1977 Green Paper (*Housing Policy*, Cmnd 6851), following the monumental review (proof that if ones wishes to make radical changes of policy, then this is best done after a brief and secret review, not a full-scale public review), if nothing else recognised that home ownership was the preferred tenure of most people and that Government policy should be framed accordingly. The one concrete policy initiative to come out of the review was the home loan scheme through which people were given a small grant and an interest-free loan towards house purchase if they saved for a given period of time. This must count as one of the most unsuccessful initiatives in housing policy of all time. Take up was virtually nil. This was because the benefits were minimal and the scheme was complicated. Nevertheless, it was a signal that the Labour Party wanted to encourage home ownership. Throughout its period in office, the Labour Government also took some steps at the micro level to increase home ownership, notably through encouraging the building societies to make higher percentage advances, a strategy that was to come under severe criticism 20 years later.

The 1980s are seen as a period in which the Conservative Government overtly encouraged the growth of owner occupation and the decline in local authority housing. In some ways, this perception is a triumph of politics over reality as the subsequent analysis will show.

Prior to the 1979 election, the Conservative Party in opposition did a great deal of work on housing policy. It developed the flagship policy of the sale of local authority houses. This was a policy waiting to happen. By this time, local authorities owned a third of the housing stock in England and Wales. Many local authority tenants had the means to purchase their own homes and, indeed, a steady stream transferred to the owner occupied sector each year. The management of local authority housing was in many cases far from satisfactory, but most important, people simply had no choice as to how much housing they occupied or where that housing was. Local authority housing had been heavily subsidised such that the rental stream covered only a fraction of the capital costs.

The policy of selling local authority houses at a discount to sitting tenants was developed in response to these circumstances and to clear survey evidence that many council tenants wished to become home owners. Within the Conservative Party there was much discussion about the merits of this policy. Some argued that it would mean giving a further subsidy to people who had already been heavily subsidised by virtue of living in local authority accommodation. The more pragmatic view prevailed, that people received a huge subsidy the moment they were allocated a local authority house, and if they were allowed to purchase the house then all they would be doing was capitalising that subsidy. Moreover, if the discount was fixed at the right level then the local authority could actually gain from the transaction in that the sale price it would receive would exceed the value of the property to them as a going concern.

The salami-slicing technique was adopted with respect to eligibility requirements. The 1980 Housing Act for England and Wales and equivalent legislation for Scotland gave the right to buy. The qualifying periods of occupation and discounts were gradually liberalised over a period of years thus maintaining the volume of sales. Many local authorities overtly opposed the policy and did what they could to obstruct sales. In the event, however, political realism prevailed. The fact is there was no effective constituency against the sale of local authority houses. The policy was popular with those people who purchased, and those who did not purchase could not see themselves as being losers. Notwithstanding eminent economic studies which argued that as a result of the sales policy fewer people were able to have access to local authority housing, the policy continued to be popular. There were sufficient embarrassing stories of Labour councillors and MPs purchasing their own houses to mute the political opposition. At any election the Conservatives might hint at the threat of Labour purchasing back houses or stopping purchases which itself would have a disadvantageous effect on those who had bought because of the impact on the value of their homes.

The merits of the policy became generally accepted. Those who bought acquired a capital asset at substantially below its open market cost, even if in reality they were doing no more than capitalising their subsidy. Many areas were improved considerably as a result of tenants purchasing their homes and subsequently improving them. The tendency for better-off people to move out of council estates was, in many areas, diminished, helping to preserve a reasonable balance in those communities. Local authorities found themselves benefiting from increasing capital receipts, and the financial argument to the effect that the sale policy was costly was transformed into a wholly separate argument that local authorities should be allowed to spend more of their capital receipts.

Politically, it is difficult to think of a more successful policy. Over a million council tenants bought their homes, and opinion surveys showed that all but a small fraction were very content that they had done so, and the vast majority benefited by so doing. Local authorities received capital amounts which they could use for other purposes. The Government achieved its objective of increasing home ownership. Labour gradually muted its opposition to council house sales and eventually came to endorse the policy fully.

This episode is significant for the total divorce between the real political debate and the academic/housing lobby debate. If one took a poll of housing activists and commentators, then probably under 10% would have supported the policy of selling council houses. Numerous learned articles were published in housing and other journals suggesting that the policy was disadvantageous to the community, to local authorities and to the individuals. This debate was wholly ignored by politicians on both sides. The political reality was that the policy was immensely successful. Its cost to the Government was nothing and its value was substantial. There are few such policies.

This policy was accompanied by others aimed at increasing the proportion of homes that were owner occupied. Local authority new house building was substantially cut back. Of all cuts in public expenditure, this is the most painless. If one wishes to buy votes then building a council house in order to house a committed Labour voter is an expensive irrelevance. Those who lost out as a result of fewer council houses being built did not realise they had lost out, and in any event their votes were not likely to be swung by being housed by the local authority. Again, the howls of outrage in the housing lobby had no impact on the political debate.

Other policies designed to encourage home ownership included shared ownership and homesteading. These were all useful for publicity purposes in that they kept attention on the Government policy to increase home ownership. They cost very little and few had any impact. This does not mean that the policies were unwise. A good political ploy is to promote policies which give the impression of something happening, while imposing no cost on the Government. Much of the home ownership policy should be seen in this light.

Reviving the private rental sector

The Government also took the first steps towards encouraging the revival of the private rental sector. Again, in political terms its achievements were remarkable. The private landlord has been an even fiercer political battleground than the owner occupation/council housing debate. The Labour Party has traditionally seen the landlord as being the enemy of the people, and regarded the only thing worse than being a private landlord as ceasing to be a private landlord. The huge decline in private rented accommodation has largely been attributed to legislation, although some have argued that it is a natural consequence of economic forces that have been replicated in other countries. The consensus at the end of the 1970s was that nothing could be done to revive the private rented sector because there would never be any political confidence that a reasonable fiscal and regulatory régime would be permitted. The Government introduced the assured tenancy concept in the Housing Act 1980. This freed newly-built homes from rent control, and its impact was virtually zero. Largely for this reason little account was taken of it. However, the concept had been firmly established. Later in the 1980s, the Government, with scarcely any debate, extended the assured tenancy concept to all new lettings in the private sector, and also to housing association lettings. It was not a question of 'repealing the rent acts' which was politically emotive. Rather, what the Government did effectively was to disapply the rent acts through extending the assured tenancy concept. It was a remarkable piece of policy development by stealth.

The Government largely had a clear run on housing policy in the 1980s. Its policies were seen to be in tune with public demand, while Labour was undergoing an internal debate and much soul-searching. The traditionalists wanted to maintain local authority housing, while the pragmatists recognised that the policy of council house sales was one that could not logically be opposed. There was very little opposition in the House of Commons to Conservative policy. Indeed, housing ministers were heard to complain that the lack of opposition meant that their negotiating position with the Treasury for more money was sharply diminished. As the focus of public debate was on the health service and education, so it was these government departments that were able to attract more funds at the expense of housing.

The point has been made already that the overt policy of encouraging owner occupation concealed the reality of the position. In practice, there were many in the Conservative Party, in particular the influential Chancellor, Nigel Lawson, who wished to reduce the privileged tax position of owner occupied housing, and, indeed, who saw it as a serious economic disadvantage. The Conservatives here built on a policy that Labour had introduced. In 1974 a ceiling on tax relief for mortgage interest of £25,000 had been introduced. The Conservatives took an early opportunity to increase the figure to £30,000. This was nowhere near sufficient to compensate for the increase in house prices since 1974. The £30,000 figure stayed as house prices continued to rise. As importantly, as the policy of cutting taxes came into effect, so the value of tax relief was sharply diminished. In 1979, a higher rate tax payer could easily find that 83% of his mortgage interest was, in effect, met by tax relief. As the highest tax rate came down to 40%, so the maximum amount of tax relief was correspondingly halved, this combining with the sharp reduction in real terms in the loan ceiling for mortgage tax relief. The Government also chipped away at the edges by abolishing tax relief for home improvements, abolishing double tax relief, then abolishing higher rate tax relief and, finally, reducing the rate at which tax relief was given from 20% and then to 15%. The combined effect of all of these measures has been that the proportion of total mortgage interest met by tax relief has fallen from about 40% in 1980 to under 10% in 1995/96. The saving to the Exchequer runs into several billion pounds annually. Furthermore, this sharp reduction in the support for home ownership has been achieved with scarcely any political debate, and also at a time of the most severe depression in the housing market with record numbers of people losing their homes and substantial negative equity, particularly in the southern part of the country.

Home Ownership Under Threat

The point has already been made that in the 1970s and much of the 1980s housing was a good investment because of a combination of favourable circumstances. Housing was treated favourably by the tax system, notably through exemption from capital gains tax and tax relief on mortgage interest. Relatively high levels of inflation boosted the demand for real assets, such as housing. Also, high inflation meant that real interest rates were often negative, sometimes substantially so. Accordingly, there was also an artificially high demand for mortgage finance. The prevailing wisdom was that even though initial mortgage repayments might be high, they soon rapidly reduced in relation to incomes, which could be expected to rise by over 10% a year.

It was inflation that largely took the risk out of house purchase. Even a rate of inflation of 5% a year meant that within a few years of purchase, what had been a high loan to value ratio generally became a relatively low ratio, and what was initially a high loan to income multiple also rapidly diminished. In retrospect, there is little denying that for much of the 1970s and 1980s, the real security on which mortgage lenders lent, on which insurers relied, and on which valuers also relied, was inflation rather than any implicit value of bricks and mortar as an investment.

Since the mid-1980s, one by one the factors which made housing such a good investment, and virtually risk-free, have been eroded, if not totally removed. The Government's sharp reduction in support for owner occupation through tax policy has already been noted. Housing itself no longer enjoys a favourable tax treatment in relation to capital gains. There are other tax incentives for long-term investments including the business expansion scheme, personal pensions and, perhaps most significantly, Personal Equity Plans.

Most importantly, inflation has been reduced substantially. Commentators now believe that the country is in a new long-term situation in which the rate of inflation will be under 4%. In turn, this has led to a reduction in interest rates which, of course, is favourable for house-buyers, although not necessarily for mortgage lenders. It is a reasonable expectation that lower inflation implies higher real interest rates, and this alone marks a significant change from the 1970s and 1980s.

A risky investment

For these reasons, housing is now a risky investment. There is no longer the virtual guarantee that prices will rise in nominal terms, while the mortgage debt stays fixed. Indeed, as has been seen over the last few years, there is no natural economic law preventing house prices falling. On average, prices have fallen by over 10%, and in the southern parts of the country, the fall has been over 30%. This should not really have come as a surprise. It replicates trends in many other countries, particularly Holland in the 1980s.

Real house prices, that is house prices relative to the general level of prices, have always been very volatile, but the impact of this volatility is greatly reduced if inflation is at a high level. For example, between 1973 and 1977 real house prices fell by 35%, but in nominal terms prices increased by over 20%. The fall in real house prices in the current recession is less than in the mid-1970s, and little different from that in the early 1980s. However, because inflation itself is at a lower level, house prices have fallen in nominal terms, hence the huge increase in mortgage possessions, the problem of negative equity and the losses incurred by mortgage lenders and insurers.

Some investment advertisements carry with them the obligatory statement that past performance is not necessarily a guide to the future. Given an economy in which inflation is permanently under 4%, it is an absolute guarantee that, in respect of nominal house prices, the experience of the past is not a guide to the future. With inflation at a low level, real assets are no longer seen as a hedge against inflation. The past few years have shown to everyone that prices can fall substantially in nominal terms.

The New Housing Market

There is now a new housing market which reflects economic realities. Housing is now purchased as a consumer good, rather than as an investment. It is no longer seen as being imperative to purchase housing at the earliest possible age with the largest mortgage that one can afford. The rented sector is now an attractive alternative for many, especially young, mobile households, who in the past have been pushed into owner occupation earlier than was desirable or necessary for them. Borrowers increasingly are seeking the minimum mortgage that is necessary to acquire the housing that they want, and should they receive lump sums, they are now likely to use them to help pay off the mortgage rather than, as previously, invest elsewhere, with the mortgage being retained. This situation is evident not only from the behaviour of consumers, but also from various opinion surveys.

One can do no more than look at the present situation to see just how much the housing market has changed. House prices are now relatively low as against incomes, and mortgage rates are near the lowest that they have been for many years, especially with attractive teaser rates available. The NHBC's First Time Buyers' Ability to Buy Index is standing at an all-time high. Notwithstanding this, and even signs that house prices are rising again, demand for house purchase remains weak. It is not that consumers have failed to understand what is happening in the marketplace – they have understood all too well, and perhaps it is some in the marketplace who have not yet understood just how much has changed.

The Market Response

The new market requires appropriate responses from the institutions that participate in the market and from the Government.

The need for a private rental sector, especially to serve young people, is now universally recognised. It is correctly seen as a complement to owner occupation as well as being in competition with it. The Housing Act 1988 provides a legal framework that is satisfactory for private rental housing. The demand is clearly there, from young people who do not yet wish to put down roots, from those moving house from one area to another, and from those seeking to live in an area for only a short time.

Over the last few years there has been a supply of private rented accommodation to match the demand. However, to a large extent, this has reflected the state of the owner occupied market. Both developers and individuals have been unable to sell houses, and have preferred to rent them out and thereby receive some income, rather than leave them empty and not only receive no income, but necessarily incur significant costs. It is fair to say that the supply of housing for the market rented sector has not been entirely fortuitous. Much of it would not have been possible without the provisions of the Housing Act 1988. It might also be observed that there is very little information on the extent of what might be called the new private rented sector. There are no statistics available from Government and no reliable market estimates from other sources. One can, however, observe from the columns of any local newspaper that there is now a thriving private rental sector.

The Government has given encouragement to the private rented sector through the extension of the Business Expansion Scheme to rented housing. In the event, however, this has not been used significantly to increase the stock of private rented houses in the long-term, but rather has been used by housing associations to increase the stock of social rented housing, and by mortgage lenders to help deal with their possessions problem. The Business Expansion Scheme has now ended, and bearing in mind the huge cost of it, it is no surprise that it has not been replaced by any new incentive to invest in rented housing.

The Government would like to see large institutional landlords in the market, but as yet few institutions have shown any interest. Rather, the market has developed with many small landlords, often individuals owning just one property they are unable to sell. This points to the need for an industry which can manage such housing, and one can see evidence of some competition in this market between traditional letting agents and housing associations.

It is interesting to ponder the question of whether institutions can be attracted into ownership of private rented property or the financing of it. Here, one is talking not only about economics, but also about psychology and, occasionally, inertia. The fact is that institutional bias develops in relation to certain types of investment. There is sometimes a failure to recognise simple supply and demand factors, and different criteria are used to evaluate existing investments which, by definition, are deemed to be wise, and new investments, which, by definition, are often deemed not to be. For years, some argued that investment in rented housing would not be possible because the interest on mortgage loans exceeded the rental yield. Those commentators failed to explain how, on this basis, there could be any investment in commercial property. The fact that interest rates have fallen below the rental yield does not seem to have shifted such people in their arguments either. Some institutions will not own or invest in rented housing simply because they have not owned or invested in rented housing, and a very significant change of attitude will be needed before they will do so. If one asks an institutional investor why they will not invest in rental housing, they could well give a series of answers which would explain fully why they would not invest in commercial property. Alternatively, they may give a simple or more truthful answer, that is that they do not want to.

The consensus in the property industry at present remains that it does not make sense to develop private rental housing ab initio. It is worth exploring whether this is really the case. Logically, the argument that one should not invest in private rented housing should be that private renting cannot compete with either owner occupation or social housing. One accepts that it cannot easily compete with social renting housing, but then this caters for a very different market from the private rented sector. The vast majority of people who might be in the market are simply not eligible for the social rented sector. However, it is difficult to see why private renting cannot compete with owner occupation given the huge reductions in tax relief on mortgage interest over the last few years and the possibility of further reductions to come. There is also the possibility that rented housing can command a premium over owner occupied housing because the risk element is taken out.

If it remains the case that investment in rented housing is not viable then the reasons for this need to be clearly understood so that Government is in a position to take remedial action should it wish to do so.

Loss of lenders' confidence

Mortgage lenders and insurers must react to the new housing market, in particular the greater element of risk. Initially, one would expect, and one has seen, a knee-jerk reaction, that is steps have been taken to deal with the very obvious problems of the recent past. Mortgage lending criteria have been substantially tightened, and mortgage insurers have equally tightened their underwriting criteria. As a result, some borrowers, for example some of those who have defaulted through no fault of their own on their loans, even if subsequently they were able to put themselves back on a sound footing, are excluded from the market. The problem of raising the deposit has, once again, become a real one. One wonders whether lenders have not gone too far in this direction. They clearly have less confidence in the owner occupied housing market. It is hardly surprising if this filters through to their potential customers.

The recovery of the housing market has now been confidently forecast for three or more years. The reality has now dawned that there will not be a traditional recovery, let alone a boom. This housing cycle is different from others. There is no longer the perception that one has to buy a house as soon as possible with the largest mortgage that one can obtain, hence demand is remaining weak, notwithstanding the fall in real house prices and low interest rates. Negative equity is a major drag on the market. Lenders have taken some steps to help those borrowers who need to move house. Little, however, can be done to help other borrowers in a negative equity situation. In the past, it was the existence of positive equity that led people to trade up and which generated much of the activity in the market. Merely enabling negative equity borrowers to move is not going to create demand. Rather, it will enable the very limited demand that exists to be met. While this needs to be done it is of little relevance to the overall health of the market.

Mortgage lenders and their insurers have the difficult task of balancing a number of conflicting forces. On the one hand they wish to learn from the lessons of the past and avoid the actions that have led them into such difficulty. There is an abundance of evidence to show that high loan to value ratios, and loans to borrowers who previously have had arrears experience, represent relatively high risks. The reaction of some lenders is simply to refuse to lend to certain categories of buyer, citing, whether realistically or not, difficulty in obtaining mortgage indemnity insurance cover. If, however, a significant proportion of potential homebuyers is to be excluded from the market, then the recovery of the market will be hindered. There is also a moral point if one dare mention this. Some of those who have defaulted did so through no fault of their own. There are, for example, people on the mortgage possessions register who were innocent parties, for example, deserted wives or husbands, and it is wrong that they should be arbitrarily excluded from the housing market.

The Government Response

In considering the Government's response to the new market situation, it is necessary to take a wide view rather than looking at housing in isolation.

Housing remains a relatively unimportant political issue. It did not feature in the last general election or in the election before that. It does not appear high on the list of issues about which the public is concerned. Unemployment, healthcare and education are the major political issues. The reason for this is straightforward. Housing is not what economists call a 'public' good. It is clear that people cannot provide for their own defence or personal security, and thus there is no dispute that the Armed Forces and the police service should be funded by the taxpayer. Health and education do not quite come into the same category, but still few people can afford to provide for their own healthcare or for the education of their children. Accordingly, there is an expectation that the state will provide these services. Moreover, as incomes increase, so people expect a higher standard of such public services.

Housing is very different from health or education. Most people can house themselves, and most want to take responsibility for their own housing. There are very few externalities in housing, unlike education or healthcare. That is, the services which housing provide are to the benefit of the individual occupying that housing rather than the community as a whole. People are well satisfied with their housing. An opinion survey commissioned by the Council of Mortgage Lenders in 1993 showed that 89% of those questioned were satisfied with their accommodation, 5% were neutral, 4% were quite dissatisfied and 2% were very dissatisfied (Boléat and Taylor, 1993). If people are not satisfied, the remedy lies largely in their own hands. That is, the majority of the population are in a position to purchase more or less housing, or to purchase different housing, or to change the quality of their housing through their own labour. By contrast, very few people are in a position to change the quality of the healthcare they and their families receive, and still less are they able to influence the quality of their children's education.

In these circumstances, it is not greatly surprising that housing has not been a political priority and that capital expenditure on housing has been a target for government cuts. It is easy to cut public expenditure on housing because there is very little effect on the direct provision of services. There are those who wish to see housing at the top of the agenda, and while all the appropriate noises will be made, housing will remain relatively low in terms of political priorities. While some of the housing indicators are now beginning to point in the right direction, it is significant that record levels of homelessness, record repossessions and the most depressed owner occupied housing market in history, have not been regarded as serious political problems for the Government although they have undoubtedly contributed to the lack of a 'feel good' factor.

In considering government policy, one also has to be conscious of its overall objective of reducing intervention in the economy and privatising services wherever possible. The reduction in tax relief can be seen as part of the programme of reducing government intervention, and the more recent cuts in income support to meet mortgage interest can be viewed similarly. The policy of privatising social housing by various means is bound to continue.

Turning directly to the owner occupied market, there are few actions that the Government can take aimed at producing more stability, and thereby reducing the risk element. Rather, if there is an adequate policy framework, combined with a stable economy, then the housing market itself will be stable. Housing is the most durable of durable goods, and it is unrealistic to expect a stable housing market with an unstable economy. The violent fluctuations in the housing market over the past few years have not been caused largely by housing market factors, but rather by macro-economic factors.

It is in the rented market where I see the focus of Government attention over the next few years. This is relevant to the health of the owner occupied market because increasingly there will be competition between the private rented sector and owner occupation, and also of course to those seeking to own, invest in or manage rented property. The objective of the Government should be to secure parity of treatment between the owner occupied sector and the private rented sector, and increasingly also to remove the unnecessarily wide gulf between private renting and social renting. One can see a number of strands coming together in government thinking on these issues. The Business Expansion Scheme was withdrawn at the end of 1993, having, one suspects, largely failed to establish a viable long-term private rental market, independent of the problems of the owner occupied market. In the social rented sector, grant rates are being sharply reduced. It was only a few years ago that housing associations had near 100% funding for new projects. Now, the average grant is under 60% with the prospect of further reductions to come.

Within the social rented sector, public policy must now recognise that we are in a low inflation and low interest rate environment. A combination of falling grant rates and the high repair and management costs inherent in the housing association system, mean that, in some parts of the country, social rents now equate with or exceed the cost of owner-occupation and private sector rents. This must lead to questions about the continued development of social housing units. Also, the huge increase in the cost of housing benefit, now running at over £10 billion a year, must be a major source of concern for the government. Any programme which guarantees to meet 100% of housing costs is bound to lead to mushrooming costs as consumers react accordingly. Also, there can be little justification for the massive subsidisation of low income tenants, when, at the same time, support of owner occupation through mortgage tax relief is being sharply reduced.

The Government will be forced to take action to deal with the problems of the rented sector in two different ways. Firstly, it will substantially reduce funding to housing associations, and no doubt is contemplating the possibility of ending the existing system completely, and rather making a lower grant, say, 25%, available to any landlord who undertakes to keep rents within a certain range, or who even undertakes to keep the accommodation available for renting for a certain period of time. Secondly, 100% housing benefit must be ended, otherwise it will cause quite unacceptable distortions in the market.

The present system benefits those of the poor who consume large amounts of rented housing. There is no reason why this group should benefit at the expense of other poor people. A substantial reduction in the overall housing benefit bill would free resources which could be better targeted and, at the same time, would lead to a more efficient rental market.

Is the Current Market Sustainable?

It is legitimate to ask whether the current structure of housing tenure, with nearly 70% of households owning their homes, is politically sustainable given the radical changes in the economics of the housing market. The answer is almost certainly that it is. There are problems at present with people having substantial negative equity and some people who, at the margin, should never have purchased. These problems are gradually being worked out of the system in one of a number of painful ways, ranging from a lender taking possession, to negative equity gradually reducing as house prices begin to rise and as mortgage debts can be paid off. The market for new purchases adapted very quickly, far more quickly than commentators, house builders and mortgage lenders had expected, hence the downturn being so prolonged and deep. Marginal purchasers have been properly deterred, both by observing the experience of others and also by the more cautious lending policies of lenders.

In the longer term, there is no reason why a 70% home ownership level is not sustainable as it is in other countries. However, the pattern of housing tenure by age will change quite significantly. People will become homeowners at a later age with the proportion of homeowners in the 25–29 age group falling from 59% in 1991, probably to well under 50%. However, there will be a rise in the proportion of elderly households who are homeowners simply as middle-aged homeowners become old. A limited number of elderly households will continue to transfer to rented accommodation.

Given that house purchase is more risky, it is proper that lenders and borrowers should take steps to reduce risk and that, where possible, government should also play its part. Borrowers are already more risk averse, reflected in the weak demand for home ownership. Lenders have become more risk averse, reflected in lower loan to value ratios and generally stricter underwriting criteria. Partly encouraged by lenders, an increasing proportion of borrowers have taken out mortgage protection insurance to help them in the event of being unable to work through disability or redundancy. At the end of 1994, the Department of Social Security announced that income support to meet mortgage interest payments would be reduced, the main change being that for new borrowers no benefit will be paid for the first nine months of unemployment. This was generally heralded as a marked reduction in government support for home ownership. However, it might also have the opposite effect by encouraging many more people to take out commercial insurance policies which give much better protection than does income support. There is also a gradual change in the balance between endowment and repayment loans. Endowment loans are less attractive the lower inflation is. If house prices are not rising rapidly, then it is obviously safer for the borrower to reduce the real value of his debt in the alternative way, that is of actually making debt repayments through the loan rather than building up a savings account. There has been much public criticism of endowment policies as a means of repaying loans, and while they remain valid for many borrowers, it is certainly proper that less use should be made of them. There is also scope for lenders to introduce more flexible loan arrangements that take account of the more risky nature of house purchase. While low start loans may have been popular in the past and were appropriate to a high inflation environment, high start loans may well now be more suitable for many borrowers, particularly when they can be combined with the option of a repayment holiday in the event, for example, of unemployment or sickness.

Conclusion

Everyone in the owner occupied housing market had it too good until recently. Owner occupiers, home buyers, mortgage lenders, mortgage insurers, valuers and house builders could hardly go wrong, protected, as they were, by a favourable fiscal régime and a high rate of inflation. The transition to the present situation is, inevitably, a painful one, although probably it is desirable for the economy as a whole. Fundamentals affecting markets can often change very quickly, and this has been the case with the owner occupied housing market. The participants in the market are slower to change; many are wedded to the market realities of the past and continue to behave accordingly. Others perhaps over-react, and in doing so threaten their ability to undertake business in the longer-term. The consumers perhaps are first to react sensibly, and that we have seen with their attitude towards house purchase.

The housing market of the late 1990s will, in many ways, be a far healthier one than that of the 1970s and 1980s. It will no longer be a case of boom or bust with people being able to earn more from the appreciation of their housing than they can from doing a job. Housing will be what it properly should be, that is a consumer good, and the production of it, for sale or for rent, should be governed by very much the same factors as govern other durable goods.

CHAPTER 5

Ideology, Public Policy and Private Rental Housing Since the War

PETER A KEMP

In recent years privately rented housing has been the subject of increasing attention from policy makers and in housing policy debates in Britain. Some commentators have sought to define a new consensus about the need for a commercially viable privately rented sector (e.g., Best *et al.*, 1992). The Conservative Government of John Major has expressed a keen desire to see a reversal of the sector's long term decline and is believed to be considering introducing new subsidies to encourage the provision of private housing to let.

This new focus on private renting follows over half a century of decline in the size of the sector and relative policy neglect. Until recently, the decline of the privately rented sector has sometimes been discussed as if it were inevitable, a function of progress towards more modern forms of housing tenure such as owner occupation. Indeed, as Whitehead points out in her contribution to this volume, some commentators have virtually assumed that the private landlord would (and perhaps should) disappear from the housing market.

This chapter reflects upon the decline of privately rented housing in Britain and examines the new interest in reviving the sector in the light of that decline. It argues that an historically informed analysis is essential to an adequate understanding of the privately rented sector. It also seeks to show that the extent and form of its decline was not inevitable but was in some respects a contingent development. It is further argued that public policy has significantly affected the nature of the privately rented sector and is deeply implicated in its decline. It is suggested that a major and sustainable revival of the market for private renting is in turn likely to require significant state orchestration, not the least to compensate for the intended and unintended consequences of previous and current housing, fiscal and economic policies that have affected the sector. Finally, it is argued that an expansion in the private management of rented housing, and possibly also in the private ownership of rented housing, could well take place over time as a result of the introduction of compulsory competitive tendering in local authority housing.

In surveying the development of the privately rented sector since the Second World War, the chapter covers a lot of ground and, consequently, risks over-simplifying a complex set of developments. Nevertheless, it can be helpful to take a broad sweep and not get bogged down in the details in order to identify the key features and forces behind the development of the privately rented sector in Britain.

The private rented sector at the end of the 1930s

At the end of the 1930s, few commentators would have predicted the pace and extent to which the privately rented sector has subsequently declined. At that stage it was still by far the largest housing tenure, accounting for nearly three out of every five dwellings (Table 1). It is true that the sector had declined in relative importance between the wars, as owner occupation and council housing developed as important housing tenures. But even in the 1930s, when owner occupation underwent a massive house building boom, over 66,000 units a year were produced for private renting (Kemp, 1984); this was a bigger total than was then, and is currently, being constructed by social housing agencies. Moreover, rent control had been gradually relaxed during the 1920s and 1930s in Britain, as in other European countries where it had been introduced during the First World War (Harloe, 1985).

Table 1   Housing tenure in England and Wales in 1938 and 1975

	1938 dwellings		1975 dwellings	
	(millions)	(%)	(millions)	(%)
Privately rented	6.6	58	2.9	16
Owner occupied	3.7	32	9.9	55
Local authority	1.1	10	5.2	29
Total	11.4	100	18.0	100

Source: DoE, *Housing Policy Review, Technical Volume I*, HMSO, London, 1977, p39; Inquiry into British Housing, *Supplement*, NFHA, London, 1985, pxii.

Nevertheless, the Second World War marked an important turning point for the privately rented sector in Britain. Thereafter, the sector declined rapidly, both in relative and in absolute size, and to a greater extent than in most other advanced industrial nations. Whereas in 1938 the privately rented sector accounted for 6.6 million dwellings or 58% of the housing stock in England and Wales, by 1975 it contained only 2.9 million dwellings and represented only 16% of the stock (Table 1).

Table 2   Components of change of the privately rented sector in England and Wales 1938–75

1938 stock	6.6
Sales to owner occupation	−2.6
Sales to local authorities	−0.3
Demolitions and changes of use	−1.2
New building and conversion	+0.4
Net change	−3.7
1975 stock	2.9

Source: DoE, *Housing Policy Review, Technical Volume I*, HMSO, London, 1977, p39.

This sharp decline was the outcome of a complex set of factors (see Hamnett and Randolph, 1988; Kemp, 1993) which operated on both the demand and supply sides and which reflects elements of both choice and constraint. As for how the sector has declined, Table 2 shows that the *existing stock* of privately rented sector dwellings was denuded in three main ways.

First, the major source of loss from the privately rented sector was sales of dwellings to the owner occupied housing market. Thus between 1938 and 1975, 2.6 million dwellings were sold into the owner occupied sector, a process that accounted for a substantial share of the growth in owner occupation over this period (DoE, 1977).

Second, 1.2 million dwellings were demolished in slum clearance schemes or – to a much lesser extent – were switched from residential into commercial uses such as offices. Holmans (1987) points out that nearly 30% of the stock of dwellings rented from private landlords in 1939 had been demolished or destroyed by 1981.

Third, a further 0.3 million dwellings were acquired by local authorities. In many cases, this acquisition of privately rented dwellings by local councils involved compulsory purchases necessary to effect developments such as road traffic improvements but in some cases it was part of an explicit municipalisation strategy. More recently, since the 1974 Housing Act, an unknown quantity of privately rented dwellings has been acquired by housing associations undertaking inner city rehabilitation schemes.

In addition, as is apparent from Table 2, there was very little *new construction* for private renting following the Second World War. This lack of new construction in the post war period is a key feature of the decline of private renting in Britain. It is also something that marks it out from most other advanced industrial nations, for elsewhere new building for private rental is not uncommon.

Control and disinvestment 1939–53

The post war housing shortage and the election of a Labour Government in 1945 were important reasons for the lack of new construction for private renting. One consequence of the post war housing shortage was that blanket rent controls were continued once hostilities had ended. The 1939 Rent and Mortgage Interest Restrictions Act had extended rent control to virtually all rented housing and froze rents at their September 1939 level. The second Ridley Committee, which reported in 1945, recommended that, in view of the housing shortage, rent control should be continued for a considerable period. The Committee also proposed, however, that rent tribunals should be established to determine fair rents in the unfurnished privately rented sector. Another proposal was that new construction should be exempt from rent controls, as it had been between 1919 and 1939 (Ridley Committee, 1945).

While the post war Labour Government accepted the recommendation that rent control should be continued, it did not exempt new construction from rent controls and nor did it take up the Ridley Committee's proposal on rent tribunals for unfurnished housing. The failure to exempt new construction from rent controls made it almost inevitable that little *new construction* for private rental would be undertaken in the immediate postwar years. And the failure to address the anomolies produced by previous, relatively inflexible forms of rent control or to introduce a more flexible system such as rent tribunals, made it highly likely that the *existing stock* would decline in size as rents fell in real terms.

While the existence of rent controls on new construction was obviously a major deterrent to building for private rental, it was not the only factor. As Minister of Health, Bevan persuaded the Labour Government (against considerable opposition in Cabinet) to focus the post war building programme very largely on council house building. Whereas the Conservatives had promised to provide subsidies for both private and local authority house building (Kemp, 1991) Labour reserved them exclusively for local authorities. Under the system of building licences, local authorities were expected to provide 80% of new construction. Given the existence of rent controls, the lack of subsidies and the limited permission to build, it was hardly surprising that the private sector focused its output on the market for owner occupation rather than housing to let.

When the Conservatives returned to office in 1951, the housing shortage was still very great and hence so was the political imperative both to maintain rent controls on the existing stock of privately rented dwellings and to increase the output of new houses. As a 'plannable instrument' it was hardly surprising, therefore, that local authorities continued to dominate the construction of new houses. The Conservatives at this time were more concerned with reaching the target of 300,000 new homes per annum that they had promised in the 1951 election campaign than by whom the houses were built (Holmans, 1987). With the private sector gradually recovering as building controls were removed, it was difficult to argue a case for the extension of subsidies to the private sector.

Meanwhile, since private sector rents were frozen at their September 1939 level – which in many cases was the August 1914 level plus 40% – they fell in real terms as house prices, earnings and retail prices all increased following the war. Thus the consumer price index increased by 105% between 1939 and 1951, while the price of building maintenance trebled (Holmans, 1987). Static rents combined with rising property values meant that rental yields fell. With a substantial gap opening up between tenanted and vacant possession house prices, many landlords took whatever opportunities that arose to sell up and invest elsewhere.

Decontrol and disinvestment 1954–63

While the new Conservative Government sought and succeeded in raising housing output to 300,000 a year by 1953, it also began to focus attention on the condition of the existing stock of (mostly privately rented) houses, much of which was seriously substandard. As Merrett (1982) has pointed out, the Conservatives' white paper *Housing – the Next Steps* (MHLG, 1953) saw the problem of substandard housing as one of the privately rented sector. Apart from the age of the stock, the white paper identified two causes of 'the neglect which privately-owned houses have suffered in recent years' (MHLG, 1953, p 6). These were (i) controls on building works and materials such as timber and steel, and (ii) 'the more serious cause', rent control.

The structure of rents in the privately rented sector was described in the white paper as 'hopelessly illogical', with, for example, different rents being charged for identical houses in the same street. In addition, many rents were insufficient to enable landlords to maintain their houses in adequate repair. Since the housing shortage was still sufficiently severe as to prevent rents from being completely decontrolled:

> The main question resolves itself, therefore, into the most equitable way of allowing such increases in the rents of privately-owned houses as will enable the landlord to keep the house in good repair. (MHLG, 1953, p 7)

The subsequent House Repairs and Rents Act 1954 permitted limited increases in the rents of dwellings which had been let before September 1939 and which had been maintained or put into a good state of repair (Doling and Davies, 1984). The aim was to give landlords an incentive to increase their expenditure on repair and maintenance. In addition, rent control was lifted from newly constructed houses.

Some dwellings were beyond repair. From the mid-1950s the Conservative Government began a new drive towards the replacement of the slums (Merrett, 1979). This new approach involved the large scale clearance of mainly privately rented terraced housing, much of it built to low standards in the nineteenth century and suffering from poor maintenance expenditure because of the low rents produced by decades of crude rent controls. The cleared stock was replaced by new council housing, built to modern standards and with the help of substantial subsidies from the Exchequer, which made it much more attractive for tenant households than privately rented accommodation. This process further hastened the decline in the privately rented sector.

Although rents had been decontrolled on new construction, there is little evidence that this led to a resurgence of building for private rental. The demand for new private housing was focused on the owner occupied market. Decades of rent control in the private sector and large subsidies for council housing had created a low rent environment which was not easily shed. Rent to income ratios in the 1950s were relatively low. The provision of subsidies to the privately rented sector seems to have been politically out of the question, even for a Conservative Government.

Political polarisation

The unwillingness of even the Conservatives to provide subsidies to private landlords in the way that other west European countries had done reflected the political controversy which surrounded the privately rented sector from the mid-1950s onwards. This period witnessed a growing polarisation in political debates on the privately rented sector.

Labour became actively opposed to the privately rented sector, its 1956 conference resolving, for example, that 'private landlordism had failed' (quoted in Wicks, 1973). It had evidently failed because slum housing was owned and let by private landlords. Hence the problem of the slums was seen as being due, not so much to the facts that the dwellings were old, had been built before the introduction of building standards, and had been constructed without state subsidies for tenants who could not afford to pay for anything other than poor quality housing; nor was it due to decades of inflexible rent controls, which made it uneconomic to maintain such housing in an adequate state of repair; instead it was largely seen as being a function of *ownership*, of the fact that it belonged to private landlords.

The answer to this perceived failure of private landlordism was seen to be municipalisation of the existing stock of privately rented housing. That municipalisation should be seen as the best way to deal with the problems of the privately rented sector was a reflection not only of Labour's distrust of the private landlord but also the statist welfare state regime which marks Britain out from many other west European countries (see Dunleavy, 1989). In housing policy, this statist approach during the 1945 to 1975 period was reflected in the heavy reliance on local authorities – rather than on voluntary organisations or the private sector – to provide new housing to let. At the same time, it reflected a tendency in housing policy in Britain towards uniform solutions being applied to what were often diverse housing problems.

From 1953 official Labour Party policy on privately rented housing involved comprehensive municipalisation of the sector. This remained the official line until 1961, when it was replaced with selective municipalisation on default where there was persistent neglect by the landlord (Wicks, 1973). Although there was little prospect, on cost grounds alone, of a policy of large scale municipalisation being put into practice, it can only have added to the political risk to which investment in the privately rented sector was subject. It also reflected a view that the decline and indeed death of the private landlord was a desirable, if not an inevitable, outcome and that nothing should be done to encourage them. In the meantime, rent control was necessary to prevent unscrupulous landlords from exploiting their tenants by charging 'exorbitant' rents for slum housing.

For the Conservatives, the privately rented sector had not failed but if problems existed it was because of rent controls. By keeping rents at below the market level, disinvestment from the sector was inevitable. Rent control also meant that private landlords could not afford to undertake the necessary repairs which they would otherwise have done. It was imperative, therefore, that such controls should be lifted as soon as the housing shortage had sufficiently abated to make that sensible. Once controls were lifted, it was argued, rents would rise, the sector would be profitable once again and investment would return. It followed from this argument that, since the problem was rent control, decontrol would be sufficient to revive the fortunes of the privately rented sector; subsidies were neither necessary nor desirable.

This polarisation of views was exhibited most clearly in the debates surrounding the passage of the 1957 Rent Act, one of the most controversial Acts to be passed in the 1950s. The parliamentary debates on the Bill, as Cullingworth (1979, p 117) has pointed out, had 'a curious air of unreality about them'. Barnett (1969) has noted that these debates were heavy in 'political symbolism in which myths about landlords and tenants defied rational discussion' (quoted in Stafford and Doling, 1981).

The impact of the 1957 Rent Act was much less dramatic than many of its supporters hoped or its opponents feared (Cullingworth, 1979). A study funded by Rowntree found that many landlords increased their rents (some by a considerable amount) but others did not (Donnison et al., 1961). Decontrol did not bring a halt to disinvestment by landlords. Rather, landlords continued to get out of the sector by selling to owner occupiers, including their own sitting tenants.

Disinvestment from the privately rented sector by sales to owner occupation was facilitated and accelerated by the Housing and House Purchase Act 1959 (Merrett, 1982). This Act made loans from the Exchequer available to building societies for lending to buyers of pre-1919 (and hence mainly privately rented) houses. As Holmans (1987, p 155) points out:

> It was part of a policy to promote improvement of older houses, but by making them more readily saleable it could only accelerate the transfer of houses out of private renting into owner occupation.

It was partly in response to the failure of the 1957 Rent Act to halt the decline of the privately rented sector that the Conservatives introduced an initiative in the 1961 Housing Act to encourage 'new style' housing associations. This involved £25 million of Exchequer loans to approved housing associations who were to operate on a cost rent basis and, so the Government hoped, 'serve to show the way to the investment of private capital once again in building houses to let' (quoted in Cullingworth, 1979, p 118). However, a number of reports commissioned by the Government at about the same time demonstrated that it was not possible to provide new houses built to modern standards without subsidies and still obtain a competitive return (Holmans, 1987).

The 1964 Housing Act increased to £100 million the amount of Exchequer loan available for housing associations. However, the emphasis was shifted from stimulating a revival of investment in private letting, to 'the development of a housing society movement which will build and manage houses for people at large who are able to meet the cost' (quoted in Cullingworth, 1979, p 118).

Thus from the early 1960s the Conservatives began to encourage the development of the housing association sector, in the first instance as a stimulant to the return of investment in new privately rented housing, and then when that failed, as a cost rent alternative to the privately rented sector. The development of this 'third arm' of housing provision (that is, in addition to owner occupation and council housing) was seen by the Conservatives as being especially important to counter the growing monopoly of council housing as the privately rented sector shrank and municipal housing increased through new building. The option of providing subsidies to enable the private sector to build new housing to let seems not to have been given serious consideration. This was perhaps hardly surprising given the political controversy surrounding the 1957 Rent Act and the subsequent Rachman scandal in the early 1960s.

The Rachman scandal

It was not until the early 1960s that many of the darker consequences of rent decontrol became apparent, partly because some of the 1957 Act's provisions were postponed until 1961. By then, the housing shortage in pressure areas such as inner London was acute, especially at the bottom end of the market. With controlled rents well below market levels, creeping decontrol (that is, decontrol on vacant possession) gave landlords an incentive to remove their sitting tenants by whatever means they could, in order to charge a higher rent. Because of the gap between sitting tenant and vacant possession house values – though this was not due to the 1957 Act – they also had an incentive to get rid of their tenants and sell their properties in the owner occupied housing market, a process that (as noted above) was facilitated by government measures which made it more feasible to obtain mortgages on pre-1919 dwellings.

In the late 1950s and early 1960s, stories began to appear in the local papers in London about intimidation of tenants, evictions and homelessness. The issue became highly politicised as a result of the publicity – which emerged in the wake of the Profumo scandal in 1963 – surrounding the activities of the West London landlord Peter Rachman. It turned out that one of the call girls involved in the Profumo 'sex and security' scandal had earlier been Rachman's mistress. The addition of slum landlordism to the already potent media cocktail of sex and national security allowed the press to inject new life into the controversy. The fact that Rachman was dead by this stage conveniently removed fears of libel writs being issued that might otherwise have restrained the media. For a couple of weeks, the public was fed a daily dose of stories about the violence and intimidation that Rachman was said to have used against his tenants (Banting, 1979). This publicity confirmed and strengthened the negative image with which private landlordism had come to be associated in Britain.

The Labour Party made considerable political capital out of the episode, which it linked to the Conservatives' 1957 Rent Act and its approach to housing policy. The party generalised the problems which the Rachman scandal highlighted to the privately rented sector as a whole; it was yet more proof that private landlordism had failed. Indeed, the new Labour leader, Harold Wilson, argued that 'rented housing is not a proper field for private profit' (quoted in Cullingworth, 1979, p 61).

In the wake of the Rachman scandal, the ailing Macmillan Government was forced to set up the Milner Holland Committee to investigate the problems of housing in London. The Committee's report, which was published in 1965, concluded that there was an acute shortage of rented housing in London. The surveys commissioned by the Committee found that, although most tenants were satisfied with the way their landlords treated them, landlord abuse was too common to be treated as an isolated problem (Milner Holland, 1965).

The Committee also demonstrated that, because of the tax and housing subsidy arrangements then in place, an identical house would cost a household less to buy with a mortgage or to rent it from a local authority than it would to rent it from a private landlord.

Crossman's legacy

The Labour Party, which came to power in 1964, pledged to reintroduce security of tenure for private tenants (Banting, 1979). The Rent Act 1965 established the system of regulated tenancies and 'fair rents' assessed by independent rent officers that the Housing Act 1988 has now abolished for new lettings. The system thus remained intact for nearly a quarter of a century.

Labour's new system of rent regulation was an attempt to provide a fair balance between the interests of landlords and tenants. It aimed to restore tenants' security of tenure while providing landlords with regular rent increases. In doing so, Crossman, the Minister for Housing, hoped to 'take rents out of politics'. But he also believed that it was too late to save the privately rented sector and that the future lay, on the one hand, with owner occupation and, on the other, with local authorities and housing associations (Banting, 1979). Perhaps it was because of this view that Crossman's Act re-imposed rent control on new construction, for it is difficult to find any other rationale for this measure, which made it almost inevitable that little new private housing to rent would be produced.

New construction was very largely confined to local authorities and the market for owner occupation. As Murie points out in his contribution to this volume, both Labour and Conservative governments supported major local authority house building programmes from the Second World War through to the 1970s. The completion of new local authority dwellings in Britain increased rapidly after the war, reaching 190,000 by 1948; thereafter completions remained at over 100,000 a year for the next quarter of a century (Merrett, 1979). Local authorities were able to offer their tenants housing that was cheaper, more modern, built to higher standards, and – in practice if not in law – stronger security of tenure than that provided by private landlords.

Whitehead (1979) has examined the benefits of home ownership and its potential advantages over private renting. It is not surprising that the number of home owners grew as real incomes increased. The attractions of home ownership for households that could afford to buy increased in the 1960s and 1970s, in part as a result of government policies, which further helped to shift demand away from private renting and towards owner occupation.

During the 1960s, as Holmans (1987) has remarked, the fiscal treatment of owner occupation changed from one of relative indifference to one of active support. One such measure was the abolition of taxation on imputed rental income in 1963. Another was the introduction by Labour of the option mortgage scheme in 1967, which gave non-taxpaying households a subsidy equivalent to that provided by mortgage interest tax relief. And whereas tax relief on the interest payments on consumer loans was abolished, it was kept in place on mortgages, though a £25,000 limit was introduced by Labour in 1974 (raised to £30,000 in 1983 by the Conservatives).

The effect of inflation

The preference for home ownership over private renting was further enhanced by the rising trend of inflation in the 1960s and its acceleration after 1973. Inflation eroded the real value of mortgage repayments and outstanding debt, thereby allowing households to borrow larger multiples of their income than previously, safe in the knowledge that a few years of inflation would reduce the debt to more manageable proportions. Moreover, for much of the 1970s the level of inflation was greater than nominal interest rates with the result that in real terms interest rates were negative. Building societies (or rather their investors) were virtually paying borrowers to buy a home with a mortgage (Merrett, 1982; Ball, 1983).

The failure of British economic policy to contain inflation was thus a contributory factor in accelerating the decline of private renting, by making it more attractive to buy than to rent. At the same time, the high rates of inflation prevalent during the 1970s had the effect of sharply reducing the rental yield on accommodation let on regulated tenancies with a fair rent (Holmans, 1987).

Since rents fell in real terms during the 1970s while vacant possession house values increased, landlords had a strong incentive to sell to owner occupiers and invest their money elsewhere rather than re-let when a property became vacant. Although landlords could make capital gains from rising property values, the rent acts gave tenants relatively strong security of tenure (in law if not in practice), which made it difficult for them to repossess their properties. Because of the gap between vacant possession and tenanted investment values, it was economically rational for landlords to realise their investment by selling when the property became vacant. This value gap was in large part a function of rent controls and the tax advantages of home ownership (Doling and Davies, 1984; Hamnett and Randolph, 1988).

The gap between vacant possession and tenanted investment values created a space for property dealers to make large profits by purchasing tenanted property, encouraging the tenant to leave and selling at vacant possession values (Hamnett and Randolph, 1988). In some case, developers were able to obtain improvement grants to improve run down privately rented houses which they then sold at a substantial profit (Williams, 1978).

By the early 1970s, owner occupation had become the mainstream tenure to which a majority of households aspired, while council housing had become the largest rental tenure. In contrast, private renting had become a minority sector and one that was rapidly disappearing. It had also become much less central to policy debates. This was reflected in the legislation enacted and government papers published in the 1970s. Although a number of measures were passed which dealt with the privately rented sector, the changes they introduced were relatively marginal. Even the Conservative Government under Prime Minister Heath failed to address the problems facing the privately rented sector, though one important measure which it did introduce was rent allowances for tenants of unfurnished accommodation in the 1972 Housing Finance Act and for furnished tenants in 1973 (Cullingworth, 1979).

Following the recommendations of the Francis Committee (1971) the 1974 Rent Act brought furnished accommodation within the regulated rent system, mainly because some landlords were seeking to avoid rent controls by letting their accommodation with a minimal amount of furniture included in the letting. At the same time the 1974 Act excluded lettings made by resident landlords from the regulated tenancy framework.

The 1977 Housing Policy Review (DoE, 1977) focused very largely on the two main tenures of owner occupation and council housing and gave little consideration to private renting, which was instead relegated to a Review of the Rent Acts. But as Cullingworth (1979) has pointed out, the Review was concerned mainly with tidying up and rationalising the existing system of controls rather than with a fundamental appraisal of the role of the sector in the modern housing market. The 1977 Rent Act did little more than consolidate the legislation that was already in place and introduced no major innovations (Stafford and Doling, 1981).

Developments since 1980

With the return of a radical Conservative Government committed to dismantling the post war settlement, rolling back the state, and releasing market forces, it was only to be expected that reviving the privately rented sector would become an important goal of housing policy when Mrs Thatcher came to power. In fact, although her first and second administrations were keen to halt the decline of the sector, it was never a central focus of their policy making. Instead, the emphasis – almost the obsession – of Conservative housing policy was on expanding home ownership; another example of uniform solutions being promoted for what were diverse housing problems. Key secondary objectives were reducing public expenditure on housing and minimising the role of local housing authorities. The beauty of council house sales, so far as the Conservatives were concerned, was that they did all three things – expand owner occupation, reduce council housing and lower the public sector borrowing requirement – simultaneously (Kemp, 1992).

As well as the Right to Buy and other measures concerned with social housing, the 1980 Housing Act introduced a range of measures aimed at making privately rented housing more profitable. The remaining controlled tenancies, extant from the pre-1965 period, were converted into regulated tenancies. The phasing in of increases in fair rents and the interval between fair rent registration, were both reduced from three to two years. It was made easier for resident landlords to regain possession. And two new forms of tenancy were introduced. Shortholds were regulated tenancies of from one to five years after which the landlord could regain possession. Assured tenancies were lettings by approved landlords of newly built housing let at market rents (in 1987 assured tenancies were widened to include refurbished housing).

Thus new privately rented construction – which had been subject to rent regulation since 1965 – was deregulated in 1980, provided the landlord was approved by the Department of the Environment. The landlord approval scheme can be seen as an attempt to shed the private landlord of the Rachman image that had dogged it since the early 1960s. Meanwhile, in order to attract new investment into the private rental market – in what was a significant departure from previous policy on the sector since the war – capital allowances were made available following the 1982 Budget to approved landlords building homes for letting at market rents (Kemp, 1988).

The impact of these measures was not very considerable. Relatively little use was made of shortholds tenancies (Crook, 1986). Although the availability of capital allowances did prompt a number of firms to register as approved landlords, the premature withdrawal of this subsidy after only two years ensured that little new privately rented construction actually took place (Kemp, 1988). During the 1980s, the sector continued to decline, albeit at a slower rate.

The Select Committee of the House of Commons investigated the privately rented sector in 1981/82. Its report concluded that there was a gap between the rate of return that investors required in order to remain or invest in the privately rented sector and the level of rent that many tenants could afford to pay. The Committee argued that this gap could only be closed if there was a significant increase, or redistribution, in housing subsidies (HCEC, 1982).

Conservative housing policy entered a new phase following the re-election of the Conservatives under Mrs Thatcher for a third term of office in 1987. Although expanding home ownership remained the Conservatives' major housing goal, reviving the private rented sector was given much greater attention than previously. This new approach was part of a wider strategy of demunicipalisation and privatisation of rented housing, as set out in the 1987 housing white paper (DoE, 1987). It reflected and built upon both the growing disenchantment with the public sector and what Piven (1986) has called the 'revivalist romance' with markets, as well as the ideological orientation of the Conservative Party under Mrs Thatcher.

The subsequent 1988 Housing Act made it easier for landlords to regain possession and deregulated all new lettings. At the same time, a short term subsidy via the Business Expansion Scheme was made available to companies letting accommodation on assured tenancies in order to give a kickstart to new investment in the sector (Whitehead and Kleinman, 1989; Crook *et al.*, 1991).

In fact, the privately rented sector ceased its long term decline by the late 1980s and then proceeded to grow somewhat following rent deregulation. Between 1988 and 1993 the number of households renting privately in England and Wales increased from 1.8 to 2.1 million. The sector's share of the housing stock also increased, from 8.7 to 9.8% over the same period (Table 3).

Table 3   The stock of privately rented sector dwellings in England and Wales 1988–92

Year	000s	% of total stock
1988	1,771	8.7
1989	1,857	9.0
1990	1,976	9.5
1991	2,047	9.8
1992	2,068	9.8

Source: DoE, *Housing and Construction Statistics 1982–92*, HMSO, London, 1944, p129.

Recent research has indicated that not all of this increase in supply can be attributed to rent deregulation (Crook *et al.*, 1995). For at the same time as rents were deregulated, the owner occupied housing market entered into a slump in which house prices fell in real – and for the first time since the war – in nominal terms, transactions declined, mortgage arrears and repossessions increased sharply (Forrest and Murie, 1994b) and around a million home owners found themselves with negative equity (Dorling and Cornford, 1995).

Crook *et al.* (1995) estimated that about one in ten of all privately rented addresses were owned by 'property slump landlords' who were unable or unwilling to sell because of the state of the owner occupied housing market; and that they accounted for around half of the increase in lettings since 1988. Moreover, the yields on private letting were found to be uncompetitive with alternative investments, taking into account relative liquidity and risk.

Meanwhile, although over £3 billion had been raised by assured tenancy property companies in six years, most directors of BES companies reported that they would probably sell their dwellings as and when property prices picked up. The net yields on BES companies were uncompetitive compared with alternative investments and, consequently, even those directors who wished to keep their company going thought it unlikely that they would be able to continue in business (Crook *et al.*, 1995).

The same research also found that there was little prospect of the financial institutions investing significant sums of money in the privately rented sector, either in the form of debt or equity. This was not only because of the low yields but also because of the lack of regular and detailed information about rents and yields compared with other investments, the poor image of private landlords, and what they perceived to be the relatively high degree of political risk attached to investment in the sector.

Finally, Crook *et al.* (1995) also found that the future size of the sector was likely to be determined, to a significant extent, by the future course of house prices and rents. If rents increased in line with house prices the sector would remain at about its present size. If rents increased faster than house prices, the sector would continue to expand. And if house prices were to increase faster than rents, as had happened for much of the 1970s and 1980s, then a significant proportion of privately rented properties would be sold. Thus although the decline of the sector has ceased, the recent increase in lettings could prove to be only a temporary phenomenon rather than a robust recovery.

Emerging trends

A new phase of policy making under the Conservatives now seems to be emerging in which the private sector is likely to have a pivotal, rather than a peripheral, role to play. In part this new dawn for private renting stems from a growing belief that the polarisation of housing provision has gone too far. On both the left and the right of the political spectrum there is greater acceptance of the need for a privately rented sector to cater for particular market niches – such as young adults, new and mobile households – whose needs are not being adequately met by social housing or owner occupation (Whitehead and Kleinman, 1986; Best *et al.*, 1992). A related argument is that the heavy emphasis on owner occupation is harmful to the macroeconomy and that a healthy private rented sector is important for economic, and not just housing market, reasons (Maclennan, 1994).

There appear to be at least four elements to this newly emerging phase in housing policy under the Conservatives. First, the Government has begun to encourage local authorities to make greater use of the privately rented sector to accommodate households accepted as homeless, instead of their own stock or nominations to housing associations (DoE, 1994). This has proved to be a highly controversial proposal and has been interpreted as an attack on social housing. Although there is much agreement, if not consensus, that the privately rented sector can and should play an important role in meeting housing needs, there is much less support for using it to discharge local authorities' responsibilities under the homelessness provisions of the Housing Act. Thus while the new realism about the role of the privately rented sector has helped to create the context within which the emerging housing policy has been developed, the latest proposals go well beyond what many supporters of the new realism would accept.

Second, as part of the 'fundamental reviews' of public spending which are currently being undertaken across Whitehall, the Government has reduced the subsidy on owner occupiers' mortgage interest payments provided by MIRAS and cut back the help provided by Income Support mortgage interest payments. These developments, especially given the trend towards more flexible patterns of employment, are likely to shift demand at the margin away from owner occupation and towards private renting. These are important changes because they appear to reflect a decision that, if there is a trade off between reducing public spending and maintaining the level of owner occupation, the former is (currently) preferred to the latter, a reversal of the position under Mrs Thatcher. These changes imply a more central role in housing provision for private renting than has been the case for many decades.

Third, and again as part of the fundamental reviews of public spending, it appears that active consideration is being given to the provision of grants to private developers, instead of simply to housing associations, to provide low cost rented housing. While the detail, still less the policy, has not yet been announced, it seems likely that these grants will be targeted on low income households rather than single people and moderate income renters. While support has built up for the provision of subsidies to private landlords, this had generally been seen as being targeted on the niche groups referred to above rather than as a replacement for social housing.

Fourth, the introduction of compulsory competitive tendering (CCT) into local authority housing will lead to the involvement of the private sector in the management of council housing estates. Various private firms have expressed an interest in bidding for contracts under CCT. One of the largest sponsors of BES companies is also preparing to be an active bidder for housing management under CCT.

While CCT is about the management of existing council housing estates, it could eventually result in an increase in the privately rented stock. It could well lead to bids being made by successful management organisations via the Tenant's Choice provisions of the 1988 Housing Act which allow non-municipal landlords to bid for the ownership of council housing. As well as bids from housing associations, Tenant's Choice bids could come from management buy-outs by existing council employees – as has happened under other privatisation initiatives – and from private sector management companies who have won CCT contracts and established a successful relationship with their tenants.

Thus CCT is unlikely to be an end-point but could, over the long term, herald the way for a major restructuring not only of the management but also of the ownership of council housing and pave the way for transfers to the privately rented sector. This process may prove more attractive than investment in new private rental stock because the transfer price is likely to be based on tenanted investment income (and also reflect the need for major repairs) rather than owner occupied house prices.

However, one conflict which faces the Government is between, on the one hand, reviving the privately rented sector and, on the other, containing the rising cost of Housing Benefit. The average private sector rent has increased by far more than the rate of inflation since 1989, while the number of private tenants receiving Housing Benefit has also risen and hence so too has the cost of the scheme. This led to reductions in Housing Benefit in January 1996, again as part of the fundamental reviews of public spending, the effect of which – other things being equal – is likely to reduce rents and hence both yields and supply at the margin. This reinforces the point that the state is a major determinant of the aggregate level of effective demand in the privately rented housing market (Kemp, 1994b).

Towards a sustainable future?

It follows from these conclusions that the privately rented sector will continue to be affected in important ways by public policy; not only that which is specifically addressed to private renting, but also policy towards other tenures, taxation, social security and macroeconomic management.

A 'sustainable' or at a least healthy private rental housing market therefore requires action in these other policy areas and not just in housing policy. The

ingredients of a more successful approach to private renting than has characterised the postwar period as a whole seem to be the following: a sustained low
inflation environment; a more tax neutral approach to private housing; a well
administered and more efficiently structured housing benefit scheme; and long
term political agreement that the sector can and should make an important contribution to housing provision in Britain.

Leaving aside the privatisation of social rented housing, the future size of the
sector will be affected at the margin not only by public policy but also by trends
(which are themselves affected by policy) in house prices, rents and inflation. Yet
even so, the sector seems unlikely either to grow or to shrink very much from its
present size (Crook *et al.*, 1995). In any case, what is more important than the
precise size of the sector is the way in which it is operating and how it fits into the
housing system as a whole. Housing policy should be less concerned with the
question of size and more focused on ensuring that the privately rented market is
able to provide accommodation that is secure, meets minimum standards, is
reasonably affordable and provides a competitive return. At present those conditions do not exist.

Conclusions

A number of conclusions can be drawn from this overview of key developments in
the privately rented sector since the Second World War and of emerging trends.
The first is that the scale and nature of decline, in important respects, has been a
contingent development. It was fairly inevitable that the privately rented sector in
Britain, as in other countries, would shrink somewhat in size but it was by no
means inevitable that it would shrink at the scale and in the manner that it has
done.

Second, the pace and nature of decline, to a significant extent, has been affected
by public policy (cf. Whitehead and Kleinman, 1986). So far as housing policy is
concerned, decades of rent regulation, the unwillingness to provide investment
incentives for private landlords, and a desire to promote other tenures, have all
been important factors behind the decline of private renting. But decline has also
been due to economic management and in particular Britain's poor performance
on inflation, which has made private renting less attractive than house purchase.

Third, the relative neglect of the privately rented sector in policy terms has
reflected what Hindess (1987) has referred to an 'essentialist' perspective on the
market, which has been shared by ideologues on both the left and the right. By
essentialism Hindess (1987, p 149) means that 'the market has been analysed in
terms of an essence or inner principle which produces necessary effects by the
mere fact of its presence'.

This essentialist perspective has permeated the attitudes of the two major parties towards housing tenure. For the Conservatives – as the debates on the 1957
Rent Bill and the 1987 Housing white paper illustrate – the private provision of
rented housing has often been portrayed as self-evidently beneficial; the problem
is merely that the governments have imposed rent controls on the sector which
have made it unprofitable and which only need to be removed for the sector to
revive. In contrast, for Labour, the private provision of rented housing is just as
obviously pernicious; and rent regulation is needed to curb the worst excesses of

the market and in particular to prevent unscrupulous private landlords from exploiting their tenants (Kemp, 1990).

Partly in consequence of these polarised and over-simplified views – but for different reasons – both parties have acquiesced to and encouraged both the bifurcation of the housing market into owner occupation and council housing and the virtual collapse of private renting.

There are signs that a less emotionally charged and ideologically driven approach to the privately rented sector is now beginning to emerge. Labour has begun to accept that the sector can have some important, if limited, roles to play and that rent regulation is not necessarily an answer to the problems which exist in part of the market. The Conservatives have accepted that rent deregulation was a necessary but not a sufficient condition for a sustained revival of the privately rented sector and that a more even subsidy playing field with owner occupation is required to make the sector economically viable.

Nevertheless, the proposal that the privately rented sector should be used to house the homeless represents something of a departure from the more widely accepted view that private renting is a suitable option for certain types of housing demand, such as young people, job movers and new households, as well as people who cannot afford owner occupation or gain access to social housing. The homelessness proposals have been subjected to heavy criticism from housing organisations and pressure groups. Some critics have interpreted them as being an attack on social housing and one response has been to focus attention on the perceived shortcomings of the privately rented sector. These proposals are consequently in danger of undermining the more bi-partisan approach that had begun to develop. While a viable privately rented sector will require cross party agreement on private renting, it may be that that will only be possible if there is also similar agreement on the role of social housing.[1]

Note
1. This chapter was written prior to the publication of the 1995 Housing White Paper.

CHAPTER 6

Beyond State Housing

ALAN MURIE

Housing problems and policy debates in Britain in the 1990s have very different elements from those which have dominated most of the century. Problems of unhealthy housing, of overcrowding, of unfit and slum housing and housing lacking modern amenities, of gross shortages of adequate housing and of insecurity and exploitative landlordism had been radically transformed (although not completely eliminated) by the mid 1970s. Any account of these changes identifies the impact of public policy and the role of local authorities and new towns in building high standard housing for rent and purchase as of key importance. (Lansley, 1979; Murie, 1983) The British experience in these respects has similarities with other advanced industrial economies. The driving forces for developing policies to improve housing conditions were not simply about recognising and meeting needs and did not result in the same approach in all countries (see e.g. Harloe, 1989; Pooley, 1993). Nevertheless and especially in the Northern and Western European democracies a substantial non profit rented sector was developed. The British approach to non profit housing was unusual because it placed the dominant role in the hands of local government. Elsewhere it was more common to use non statutory agencies – although often with local authorities having a strong direct or indirect influence.

Britain was generally more active in developing non profit or social rented housing in the period before 1939 and early British planning and public housing activity and the approach adopted after 1945 had a considerable influence on other countries. The approach to planning new communities and to the standards of new public sector housing were widely held up as models. The dwellings which were built were predominantly traditionally constructed houses with gardens designed for working class families and those seeking to rent. They represented dramatic improvements on what was generally available elsewhere in a declining private rented sector and formed a privileged sector of the housing stock for which there was considerable competition to gain access. At this point council housing can be presented as having attributes which promised a sustained and successful role:

- it formed a key element in the welfare state in the attack on squalor and through low rents in social security strategies;
- it provided a high standard and highly valued service at rents which ordinary households could afford;

- it involved a level of development which could be adjusted in the light of macroeconomic circumstances and economic management;
- it involved a pattern of development which took account of local housing needs and of local planning policies and was accountable to elected local representatives;
- it largely involved private sector contract construction and provided a source of stability for the construction industry;
- as the sector matured it had an increasing capacity for pooling of costs or cross subsidy between older properties with limited outstanding debt related to historic costs and properties burdened by the high debt associated with new building;
- because of subsidy systems and pooling arrangements the sector was successful in breaking the association between low income or other measures of social disadvantage and poor housing;
- and as the sector developed a mix of properties and catered for households with different housing needs associated with different and changing circumstances it had the capacity to develop active transfer and exchange strategies and to manage housing to achieve efficient use of the stock and meet the choices and preferences of tenants.

The potential of the council sector, as outlined above, was not always realised. Local housing authorities were often slow to recognise the potential for policy change and to respond to criticisms of their approach. But at the point where the greatest potential for such change was being created municipal housing lost favour. It has not formed the key element in the development of British housing since the 1970s. Rather than regarding the council sector and the energies and experience associated with it as assets, policy makers in the 1980s have sought to dismantle the sector and have seen the electoral, fiscal and individual choice or exit potential of dismantling the sector as more compelling than any opportunities foregone. As a result council housing has come under attack and policy changes have changed the sector in ways which leave it with fewer strengths and less likely to attract political support. Changes which have been partly justified by the shortcomings of council housing have had the self fulfilling effect of confirming and adding to shortcomings.

Leaving this aside the provision of council and new town housing transformed housing conditions, rights and opportunities and changed the nature of the built environment and social and spatial patterns within cities, towns and rural communities. This legacy will continue to have an important impact but the nature of this impact is changing. Furthermore by the 1990s the role of local authorities and new towns in providing new rented housing had declined to the lowest peace time level since 1920. The changing role of council housing arose from the interaction of different elements. Three elements have been of particular importance: those associated with financial maturation and changes in the age of the stock in council ownership; those associated with a changing social and tenure environment; and those associated with policy choices to alter the size and role of the sector. This chapter does not seek to review the origins and development of council housing in Britain or to evaluate the achievements and failures associated with the tenure. It refers to some of the key issues in such discussion but its focus is on changes in the tenure which have affected its role and reputation. This particularly refers to the changing social role of the tenure. It is argued that the council sector has changed as a result of wider social processes as well as policy changes and that the inevitability of change means that no part of the housing system can insulate itself and reproduce successful formulae from the past.

In view of this the key questions for a sound and sustainable housing policy relate to the capacity to adjust to change and to sustain progress in relation to the condition of the housing stock and the opportunities of households with different resources. In relation to the latter the key questions relate to the position of households with limited resources and bargaining power in relation to the housing market. The key questions for a sustained attack on poor housing conditions and on housing inequality are not about reproducing or defending council housing but do relate to conditions and relationships which council housing has been at least partly successful in modifying. Whether local housing authorities or council housing has a role in a future sustainable policy package depends upon whether there are better ways of resolving key problems. Whatever the answer to this is, state housing in Britain and the legacy of production of housing by local authorities and new towns will continue to be important. This chapter ends with a consideration of this issue and of alternatives for a continuing role for council housing.

Background

Accounts of the nature and development of housing policy in Britain refer to nineteenth century measures to deal with the problems of the health of towns and a succession of measures to replace slums, improve dilapidated dwellings and build model houses and model estates (see, e.g. Merrett, 1979; Malpass and Murie, 1994). The major inroads made into housing problems were associated with changes in housing finance and the process of housing development. The declining interest of private investors in rentier landlordism was apparent before the First World War and the introduction of rent controls. New speculative development for home owners expanded in the inter war years and made a major contribution along with council housing supported, after 1919, by subsidies from the exchequer and the rates. The expansion of both home ownership and council housing through new building and transfers from the private rented sector contributed to a dramatic restructuring of housing tenure with the near monopoly position of private renting being replaced by a dual tenure system in which home ownership was the senior partner and council housing the junior.

The introduction of exchequer subsidies in 1919 made it possible for local authorities to build high quality houses with rents which were at least within the reach of affluent working class households (see Murie, 1983). In the ensuing 60 years the quantity and quality of what was built by local authorities was affected by changes in subsidy arrangements (see Malpass, 1990) but local authorities organised themselves to become energetic and creative providers and developers of housing which was mostly popular at the outset and continued to be in high demand.

The impact of the Second World War on housing in Britain was profound with a dramatic scaling down of new production and the reintroduction of rent controls as well as severe damage to the housing stock through aerial bombardment. In spite of the deterioration in the housing situation, there was no major enquiry into housing. There was no equivalent of the Beveridge Report for housing. While it would be wrong to imply that there were no innovations and initiatives in policy there was no comprehensive reassessment of housing policy sufficient to meet this agenda. After the end of the war there was no nationalisation of defined sectors of the housing stock, and any municipalisation proceeded on the basis operating in the past. There was no nationalisation of land or of the building industry and the nationalisation of development rights (under the Town and Country Planning Act 1947), designed to remove problems of speculation and profiteering, was a substantial retreat from Labour's earlier commitment (Merrett, 1982).

In an environment of reconstruction and radical reorganisation, in housing Labour chose to work with existing structures. Bevan, as Minister of Health, stated:

> if we are to plan we have to plan with plannable instruments, and the speculative builder, by his very nature is not a plannable instrument . . . we rest the full weight of the housing programme upon the local authorities, because their programmes can be planned (quoted in Donnison, 1967, p.164).

The New Towns Act 1946 provided for the setting up of development corporations to found and run new towns. This was a break with the policy of local authority responsibility which operated elsewhere. The new town development corporations went on to build over a quarter of a million houses housing 'overspill' population from urban areas and playing a role in regional policies.

Aneurin Bevan explained the role envisaged for local authorities in housing:

> Before the war the housing problems of the middle-classes were, roughly, solved. The higher income groups had their houses – the lower income groups had not. Speculative builders, supported enthusiastically, and even voraciously, by money-lending organisations, solved the problem of the higher income groups in the matter of housing. We propose to start at the other end. We propose to start to solve, first, the housing difficulties of the lower income groups. In other words, we propose to lay the main emphasis of our programme upon building houses to let. That means that we shall ask Local Authorities to be the main instruments for the housing programme
> (Parliamentary Debates, 1945–6).

Bevan also commented on the disadvantages of allowing local authorities to build houses for only the lower income groups and the early postwar measures established a wider role for local authorities and government in housing. Policy was concerned not just with the poor or the working class and not just with new building, or even renting.

Local authorities, supplemented by new town development corporations and by private enterprise, achieved high rates of new housing investment with construction on green field sites and in slum clearance areas as well as housing improvement. The contribution of local authorities did not squeeze out private provision and the highest levels of new building by the private sector were achieved when local authorities were also achieving high rates of completion. Between 1938 and 1981 local authorities and new towns in England and Wales built some 4.4 million dwellings. In the years 1914–38 they had built 1.1 million. On a pro-rata basis the post 1938 achievements were much higher. In the period

1939–60, 2.3 million dwellings were built; and in 1960–75, 1.6 million. It is in the period since 1975 that the contribution has been most limited. There can be no doubt that the public sector made a major impact on housing supply. Private sector speculative house building was held back by licensing between 1945 and 1951 but in the whole period 1938–75 new building for owner-occupation was 3.9 million dwellings – the same as by the public sector. In the 1980s, when council house building was severely restricted, the private sector failed to achieve building rates in excess of 150,000 dwellings a year. It has nowhere near regained its own highest levels of investment, let alone those of the public sector and in the 1990s problems in the home ownership market led to a fall in private sector completions.

The postwar priority given to high quality council building was eroded after 1950. In 1951 the Labour government reduced 'circulation space' and subsequently the Conservative government reduced living space and equipment in order to achieve more units of output. However, this was accompanied by higher subsidies and the higher building targets set and achieved still related to good quality housing. The relaxation of controls on private building were more important in shifting the balance and after 1954 local authority building was restricted to slum clearance replacement. In 1954 Harold Macmillan said 'Local authorities and local authorities alone can clear and rehouse the slums, while the general housing need can be met, as it was to a great extent before the war, by private enterprise' (quoted in Samuel et al., 1962). This return to the prewar role of local authorities formed part of a more general 'market' philosophy in housing. The temporary and extraordinary shortages occasioned by war were now thought to be remedied. Problems were thought to arise because of mis-allocation of resources rather than absolute shortage. The market was seen as the best mechanism to reallocate – local authority action was needed to meet the peculiar circumstances of slum clearance. The view that 'a national sufficiency of housing existed and a return to economic rents would allow housing policy to be directed at real problems instead of a larger and artificial and spurious shortage occasioned by rent restrictions' (Howe and Jones, 1956) was indicative of Conservative views.

By the 1970s, the mixed economy of housing policy included a considerable public sector presence. Some 1 in 3 dwellings were owned by the state. This measure of the energy and activity of local authorities in particular and of the demise of private landlordism was not the product of a consensus over the reorganisation of housing. Disagreements over the respective roles of public and private sectors were apparent throughout the postwar years and Conservative critics of the waiting list society and of the power which municipal housing authorities had were prominent. (see e.g. Howe, 1965) Criticisms gained strength with the emergence of problems of high rise housing, older housing needing repair and maintenance and increasing concern about the management regimes applied to an ageing and changing housing stock. From the mid 1960s some key Conservative controlled local authorities also made energetic use of powers to sell council houses and actively campaigned to make this a central element in local housing policies (Murie, 1976). Proposals for demunicipalisation and privatisation were added to fiscal and other measures which were designed to encourage home ownership and had begun to dominate housing policy. With postwar housing shortages largely removed equity and redistribution became less apparent in national policy aims and housing policy was increasingly linked to individual choice, reward, accumulation and enterprise.

Both Labour and Conservative governments continued to support major public sector housing programmes until the 1980s. However, government from the mid 1950s has pursued an increasingly residual policy towards council housing. As the Labour government of 1965 stated:

> Once the country has overcome its huge social problem of slumdom and obsolescence, and met the need of the great cities for more houses let at moderate rents, the programme of subsidised council housing should decrease. The expansion of the public programme now proposed is to meet exceptional needs; it is born partly of a short term necessity, partly of the conditions inherent in modern urban life. The expansion of building for owner occupation on the other hand is normal; it reflects a long term social advance which should gradually pervade every region (MHLG, 1965).

The ambitious aims of the 1940s had given way to a more restricted vision for council housing. But it remained a positive vision in housing old and disabled persons and those unable to buy. By the 1970s government regarded the general problems of housing shortage as solved and there were major disagreements over the way forward and over how best to arrange housing subsidies (Malpass, 1990). The sharpest break with policy towards council housing and the one with the most lasting impact came in the legislation of 1980. A new subsidy scheme was introduced alongside major cuts in public expenditure and a general privatisation programme with the sale of public sector housing to sitting tenants as the core programme. These steps represented a significant break with the past. They were implemented by a newly interventionist Conservative government assuming greater power and control in what has been referred to as a nationalisation of policy (Murie, 1985). Council housing began to decline in size and became the government's largest single programme of asset sales. Cuts in expenditure had been made consistently since 1975 but the changes from 1980 onwards were much more dramatic. In the climate of the period after 1979 housing public expenditure decisions were based on 'what the country could afford' rather than on calculations of what was needed. Need itself was regarded as a moving target and the aims of policy were concerned with the promotion of market processes, incentives, choices, self-help and the redistribution of wealth through council house sales (Malpass and Murie, 1994).

A final phase of policy emerged in 1987 and legislation of 1988 and 1989. It related to further dismantling of the council sector through Tenants' Choice measures, voluntary transfers of stock on the initiative of councils and a Rent to Mortgage Scheme designed to add to the sale of council houses. The operation of the Right to Buy would continue to lead to sales of council properties as rents rose and mortgages proved an attractive alternative. Alongside the Tenants' Charter, a new emphasis on individual rights, the encouragement of tenant management, the favouring of housing associations, the emphasis on an enabling role, requirements for compulsory competitive tendering for housing management and an impending reorganisation of local government, the presentation of public policy involved little to encourage local authorities to make the positive direct contributions of the past.

A Changing Tenure

The danger of accounts of policy change are that they implicitly suggest that policy changes form the key to understanding changes affecting a policy area. For council housing changes in policy and especially those since 1980 have been very important. However, the nature, role and demand for council housing changed significantly as a result of other processes. These affected the political support for the tenure and interact with policy changes to determine the continuing role for local authorities in housing provision. Rather than housing policy being the major determinant of changes in housing it is changes in population size and structure, changes in employment and the economy, and changes in taxation, public expenditure on welfare and economic strategy which have had most impact. Increasing social inequality and the end of an era of full employment have had major consequences for council housing. The main elements in these changes have been set out elsewhere (Murie, 1993). They include changes in supply and in social role which are dealt with in turn below.

The major changes in the supply of council housing relate to the flow of properties available to households seeking to enter the sector or to move within it but also to the stock of dwellings. Whereas at one stage council housing consisted of new dwellings, greatly superior to those available elsewhere in the rented sector, the stock has aged and is much more mixed in quality and design with an increasing proportion of flats among a declining stock. In the 1990s new tenants, in contrast to their predecessors, are likely to be offered an older, second hand dwelling. This situation has been affected by the low rates of new building in the council sector since the 1970s as well as by the greater extent to which more popular properties have been sold since 1980 under the Right To Buy. The extent to which the council housing sector consists of less desirable and sustainable properties relates to processes of ageing and obsolescence, the lack of new properties and the process of sale and transfer. One inevitable consequence of this is a further identification of council housing as a sector of limited choice and a second best tenure.

Changes in the social role of the council sector merit a lengthier discussion. Council housing started as a highly desirable tenure attractive to the affluent working class. However, as the characteristics of the supply of housing in different tenures changed and as the financial advantages associated with home ownership and access to that tenure improved, it increasingly became the case that households which could afford to buy did so and, latterly, that existing tenants were encouraged to exit through various new routes – the Right to Buy, Rents to Mortgages, and choosing a new landlord. At the same time the profile of existing tenants was changing. The relative uniformity of the first cohort of tenants ceased to determine the profile of the sector. The first cohort aged and family structures changed while new tenants continued to be mainly young families with children. By the 1980s wider demographic changes were affecting council housing with more elderly households and lone parent households and a greater impact of household fusion and fission contrasting with the relative stability of household arrangements which were associated in the past with long term tenancies or housing for life.

The overall profile of those in council housing was influenced by the changing characteristics of those entering the sector. Even without slum clearance rehousing obligations and an emphasis on housing those with the greatest need the steady decline of the private rented sector removed alternatives for lower income households and this group was increasingly dependent on the council sector. As a result of these three processes the social profile changed and council housing was increasingly a sector for the elderly, the unemployed, female headed households and those with no choice of housing. This trend is evident from the 1960s and has resulted both from policy changes and wider social changes. The extent to which the sector took on a residual role has been directly affected by the decline of the private rented sector and by widening social inequality and unemployment. This is an important element in understanding the changing role of council housing. Malpass (1990, p.29) has argued that an emphasis on poverty and marginality does little to explain the processes which brought about the concentration of the least well off in council housing and that the focus should be on supply side preferences which determine where the marginalised population is housed. This is an uncompromising emphasis on one of a number of contingent factors. The refusal to recognise the importance of wider social changes inhibits clear understanding of what has been happening. If council housing had continued to operate in the environment of full employment which marked the period from 1945 to the 1970s its share of the market was sufficiently large that it would have contained a mix of households of different economic status and occupational characteristics. The extent to which the sector came to house those outside the labour market and the pace at which this occurred are a consequence of the growth of this segment of the population and what has happened in the labour market as well as of housing market and housing policy changes.

By the early 1970s evidence about patterns of residential movement left little doubt about the tendency for inequalities in financial and other resources to contribute to different experience of the housing system. (Cullingworth, 1965; Nevitt, 1966; Donnison, 1967; Murie et al., 1976). With an owner occupied sector benefiting from a range of tax advantages, those who could buy increasingly did so. As the value of the major tax reliefs increased, and as the advantages of home ownership as a source and store of wealth became more apparent this tendency was enhanced. At the same time the private rented sector was in continual and probably terminal decline. The declining private rented sector was of relatively open access but unattractive with poor quality dwellings with neglectful as well as exploitative landlords and lack of security of tenure. It was less attractive than the council sector but the latter acquired a dominant role in housing poorer households as the private rented sector's size and capacity declined.

For those unable to buy, council housing was increasingly the only option. It was also the best option in that it generally offered attractive properties at rents linked to historic cost and benefiting from a subsidy applied irrespective of income. Rationing access to council housing generally restricted access to families and required long periods on local authority waiting lists.

In this situation the residential behaviour of households was strongly influenced by existing housing situation, position in the family cycle and labour market position. Accounts of the process of residential mobility established the tendency for households with different resources to develop divergent housing histories. The interaction of the organisation and financing of housing, labour market career and family cycle events and experience sorted the population by tenure, location and dwelling (see e.g. Murie, 1974; Murie *et al.*, 1976; Bassett and Short, 1980; Murie, 1993) In a period of full employment, then, the distribution of households in any age cohort was a product of socioeconomic position and the housing position achieved at early stages in the family cycle. Subsequent adjustment was consistent with a movement of the more affluent to home ownership but inertia or attachment to home and neighbourhood irrespective of tenure meant that not all cohorts responded equally to immediate circumstances and the pattern of current advantages in the housing market. Consequently, the council and private rented sectors continued to house many who could have taken advantage of the benefits of home ownership if they had moved house.

A changing housing market and differential responses by different cohorts meant that any extrapolation from what was known about the housing behaviour of different groups of new households and the residential mobility of different groups of established households, about household formation, fission and mortality, indicated a strong underlying trend for the council sector to play an increasing role in housing the poorest. In addition to residential mobility data and the role of councils in replacing (and rehousing from) the slum districts where the poorest lived data on supplementary benefits were used to demonstrate the increasing role of council housing in housing the poor (Murie, 1983). As the private rented sector declined those who in earlier cohorts had found permanent housing in that tenure went to one of the other two high standard tenures. Which one they went to reflected their resources.

Consistent with this ongoing pattern of change it was also true that any snapshot social profile of tenures showed considerable social mix. There was no need to worry about segregation and concentrations of the poorest because the snapshot did not indicate a major problem. There was a failure to engage with how the system was changing and consequently a failure to take action at an early enough stage. In some cases this failure may have been influenced by political and electoral assumptions around housing tenure.

The evidence suggests that, irrespective of the effects of new developments from the mid 1970s onwards, there was already a strong underlying trend for a changing tenure structure in which tenures were associated more strongly with economic status and social class. The rented tenures became more narrowly based socially and while home ownership became more mixed certain groups became more exclusively home owners. The engine for what has subsequently been identified as residualisation was already working.

It has been argued that this pattern was not clear by the mid 1970s. Holmans (1991) indicates that the housing policy review carried out in the mid 1970s did not anticipate the pace of residualisation. It is certainly true that the extent of economic problems and volume of council house sales could not easily have been anticipated and that these elements have speeded the pace of residualisation. However, it is also apparent that the social profile of the tenure had already changed significantly before 1976 and that key elements leading to residualisation were in place and their impact was clear. Even without the factors emerging in the 1980s rapid residualisation would have taken place. It is not unreasonable to suggest that the cautious view taken of existing data by the housing policy review was as much informed by the existing agenda of policymakers as seeking to inform it. The issues associated with residualisation or the trend itself have consistently been denied by government. Since Bevan's stated concern about social mix government has not expressed concern with the impact of policies on the social composition of tenures. The evidence given by the Department of the Environment to the Select Committee on the Environment in 1980 illustrated this. When asked the following:

Do you accept the view that council housing is likely to develop towards 'welfare housing' (providing less popular and less advantageous housing for those with lowest incomes and least bargaining power) as a result of council house sales in the context of other developments in housing policy? What policy consideration has been given to this?

the Department's response was:

'The answer to the first question is 'No', the second question does not therefore apply'.

(House of Commons, 1981a; pp. 321–322)

It may reasonably be argued that the failure to take account of trends changing the housing system and the structure of cities was a conscious political choice.

If the process of residualisation was already under way before the 1980s, rising unemployment, growing social polarisation and the erosion of welfare benefits strengthened the trend. It is now generally accepted that in the 1980s households with below average incomes have not benefited as much from economic changes and that social and income inequality have increased (DSS, 1992). The 1980s saw a further shift in the balance of advantage for existing council tenants. The Right to Buy included in the Housing Act 1980 and the generous (and increasing) discounts available gave most sitting tenants in council and new town housing an option to adjust their tenure position to take up the advantages of home ownership without having to leave the home and neighbourhood to which they were attached. Changes in council housing stock and subsidy and rising rents reduced the attraction of council housing to anyone not qualifying for rent rebates or housing benefit. Exercising the Right to Buy made sense for those who could afford to do so including those satisfied with their house and neighbourhood. For others, and increasingly after the policy changes of 1988 encouraged the development of assured tenancies in the private and housing association sectors, the rents, rights and quality of council tenancies were preferable to those available from other landlords. Consequently demand remained high. However, the attractive terms of the Right to Buy and the lack of funds for new building or even the energetic modernisation of council properties meant that this demand could not be used to build a robust, stable sector.

Narrowing the social base of council housing

The increasing concentration of low income households in council housing represents a key element in patterns of urban social stratification. Council housing has been in numerical decline since 1980 as sales have exceeded additions to the stock. Council housing has a smaller role in housing the population as a whole. This declining role has been most marked among middle and higher income groups leaving the sector with an increased role in housing lower income groups.

This pattern is strikingly apparent from Family Expenditure Survey Data. In 1963 the proportion of households in the bottom three income deciles who were council tenants was 26.3%. In 1972 it was 41.1%. In 1979 it was 47% (Murie, 1983, pp. 187–8). These figures demonstrate that the process of social polarisation between tenures was well established before the 1980s.

In 1967 45% of households in receipt of means tested social assistance benefits (supplementary benefit) were council tenants. By 1971 this figure had risen to 52% and in 1979 it was 61%. During this period the proportion of the housing stock which was council housing had risen only very slightly – from 29% in 1967 to 32% in 1979. The greater proportion of lower income households represented an increase in concentration rather than simply a growth of the sector. This pattern of change in the British housing market has now been widely discussed as residualisation and a wide range of statistical data has been employed to illustrate it. For example this shows that in the council sector there has been a decline in the proportions of economically active heads of households, of multiple earner households, of higher income households and in the level of car ownership. At the same time there has been an increase in the proportion of households with no earners, of non-married households, of female headed households, of households with older persons, of single elderly households, of persons aged under 25 and an increasing proportion of lettings to homeless persons (Forrest and Murie, 1990a).

By 1987 the council sector in the UK had lost over 1.5 million dwellings, through sales, and had declined to providing housing for 25% of all households. There was no decline, however, in the proportion of the poorest households housed in the sector. In 1987 the council sector continued to house 61% of those in receipt of supplementary benefit. The concentration of the poorest sections of the community in the sector had increased and in many areas the only households becoming new tenants were those who were classified as homeless. New tenants in general were drawn disproportionately from those outside the labour market (Forrest and Murie, 1988; Prescott-Clarke et al., 1988; 1994). Although low income new tenants will not always have low incomes the prognosis for the sector continues to be about residualisation and a clear welfare housing role. The continuing existence of the Right to Buy and the low rates of investment in new housing in the sector seal the future. Nor is the favoured non municipal arm of the social rented sector experiencing a different pattern. The non profit, voluntary, housing association sector has grown but still provides only 3% of dwellings. Its tenants and new tenants have a similar profile to council tenants and recently concern has been expressed about creating ghetto estates (Page, 1993).

In view of these developments it is not surprising that the most up to date material on the social differences between tenures indicates a continuing trend towards a lower income social rented sector. The Family Expenditure Survey shows that between 1980 and 1991, although the overall share of the social rented sector in the housing market declined it housed a higher proportion of the lowest income decile and continued to house a considerable proportion of the next three lowest deciles. The dominance of social renting declined rapidly after the fourth decile (Table 1). The pattern of change relates directly to the pattern of financial advantage associated with different tenures (Hills, 1991).

Table 1 Income Decile, Council Housing and Home Ownership

Income Decile (1=lowest 10% of incomes)	Council Housing		All Home Owners		Home Owners in Process of Purchase	
a) Percentage of Income Decile in each Tenure	1980	1991	1980	1991	1980	1991
1	60	65	21	11	1	2
2	52	44	36	38	3	7
3	43	33	42	52	8	14
4	37	25	46	62	18	24
5	41	19	48	69	28	37
6	33	12	56	76	40	53
7	27	9	66	84	51	65
8	22	4	71	92	56	74
9	18	3	75	94	59	75
10	15	1	81	93	64	75
All Incomes	35	22	54	67	33	43
b) Percentage of Tenure in each Income Decile						
1	17	30	4	2	*	*
2	15	20	7	6	1	2
3	12	15	8	8	2	3
4	11	12	8	9	6	6
5	12	9	9	10	9	9
6	9	6	10	11	12	12
7	8	4	12	13	16	15
8	6	2	13	14	17	17
9	5	1	14	14	18	18
10	4	1	15	14	19	18

Source: Department of Employment, *Family Expenditure Survey*, *1980*, London, HMSO, 1982 and Central Statistical Office, *Family Spending*, London, HMSO, 1992

One of the most important recent contributions to this debate comes from systematic analysis carried out by Alan Holmans. Key elements of the data are presented in Tables 2 and 3. These data demonstrate the relative concentration in council housing of households with no earners or unemployed heads. They also show that the concentration effect in relation to number of earners has continued in the period in which council housing has declined. They provide a salutary commentary on the Government's view of 1981 and the slowness to acknowledge a trend already apparent to others.

There is a range of other data which demonstrates the changing composition of council housing neighbourhoods. Thus for example data on the city of Birmingham show that the characteristics of new tenants have changed over time with more unemployed and lone parent households (Forrest and Murie, 1988). Other data relating to the characteristics of new tenants and the increasing importance of homeless households reinforce the picture of a sector recruiting from a less varied population. Studies of the processes of housing allocation also show that there is a systematic tendency to steer households with least bargaining power towards certain parts of the housing stock (see Henderson and Karn, 1987;

Table 2 Main Housing Tenures in England: Number of Earners (percentages)

	None	One	Two	Three or More
Owner Occupiers				
1962	17	45	28	9
1988	23	29	39	9
1991	26	29	36	8
Council Tenants				
1962	11	34	33	22
1988	60	22	13	4
1991	63	24	11	2
All Households				
1962	16	42	29	13
1988	34	28	31	8
1991	36	29	29	7

Source: Holmans (1993)

Table 3 Main housing Tenures in England: Unemployment Rate of Heads of Household in England

	1984	1988	1991
Unemployment Rate			
Council Tenants	24	21	20
Owner Occupiers	5	4	5
All Households	11	8	9

Source: Holmans (1993)

Phillips, 1988; English, 1979; and the reviews in Willmott and Murie, 1988 and Malpass and Murie, 1990). The resulting patterns at a neighbourhood level are evident from analysis of the Census of population for 1991.

In this discussion it is important to recognise that what is happening to the council housing tenure is not always going to be apparent in what is happening to neighbourhoods. The progress of council house sales changes the profile of the tenure but does not immediately result in changes in the social composition of neighbourhoods. Those who have bought properties as sitting tenants have not been a cross section of council tenants but have been disproportionately of mature employed and more affluent households. As a result the profile of the council tenant population has shifted more dramatically towards less affluent households than would have been the case if this feature of tenure restructuring had been absent. In terms of social segregation these tenure transfers make no immediate difference and social composition only changes as people move out of the house and the area. Nor is it evident that purchaser households are more likely to move than tenants. These purchaser households are mostly well advanced in the family cycle and the asset value of their dwellings is often not sufficient to provide a wide range of choice (Forrest and Murie, 1994a). It is only when properties are subsequently exchanged and the different mechanism for exchange (the market rather than bureaucratic allocation) has an effect that spatial patterns begin to change. The available evidence shows that social change will follow behind tenure change and some 'gentrification' of former council estates will occur, especially in areas where house prices and housing shortages are greatest. This factor must be taken into account in considering Tables 1 to 3. These demonstrate the increasing association between council housing and low income groups. They are, however, the product both of population changes which change the social composition of neighbourhoods and of tenure transfers which do not initially have any effect on this.

One final comment is merited on the residualisation of the social rented sector in Britain. This relates to the experience of other countries. The extent of tenure polarisation which has occurred in Britain in recent years is significantly greater than in other comparable countries which developed substantial social rented sectors. None of these, with the exception of Ireland, had embarked upon sales of council dwellings on a comparable scale and their tenure and residential systems were more marked by continuity. The social rented sectors in these countries were not unaffected by other changes and some tenure polarisation has occurred – but nothing like to the extent in Britain. The resulting policy agenda is as a result very different. The example of the Netherlands can usefully be referred to briefly. In the 1970s Britain and the Netherlands had social rented sectors which housed similar proportions of the population. While the lack of new building and the sale of dwellings has reduced the sector in Britain, the Dutch social rented sector continued to expand numerically in the 1980s. A sector catering in 1990 for some 40% of households could not have such a narrow social role as that obtaining in Britain. While in the Netherlands in 1989 in each of the four lowest income deciles over 60% of households lived in the non-profit sector, the UK shows a clear drop of this percentage from almost 70% in the first decile to almost 25% in the fourth decile (Dieleman and Jobse, 1991; Dieleman and Van Engelsdorp Gastelaars, 1992; Dieleman, 1994). The consequences of this greater degree of social mix are apparent in low levels of segregation in the major cities (see e.g. Musterd and Ostendorf, 1992; 1993; Ostendorf, 1992; van Amersfoort, 1992). While the pressures of change in Dutch cities have included many of those affecting developments in Britain, changes in the welfare state and in housing have been very different and delay if not prevent the British pattern from emerging (Murie, 1994).

Taking stock

Council housing in the 1990s has very different characteristics than at other stages in its history. Tenures do not have inherent characteristics but are the outcomes of a range of influences. It follows from this that the capacity of a tenure to achieve policy objectives cannot be read off from a tenure label but is contingent upon various factors. At some stages in its development council housing has had considerable assets and potential to make a major continuing contribution to meeting a wide range of housing needs. The high quality of most of the housing it provided, the considerable social mix achieved in the early years and sustained because households which could have moved out preferred to stay in the family home, the security and low rents associated with a council tenancy and the increasingly favourable historic cost structure could have been built upon and represented a viable alternative to home ownership as a way of providing housing (Kemeny, 1981). They were not built upon for various reasons. These included a fundamental lack of consensus about the role of the state and a commitment to private provision, the damage done to the image and reality of council housing by the high rise and system building phase, the failings of council house management associated variously with the organisation of slum clearance, housing allocations, the management of difficult tenants, neighbourhoods and properties; a resistance to recognising the housing needs of young single people or to adjust rapidly to changing circumstances and a failure to market the positive achievements of council housing effectively.

Some of these failings arose because of the interaction between central and local government and central government became an increasingly unenthusiastic or unreliable partner in the council housing enterprise. One view of this is that central and local government had sufficiently different priorities to erode the original base which had sustained the sector. While direct contact with the community reinforced local government's commitment to the sector, central government's agenda was increasingly preoccupied with fiscal problems. Not only was council housing a claim on public expenditure but it presented an opportunity to generate capital receipts. Such an approach also fitted with the language of targeting and with concerns to cut income taxation and reduce public expenditure. The ideological and electoral appeal of the Right To Buy and attacks on municipal mismanagement were also significant factors.

Whatever the reasons for the termination of sustained political support, the council housing sector which has survived has fewer assets and less potential to play a continuing role. The policies in place in 1995 will further erode the housing stock and push up rents. Especially in a period of low interest rates the right to buy offers an immediate or short term prospect of reducing housing costs. The financial arrangements for different tenures are unlikely to do other than strengthen tenure polarisation. The stronger association between council housing and low income or homelessness is likely to affect the decisions of individual households and of policymakers. The political and social base of council housing have been weakened by events since the 1970s and have added to ideological, electoral and financial considerations to limit the possibilities of the council housing sector playing a sustained role in the future. The continuing operation of the right to buy linked with extraordinarily high discounts is incompatible with building a consistent and sustained role – where councils succeed in providing good housing and satisfied tenants those tenants are still likely to exercise the right to buy as soon as they are able and confident about the future.

At the end of the 1980s a new attack on municipal ownership and selective concern to empower municipal tenants involved providing a statutory framework to enable tenants to choose a new landlord. Two significant elements in this were the admission in 1988 by the then Secretary of State for the Environment that there was a continuing need for 'subsidised housing for the less well off' (Ridley, 1988) and the gradual emergence of registered housing associations as the only alternative landlords who could be regarded as guaranteeing that any promised package, on which tenants could decide, would be delivered. Although very little action has been taken in relation to tenants choice, its offspring – large scale voluntary transfers – has had some impact in England. By early 1995 37 local authorities in England had received both the tenants and the Secretary of State's approval and transferred their stocks (some 163,000 dwellings) to housing associations. In some cases these were housing associations newly formed for the purpose and involving former local authority staff. They were as much monopoly landlords as their municipal forebears and the Ministerial view that they had made a valuable contribution to the diversification of tenure of rented housing is misleading if not strictly inaccurate.

The reality created by this environment is that local authorities will continue to have an important influence on housing. Firstly, and depending on the pace of demunicipalisation, local authorities will remain the largest landlords and how well they function as landlords will be of crucial importance especially for lower income households. Local authorities remain the major providers of rented housing and of housing which is within the reach of poor and disadvantaged citizens. They also act as gatekeepers to some housing association lettings. The supply of their own lettings is principally determined by tenancy terminations in the existing stock and by relets. The numbers of relets are likely to decline substantially once the sale of council houses begins to take effect. The impact of this has not yet been fully felt. In addition to affecting the flow of relets, the sale of council houses will affect the types of properties available for letting. More will be in flats, maisonettes and less popular dwelling types, designs and locations. Rents in the council sector are rising but not as fast as in assured tenancies. Tenancies have more security and enforceable rights including the Right to Buy. Hence local authority housing will often remain more attractive and a better deal than a housing association letting. But the stock will continue to be eroded by the right to buy and voluntary transfers and the uncertainties about voluntary transfers, the impact of compulsory competitive tendering and rent levels will continue to encourage uptake of the right to buy.

Secondly council housing neighbourhoods will continue to provide a flow of housing opportunities. Even where dwellings are no longer owned by local authorities their role in housing provision will be sustained. The influence of local authorities in providing high quality housing does not cease with their ownership. This relates to an important third consideration – local authorities' future role may not be that of a landlord but can continue to be that of creating a flow of housing opportunities. It is doubtful if this can be most effectively achieved through the use of an enabling role and persuading others. A more active role in the planning and construction of dwellings offers the prospect of providing housing opportunities without requiring continued ownership. Rather than wait for the Right to Buy to determine the pattern of future management or pass the role to housing associations operating within a second best framework of rents, rights and accountability, the logic is to investigate different forms of relationship between local authorities and landlord organisations. Examples of such possibilities have been outlined elsewhere. For example arms length public bodies in which the council would retain a controlling interest (perhaps shared with tenants or other local bodies) would remove the bureaucracy associated with local government without removing the accountability to locally elected representatives. New arrangements which balance autonomy and flexibility with accountability to public and social interests merit consideration (Willmott and Murie, 1988; Wilcox *et al.*, 1993).

The need for a continuing concern to affect the flow of housing opportunities relates to the changing nature of housing problems experienced in Britain in the 1990s. The traditional measures of unsatisfactory housing relating to overcrowding, amenity provision and fitness no longer represent the extent of problems. There are issues related to security of tenure and to low demand properties but the central issues relate to the position of households with insufficient bargaining power to have any real choice in housing and for whom housing may exacerbate exclusion from employment and social participation. It also relates to the high levels of both homelessness and repossession of residential property which have come to typify British housing problems in the 1980s and 1990s. The obvious basis for a strategy related to poor and disadvantaged citizens starts with a partnership between local authorities and housing associations, involves mortgage benefits as part of a reformed housing finance system, and involves different conventions for public expenditure so that council borrowing against assets or the use of capital receipts for capital expenditure are not treated differently than would apply elsewhere. For this last element to apply it may be necessary to take proposals for arms length public bodies further.

These developments relating to public expenditure and partnerships between housing agencies do not fit with the approach adopted by central government in the past. In this sense the obstacle to innovations which could recreate a new and viable role for local government in housing remains the position of central government. The anti-municipal stance of government, the absence of a level playing field in finance and investment and the inability to plan and develop policies where sales and transfers of ownership bear no relation to strategies to meet need or to performance as a landlord prevent best use being made of the expertise and resources of local authorities. The partitioning of housing subsidy and financial regimes is in stark contrast to attempts in other countries to achieve tenure neutrality and some commentators convincingly represent this as an Anglo-Saxon aberration (Kemeny, 1993). Whether this arises from political or ideological factors or policy inertia and lack of concern with social outcomes it does effectively involve separating the poor. The approach fits with some notions of targeting and some have argued that it is a sign of success that council housing is more strongly catering for poor people. The doubts about the wider consequences of this are not addressed. The argument that what is needed is more than a housing policy but a policy in which housing is linked to education, training and economic development has equally not yet been addressed. For households in the social rented sector because of limited bargaining power the absence of a broad based strategy linking housing and employment (and related issues of education, training, child care and transport provision) may mean that obtaining adequate housing carries a cost of reducing chances in other spheres. And reduced social mix is generally assumed to reduce political muscle.

One prospect is that the tradition of direct housing provision is abandoned and replaced by a more comprehensive pattern of income transfers to provide assistance with housing costs. There would no more be a housing policy than a bread policy or a clothing policy. Income support or voucher schemes would be developed empowering households to use the market and exercise choice. But the consequences of this would be to strengthen links between housing and income inequality. Not only would the market fail to build to meet need but the conditions of those at the bottom of the bargaining scale would decline. The imagery of a moving column, of filtering and of trickle down in housing does not stand up to scrutiny. A filtering process has not in the past proved an effective way of improving the housing situation of lower income households and recent data again demonstrate that for these lower income households waiting for housing released through turnover in the private sector means waiting longer and obtaining poorer quality housing. For most there will be no trickle down benefit because the realities are of exclusion and barriers of access to home ownership (see Forrest and Murie, 1993).

Housing programmes cannot be expected to overcome inequalities generated through other social processes. Inequalities in income and employment have dominated housing and the limitations of social security benefits have had a continuing effect. In practice inequalities in housing have added to the problems of households disadvantaged elsewhere. A housing policy alone will not be an adequate response to inequalities but nor will the abandonment of a housing policy and a reliance purely on a benefits policy. Housing policy has ceased to be mainly about supply and housebuilding and a residual social security policy would be consistent with a withdrawal from direct roles in housing provision. The prospect is of increasing inequality in housing and a range of problems in each tenure. The possibility of transferring ownership of remaining council housing to other landlords would alter labels but not alter the associations between housing and other inequalities. In this sense the successes of council housing in breaking links between low income and poor housing are likely to be further eroded. The lessons of the postwar period are that a comprehensive housing policy with interventions in production, consumption and exchange and involving a wide range of public and private sector agencies is necessary but not sufficient. It is not sufficient because the absence of a framework of other policies related to employment, training and education, incomes and poverty limits what can be achieved.

What is the future then for council housing? The legacy of councils' role will remain in the dwellings which have been built by councils. Councils' continuing role is less clear. Enabling roles relying on planning and other powers offer an uncertain recipe for providing a flow of housing opportunities for low income households or others. But government appears antagonistic to more direct roles. Within current public expenditure conventions there is little likelihood of substantial council investment in housing and the prospect is of continuing decline in council housing associated with growing social segregation and stigmatisation. There are alternatives to this vision but they do not involve reverting to a past golden age of council housing. The changes of the 1980s have altered the sector for good. Two areas are most important in a continuing robust role. The first involves consolidating the advantages of tenancy rights and security, rent regimes and accountability by achieving better management than achieved by other landlords. The second involves using the asset base to provide a flow of high standard housing to the local community in housing need. In order to realise either or both of these missions the framework for operation would have to change. Central government would have to distance itself, put its anti-municipal stance behind it and enable councils or their arms length agencies to operate as trading companies using their asset base and entering into partnership with others.

Local government will also have to change its role to become less involved in day to day management and more satisfied to set strategic tasks related to the flow of housing opportunity and the processes of management (perhaps delegated to others) and accountability. Crucially, local government and its agencies may have to regard continuing ownership and management as less important than continuing investment and intervention to affect the pattern of housing opportunity. They may need to build or acquire to affect access to housing but only for the first occupier. Rather than securing houses for those in need 'in perpetuity' they may be better to affect initial access and release funds as quickly as possible to enable these to be used again after 5 or 10 years rather than after 40 or more years of a tenancy. They would be responsible to seek to ensure that whoever continued to own or manage operated in an acceptable manner with clear accountability, but to find a formula allowing this as well as giving priority to generating a flow of opportunity. A financial and policy framework enabling these developments is possible and involves using the assets of council housing to move beyond the historical conception of the tenure in a positive way relevant to the changing needs and resources of future decades.

CHAPTER 7

Housing Associations: The Sustainable Solution?

RICHARD BEST

This chapter traces the development of the housing association sector from the margins to the mainstream. The next stages in the sector's evolution are considered. The value of provision by non-profit bodies in maintaining supply when there are market failures is described; and the benefit of a pluralist approach to subsidised provision – with local authorities as the strategists, not the monopolistic providers – is outlined. It is predicted that in the years ahead today's 'Housing Association Movement' will incorporate – through transferred public housing and not-for-profit companies – the bulk of all rented homes. And the role of many associations will extend outwards to community development, involving a more holistic approach to meeting local needs.

Background

In the early 1900s Joseph Rowntree wanted to find out if it was possible to produce decent accommodation at rents affordable to those in modestly-paid employment, without public subsidy. He discovered that it was not: rents within the means of ordinary working households did not produce an adequate return on the investment. Although good quality housing has been produced by the Joseph Rowntree Housing Trust since its creation in 1904, it has always been dependent upon injections of charitable money or public subsidies.

Since charitable donations do not go far in providing a sustainable base for meeting the capital costs of housing, expansion of housing associations has had to depend on public money. But governments have preferred to allocate their resources to promoting the growth of public sector housing, through local authorities, or private sector provision for sale, subsidised by tax relief. Philosophically, Conservatives have favoured private enterprise and Labour governments have opted for direct provision by democratically controlled public bodies. While no party has done much to assist the private rented sector, there has also been a reluctance – at least for the first 75 years of the century – to give substantial backing to the voluntary sector. Housing associations have been the 'second best option', whichever political party has been in power.

As private renting has faded, decade after decade, the potential for housing associations has become increasingly apparent. And as the politicians' confidence in council housing and faith in homeownership for all have both receded, housing associations have gradually obtained the financial backing which governments alone can afford.

By the 1990s few would dispute that there are limits to the market for owner occupation: this tenure will not be affordable or sensible for substantial numbers of households and pushing homeownership too far can lead to personal tragedy and wider economic problems. While the role of a private rented sector has been acknowledged for those who can afford market rents and are not looking for a permanent home for life, there are inherent problems in using this sector to supply secure accommodation at rents affordable to those on lower incomes. Although housing associations provide permanent homes, private landlords may properly prefer fixed term contracts so that they have the option to sell later. Governments feel relatively safe in giving substantial subsidies to housing associations; but doing the same for private landlords – so that they can achieve affordable rents – requires elaborate regulatory machinery. Yet the alternative of subsidising rents so that tenants can pay market rents to private landlords creates distortions and disincentives to work. On the other hand, depending on the local authority as the single landlord for each area brings the dangers of insensitivity, bureaucracy and inefficiency which can afflict any monopoly.

Housing associations may be seen as the less-than-ideal solution by politicians on all sides, but they may also be recognised as essential. Associations pick up where the market sector fails, and they bring diversity, variety, and competition for quality. They are the vehicle through which gaps in supply can be filled and they enable governments to sustain the flow of provision when other providers cannot do what the country wants. This makes them – in their various forms – the necessary ingredient for any government to achieve sustainable housing policies.

Back to the 1960s

Thirty years ago, housing associations had two main characteristics: they were almost infinitely varied, and their contribution to meeting housing needs was extremely limited. They ranged from ancient almshouse trusts to new cost-rent societies, from Victorian charities like Peabody and Sutton, to fledgling 'stress-area' housing associations, and from those providing 'old people's dwellings' to self-build associations with members who actually constructed and then owned the properties. But for all this diversity, they only owned some 0.7% of the nation's stock. Across the rest of Europe, comparable organisations typically owned 25% or more of their country's homes.

In considering the 'Housing Association Movement' of the 1960s it is probably wise to exclude the Coal Industry Association with its 111,000 properties. Industrial housing associations were set up by particular industries – often the nationalised industries to house their own employees. Together these organisations accounted for more than half of the total stock of the sector in the 1960s – because of the size of the coal industry's properties. Several of the other industrial housing associations – such as The British Airways Employees Housing Society – were to go on growing over the next three decades and played their part within the wider 'movement'. Excluding those houses linked to the Coal Board, the sector represented little more than 100,000 homes at the beginning of the 1960s. And it was nothing if not diffuse: it comprised nearly 3,000 organisations, some with more than 10,000 properties, but with an average of about 35 homes each.

The post-war building boom had largely passed the associations by. While local authorities had built over 2 million homes by 1960, and private builders had constructed 1.3 million, the housing associations had only achieved 46,000 extra homes between them. Indeed, by 1960 itself, the programme of housing associa-tion work had come almost to a standstill.

Growth in the 1960s: the top down approach

In the 1960s, examples can be found of both the 'top down' approach where government seeks to use this sector to meet perceived need; and of 'bottom up' initiatives from those confronting housing problems in their communities and using voluntary housing as the means of tackling them.

First, the action by the state. In 1961, the Conservative government, concerned at the decline of private renting and the absence of choice between owning and municipal housing, set up a loan fund of £25 million – sufficient to produce about 7,000 houses – for lending to housing associations to produce homes for the middle market at 'cost rents'.

Section 7 of the Housing Act 1961 created the framework, and led to the funding, for the new type of association. The new breed differed from its pre-decessors by attempting to produce rented accommodation without subsidy from the State or from charity. The Minister of Housing and Local Government, Henry Brook, expressed the hope that one type of new housing association which would emerge from this Bill is 'what is called the co-operative housing association in which a group of would-be occupiers form themselves into a body to build and then to manage collectively houses or flats in which the members themselves will live'. He noted that such developments were common in other European coun-tries and Sir Keith Joseph, the Ministry's Parliamentary Secretary, said in the winding-up debate, 'I am sure that we all hope that we shall soon have in this country examples of the co-operative housing which has served the people of Scandinavia so well'.

But the cost rent societies were destined to be of little significance. The govern-ment's hopes that they would create a substantial 'third sector' proved un-founded. The cultural and historic background to housing provision in the UK was quite different from that in the Scandinavian countries and the co-operative model held little intrinsic appeal. Judged by potential consumers on the more pedestrian criterion of value-for-money, the demand perceived by the government – for unsubsidised cost renting – was not there. In competition with a rapidly-expanding council sector in receipt of generous tax relief, the notion of un-subsidised renting was doomed. Only 1600 homes were built.

However, with the added input of tax relief, the concept of 'middle-market' housing associations re-emerged later in the 1960s as 'co-ownership societies', this time supported by a Labour government. The Housing Act 1964 provided the framework for central government funding – the principle established by the 1961 Act – to be extended and controlled through a 'quango', the Housing Corporation. The National Federation of Housing Societies (NFHS) had

administered the funding for the cost rent societies, ending up with responsibilities for managing the bulk of these homes through a separate company
(Strand Management Limited). This had tested the concept of central government
funding for housing associations which could by-pass local authorities. But the
next stage was not only to increase the resources available from central government – this time to £100m – but to bring the arrangements more directly under
central government control.

The production line for co-ownership housing was propelled by the
'enlightened self interest' of the architects, lawyers, builders, and others who had
no financial interests – to take advantage of built-in tax subsidies. Over the
decade 1964–1974 over 1,000 co-ownership societies were formed producing
near 40,000 homes in England, Wales and Scotland. But rapid inflation in the
early 1970s pushed up the price of land and interest rates to the point where the
advantages of relatively easy mobility and some convenience of lifestyle were
overtaken by the disadvantages of higher costs than owner occupation.

Because co-owners were given the opportunity in the early 1980s (through a
simple Regulation) to acquire their homes on an individual basis, at a cost of only
the outstanding mortgage commitment, this form of accommodation was converted
into individual home ownership and is virtually non-existent today. This high-profile
chapter in the history of housing associations proved a short one. But without the
1961 initiative, testing the concept of central government funding for housing associations (albeit without subsidy), and without the 1964 creation of the Housing
Corporation to distribute and extend this funding (albeit to middle market housing
only) the mechanisms would not have been in place for the rapid expansion of
subsidised, renting housing by housing associations in the next decade.

Growth in the 1960s: the community-based approach

The 1960s also illustrate the way that Voluntary Housing can fill a gap identified
not from above, but by those in local communities who are moved to take action. In
preparing An Historical Survey of Selected Housing Associations for the Joseph
Rowntree Memorial Trust (now the Joseph Rowntree Foundation), Margaret Tims
wrote in 1968 of the role of the housing association in catering for 'the misfit who is
not acceptable to the council; the large, poor family who cannot afford council
rents; the immigrant . . . By accepting these types of tenants, the Society helps to
release council tenancies for the rather better-off families who wish to progress from
a tenement to a new flat'. It was to help these groups, for whom council housing was
not available, that 'inner city' housing associations began to emerge in the mid-1960s.
They were much helped by a new grant-raising charity SHELTER. In 1966, SHEL-
TER was created by five national housing organisations. Thanks to dynamic leader-
ship and perfect timing of a drama documentary, Cathy Come Home, SHELTER
raised £3 million in its first three years. These funds were used by the emerging local
associations principally to pay for staffing costs, thereby greatly multiplying the rate of
growth that would have been achieved by purely voluntary effort.

The big breakthrough for these 'stress area associations' came with a special
clause in the Housing Subsidies Act 1967. The Labour Government was keen to see
older properties acquired and modernised; it was recognised that the municipal
authorities – geared up to large scale demolition and estate building since the end of
the War – were ill-equipped to handle this labour-intensive task. The subsidies for

property acquisition were provided by the Act for housing associations, but were not made available to the local authorities. Over the next 20 years, about half of all housing association investment went into the buying and rehabilitation of street properties to meet the needs of those who missed out on Council housing.

The 1970s – dramatic growth

The 1970s saw a massive expansion in the work of housing associations. By the end of this decade, the sector was producing as many homes in a single year as it had done in the whole of the 1960s (or in the whole of the period from 1945 to 1960). An important mechanism for achieving this explosive growth was the use of the central government agency – the Housing Corporation – as a channel for extra funds. In retrospect, it can be seen not only how important was the Housing Corporation's investment in the years after 1974, but also how the relatively relaxed controls on local authority funding helped housing associations in the middle of the 1970s (see Table 1). Even without the Housing Corporation, housing associations would have had a good decade compared with earlier years. Nevertheless the arrival of the Corporation's funding for rented housing greatly magnified the spending power of the associations thereafter.

Cross-party agreement on the need for housing associations was the hall-mark of the sector's revolution. Although it was a Labour government, elected 1974, which passed the Housing Act 1974 and channelled substantial resources to associations thereafter, the groundwork for this had been laid by the previous Conservative administration. Their Housing and Planning Bill had contained measures for enhancing support to housing associations and also for concentrating resources in Housing Action Areas. Labour's Housing Act of 1974, introduced by Anthony Crosland, the Labour Secretary of State for the Environment, looked much the same.

In choosing Lord (Arnold) Goodman in 1973 to chair the Housing Corporation, the Conservative administration had selected someone equally acceptable to the incoming Labour government. Under Lord Goodman, the Corporation now had the resources as well as the legal powers, to promote the expansion of a fully regulated, non-profit sector concentrating on rented housing, after years spent mostly funding the side show of co-ownership schemes.

Meanwhile it had been a Conservative-controlled Greater London Council which – acting virtually as a Housing Corporation for the London area – had sponsored the growth of housing associations in the years immediately prior to the 1974 act: over the five years 1970–1975, the GLC spent some £125m in loans and grants to housing associations.

After 1974, to gain public funding, it was necessary for any voluntary organisation to obtain registration on a common basis from the Housing Corporation; to ensure some consistency of standards thereafter, the Corporation had the task of monitoring and supervising all the registered associations. Although the elements of innovation and diversity remained there was substantial consolidation of the role played by this sector. The 1970s were characterised not only by growth – inevitably with some 'growing pains' for the organisations concerned – but also by some increase in the cohesiveness of this sector. Within London, the Shelter-backed and community-based organisations had joined with established trusts to create the London Housing Associations Council (previously the 'Twilight Areas Housing Associations Committee') to represent their interests; and like-minded stress area housing associations from all parts of the country were represented within the National Federation of Housing Societies by its Improvement Action Committee. These two committees – sometimes seen as breakaway groups – became more closely integrated within the Federation when the Secretary to both became the NFHS Director in 1973. (This organisation's name changed to the National Federation of Housing Associations in 1974.)

Attracted by the lure of public funding, organisations previously concerned with cost-rent and co-ownership schemes joined the new and old charities and began to concentrate on housing those with lower incomes. Abbeyfield Societies and even almshouse trusts sought Housing Association Grants on similar terms to other associations. Some of the industrial housing associations moved beyond their original remit of housing employees for particular industries and joined the same mainstream.

Both through a much expanded programme of property purchase and conversion/modernisation, and through a continuation of the building of new homes, particularly for elderly people, the effort of this broader mainstream of housing associations in the 1970s was devoted principally to those on low income in acute need. The local authority house building programme was running at half the levels of the 1960s (having peaked at 200,000 homes in the single year of 1964). However, the public sector machine, operating on the model of newly built estates (often following clearance of private housing and frequently using industrialised building techniques) left many sizeable gaps to be filled by the growing Housing Association Movement. This grouping of independent bodies was now taking on a 'sharper image' and fighting the accusation that it was not just 'heterogenous' but 'fragmented'.

Further attempts to promote the work of co-operative housing associations emerged in the mid 70s – this time championed by the Housing Minister Reg Freeson. Legislation in 1975 (the Housing Rents and Subsidies Act) and a focus provided by a Department of Environment working party, chaired by Harold Campbell, led to some expansion of this form of tenure. However, in contrast to its manifestations in the 1960s, in the co-ownership format, these housing co-operatives were for rent on terms comparable with those of the other registered housing associations. Once again progress proved limited (although it can be argued that the real influence of co-operative housing has been the wider one of changing attitudes toward the involvement of residents in the management of local authorities and housing associations in general).

Seeds were sown for another attempt at provision for people needing less public subsidy, with the invention of *community leasehold* projects. This concept contrasted with a London experiment for 'high rent' council housing (by the GLC and Westminster) by giving something extra for the higher payment: the resident acquired a stake in the ownership of their home. The idea was similar to a pioneering project of 'equity sharing' in Birmingham and represented the first manifestation of middle tenure housing which was later to become the substantial programme of *shared ownership*.

By 1976, the National Federation was able to report that approvals had been given by the statutory bodies for associations to make a start on the building or modernising of almost 50,000 homes in England and Wales alone. And in 1977 the Federation's President, the Duke of Edinburgh, was able to celebrate the completion of 'One Hundred Homes a Day' by housing associations nationwide.

This decade of growth was fuelled by a financial system which, by any standards, was a generous one. Housing associations were supplied with funds to cover the whole cost of each home provided; rents were pegged at the 'fair rent' levels and grants reduced the loan charges to whatever levels these rents could bear. The amount of grant was adjusted to take into account any increased expenditure as projects proceeded and a revenue deficit grant was available if, despite all this help, the association ran into unavoidable difficulty. The arrangements can be criticised in retrospect as unfair in comparison with the terms available for council housing. But to weld a varied collection of organisations into a credible development body for social housing required this special treatment: not only was it necessary to entice the long-established trusts to use their skills in a programme of expansion, but the financial system had to give complete security to the penniless 'stress area' associations working on run-down properties in the worst areas (and also to persuade the sponsors of cost-rent/co-ownership housing to change direction). The legacy of the 1970s was not only in bringing together a larger group of expert, committed people – as volunteers on committees as well as professional staff – but in securing the financial base for growth in the years to come. Writing off capital debt gave housing associations equity in property which, as prices rose, proved an invaluable under-pinning to the associations' future strength.

1980s: conflict and consolidation

The Conservative administration elected in 1979 was concerned to cut public expenditure and to reduce the role of the State – particularly at the local government level – and, in its housing policies, to enhance owner occupation. These three political objectives all affected housing associations directly: the early years of the 1980s saw considerable conflict between associations and the government over cuts in the funds available from the Housing Corporation, over the repercussions from receiving less support from local authorities, and in combatting attempts to use housing associations to increase the level of owner occupation.

In each of the three years leading up to 1980, the Housing Corporation had funded an average of 33,500 association homes, in addition to the programme of some 10,000 homes each year financed by local authorities. By 1980 the Corporation's planned programme was reduced to 21,700 rented homes but the Housing Minister announced a moratorium on new projects at the Federation's Annual Conference in September, with a cut in the programme to 14,700 homes. A national campaign was mounted to fight these reductions, led by the Archbishop of Canterbury, supported by 19 bishops. These efforts seemed to have some effect and by 1981/82 the number of homes approved for funding by the Corporation had passed the 20,000 level again.

In relation to the government's commitment to home ownership, housing associations also found themselves in campaigning mode. First, there were the efforts to include charitable housing associations in the statutory 'Right to Buy'. Although passed in the House of Commons, this measure was halted in the House of Lords as a result of a major lobbying exercise, led by the Earl of Selkirk, backed by peers from all the political parties. They pointed out that if the rented stock was to be sold – at substantial discounts – the contribution of associations would gradually diminish; forcing charities to part with their assets, for the benefit of those already housed today but at the expense of those needing housing tomorrow, would have undermined the whole basis of the 75% of housing associations who were constituted as charities.

The second way in which the housing associations were to have contributed to the growth of owner occupation lay in a planned switch of the Corporation's budget from schemes for rent to those of shared ownership. Once again, conflict between the National Federation and the government resulted.

The 1981 riots in such areas as Toxteth and Brixton (repeated in Handsworth and Tottenham in 1985) increased public awareness of the problems of these neighbourhoods. Housing associations declared certain neighbourhoods 'Housing Crisis Areas' and prominent politicians and others proclaimed properties 'Future Ancient Monuments' because, in the absence of a programme of building, each house would have to have a life of over 400 years. In 1982/83, supported by the Environment Secretary, Michael Heseltine, rented housing in the inner cities received priority rather than programmes of low-cost home ownership.

If the early 1980s were characterised by conflict, the mid 80s saw some consolidation in their programmes. Homelessness was rising and the programme of local authorities was in sharp decline. The work of housing associations did little to fill the gap left by the collapse of council house building but work continued on a steady – though diminished – basis.

In 1986, the government conceded a vital administrative point: henceforth, even where the bulk of the funding for an association project came from public sources, any borrowing from private sources would not be regarded as 'public expenditure'. By using the funds from the Housing Corporation (and the, now much reduced, support from local authorities) for grants, and getting the necessary loans from private investment institutions, an enlarged programme would be possible for the same input of public money.

In 1988, new legislation built upon the breakthrough in the definition of 'public money' and heralded substantial change in the ways in which housing associations were to operate thereafter. The Housing Act 1988, closely associated with the Housing Minister, William Waldegrave, represented another landmark in the history of Housing Associations. It aimed to secure more homes for the available public resources, not just by enlarging the use of private finance, but by limited levels of grant per property and by opening the door to real cuts in grant levels by decontrolling rents: henceforth, rent increases could take the strain when Housing Association Grant was reduced. The Act was also intended to increase the cost-effectiveness and value for money provided by these organisations by making them more market-orientated and competitive. It largely succeeded in all these aims but not without costs and problems.

The NFHA had expressed its concerns about the changes in relation to the *affordability of rents* once the fair rents arrangements were removed for new lettings, about the *risks* flowing from a regime in which grant was set at predetermined levels but final costs were unpredictable (particularly for schemes of property improvement), and about *tenants rights* which would be substantially reduced.

The 1988 Act also introduced a separate measure which some predicted would lead to a huge growth in the importance of housing associations: under the tenants choice arrangements, disenchanted tenants were entitled to vote for a new landlord to own and manage their homes. This was an example of 'topdown' use of housing associations to fulfil governmental policies. Because it did not chime with the needs and aspirations of those at a local level – this time council tenants – the initiative was doomed to failure. In two small-scale instances, transfers to newly-created housing associations have been carried through under this arrangement. But in no cases have tenants decided that their homes should be transferred to an existing housing association (however inept the management of their properties by the local authority and however good the track-record of local housing associations). Although tenants had often been critical of their council landlord, the tenants choice experiment indicated that they wanted an improvement in the service, not a change in the ownership of their homes.

The 1988 Act brought opportunities for growth but these required new financial disciplines. Housing associations had to cope with a tougher funding regime, based on predetermined grant levels and reliance on private borrowing; they were keen to avoid passing on the extra costs in higher rents to tenants. But government gradually turned up the heat by reducing levels of grant and housing associations had to take steps to compensate for an era of lower subsidy:

- first, housing associations looked increasingly to local authorities to supply sites at little or no cost and in return allocated the resulting accommodation to the nominees of the council. The downside of this approach was that those nominated tended to be the homeless families with the greatest needs and lowest incomes, leading towards the dangers of segregated groups on stigmatised estates.
- second, building costs were held in check in the competitive climate which followed the drastic decline of the house-building sector in the late 80s. Adopting package-deal and design-and-build procurement methods also helped to keep down building costs – and the on-costs of paying professional advisers.
- third, some associations cut costs by cutting standards. JRF-supported studies for the National Federation of Housing Associations showed that the average floor space area of newly built homes in 1989/90 was about 9% below the 'Parker Morris' standard which was compulsory in earlier years; average floor space appeared to have fallen by 10% since 1987/88.
- fourth, some housing associations – particularly in rural areas – were able to use 'planning gain' to obtain lower-priced land: in order to secure planning consent, the landowner was compelled to part with the site for less than its market worth. But this option has limited application and it can mean development of sites in unsuitable places and/or have wider repercussions.
- fifth, housing associations could cross-subsidise their newer projects with surpluses achieved from previous work. This arrangement favours the organisations that have been active for some years and, indeed, usually means that the larger associations have a considerable advantage in bidding for Housing Corporation funds over the smaller ones. Concern that this trend might lead to a super-league of larger associations was expressed later by the Environment Committee in its Inquiry into the Housing Corporation (1993).

All these avoidance measures enabled housing associations to enter the 1990s with a substantial programme of work despite the start of a succession of cuts in

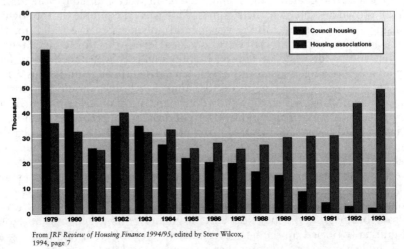

From *JRF Review of Housing Finance 1994/95*, edited by Steve Wilcox, 1994, page 7

Figure A Housing association starts 1979–1993 (England and Wales). House building switches from council housing to housing associations

Table 1 Housing Association Investment

| | £ million (1992/93 prices) (Gross) | | | |
	Housing Corporation	Local Authorities	Private Finance	Total Investment
1971/72	–	290	–	290
1972/73	–	363	–	363
1973/74	–	461	–	461
1974/75	590	665	–	1,255
1975/76	741	761	–	1,502
1976/77	898	754	–	1,653
1977/78	898	694	–	1,593
1978/79	908	511	–	1,419
1979/80	952	450	–	1,402
1980/81	1,022	342	–	1,364
1981/82	956	261	–	1,217
1982/83	1,293	229	–	1,522
1983/84	1,201	226	–	1,427
1984/85	1,086	229	–	1,315
1985/86	1,050	177	–	1,227
1986/87	1,026	208	–	1,234
1987/88	1,025	213	–	1,237
1988/89	1,009	163	128	1,300
1989/90	1,116	368	179	1,662
1990/91	1,362	213	193	1,768
1991/92	1,768	186	249	2,204
1992/93	2,371	286	950	3,607
1993/94	1,786	381	775	2,942
1994/95	1,460	304	1,002	2,767
1995/96	1,096	344	928	2,368
1996/97	967	294	823	2,074

Sources: All figures from DoE, except estimates of private finance to match Housing Corporation and local authority grants from 1988/89 onwards.
Note: 1992/93 prices derived by application of adjusted GDP deflator.

grant levels and the need to borrow more money privately. But the necessity for major rent increases had been postponed, not avoided.

1990s: further expansion – at a price

The 1990s saw the real impacts – good and bad – of the measures of the 80s.

Growth

The greater use of private finance was coupled with a 50% increase in government funding to the Housing Corporation for the first four years of the 90s, compared with the last four years of the 80s. The depressed state of the property market was causing widespread concern with a decline in real house prices in the early 1990s: a Housing Market Package in 1982/1983 involved the Housing Corporation financing the purchase of about 18,000 owner occupied houses to reduce the glut of unsold properties – a good many of them repossessed from borrowers who could not pay their mortgages – to stabilise the market. In stark contrast to the role expected of housing associations a decade earlier, housing associations now found themselves funded to switch property from home ownership into renting! With this boost, housing associations spent the immense sum of £10.5 billion in the first four years of the 1990s, compared with £5.4 billion in real terms in the last four years of the 1980s (see Table 1).

Private finance

The private funding made possible by changed rules and the end of rent controls began to flow in the 1990s, achieving progressively more housing for the same level of public spending. It also meant that housing associations had to familiarise themselves with the practices and disciplines of the private sector. Importantly, this change brought in new allies for housing associations since their investors also wished to see good quality homes and rents which are well below the maximum market levels, to provide them with greater security. But this phenomenon also carried the danger of undermining the financial strength of these organisations. The investors' need for security requires associations to pledge property other than the homes against which the lending is secured; giving up the equity on older property can undermine the asset base of the association, preventing this from being used to support other work. However, although substituting private loans for public loans may mean slightly higher interest rates, the shift to private finance on its own did not generate unaffordable rents or lower standards. The squeeze on rents and standards came from the reductions in levels of grant.

Grants and rents

Housing associations could pursue several options – as listed above – before passing on the effects of grant reductions in higher rents for their tenants. But these alternatives to rent rises are limited. As grant levels declined from 75% to 58% over the first five years of the 1990s, the impact on rents was to become of growing concern.

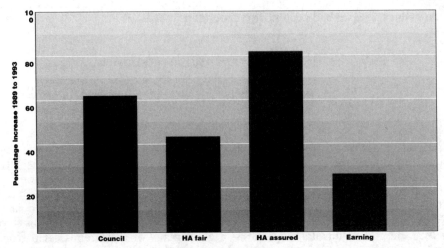

From *JRF Review of Housing Finance 1994/95*, edited by Steve Wilcox, 1994, page 13

Figure B   Percentage rent increases, 1989–1993 (England). Social housing rents rise faster than earnings

For all new housing association lettings, rents represented 28% of tenants' household incomes for the first quarter of 1994, compared with less than 23% at the end of 1989. The assured tenancy rents, outside of rent control, increased by over 80% during 1989 and 1993 whereas earnings were up by well under 25% during this period.

In so far as housing associations tenants have their higher rent paid by housing benefit, the switch from the 'bricks-and-mortar' grant to the association from the Department of Environment to a personal subsidy to the tenant from the Department of Social Security does not save public money. Moreover, recent research sponsored by the Joseph Rowntree Foundation indicates that the implications for public expenditure, which result from a higher-rent, higher-benefit regime, go further. Rent increases feed through into higher inflation which, in turn, has effects on employment. The calculation of the Retail Price Index includes a rent element; if rent is increased by 10%, the RPI rises by about 0.4%: consequently central government pays more in respect of the social security benefits and pensions which are index-linked.

Similarly, rent increases for those in work, as opposed to those in receipt of benefit, have wider implications. Employees may well be less likely to exercise wage restraint on the grounds of low inflation when their rents – a big part of the weekly budget – are escalating by three times the increase in average earnings. Measures to increase rent, therefore, can impact upon the profitability of British industry. However, the main criticism of the switch from 'bricks-and-mortar' subsidies for housing associations, to personal subsidies for their tenants, concerns the impact on incentives to work. Because tenants pay the withdrawal of their housing benefit after deduction of tax and national insurance contributions, rents which mean more

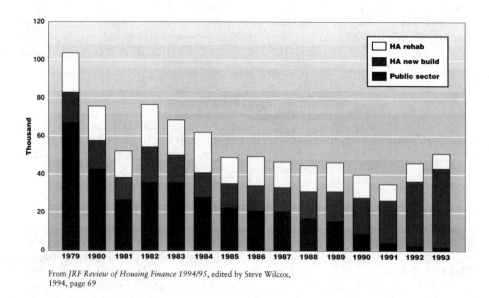

From *JRF Review of Housing Finance 1994/95*, edited by Steve Wilcox, 1994, page 69

Figure C   Starts, 1979–1993 (Great Britain). New social housing provision

people reliant on benefit create 'taxation' levels which may make it financially disadvantageous to work, or to work harder. By the mid 1990s, rents for new homes were likely to require those working as a bus driver, postman, clerical officer or bricklayer all to become reliant on housing benefit – and to face a 'tax rate' of 97p in £1 for those with children (who are entitled to Family Credit) or 89p if they are childless. The disincentive effect of these rents may become the decisive factor in halting the cuts in Housing Association Grants in the later 1990s.

Property rehabilitation

The 1990s saw a switch from property acquisition and renovation to a much larger programme of new building, driven by the need to avoid the insecurities of the rehabilitation programme. Although levels of grant were higher for 'rehab' work than for building new, it is always more difficult to predict final costs of modernising old houses; with a fixed level of HAG, it is a risky business to compete for funds for schemes of acquisition and modernisation which may turn out very differently than expected.

The sharp decline in the housing association rehabilitation programme – even though this may mean more homes for the public money – has wide repercussions. The role of associations in the decade after the 1974 Act made a significant contribution to inner city regeneration. Investment by associations encouraged private owners to modernise their properties and helped stem the decline of neighbourhoods which can bring with it more widespread social problems. Conversely, the shift of emphasis by associations into building new estates has taken them away from the 'stress areas'. The new sites may not be so convenient for public transport and amenities and there are environmental impacts from this relocation. Moreover, in concentrating those suffering from homelessness, poverty and disadvantage, within these new estates – rather than scattering them throughout a community as was the pattern in the previous era of 'pepper-potted' modernisation of older houses – the life chances of residents can be harmed and social problems multiplied.

Standards

Further JRF research, this time by Valerie Karn and Linda Sheridan (1994), indicated that pressures on costs were being translated into further reductions in space standards. The proportion of association homes 5% or more below the Parker Morris standards increased from 53% in 1989/90 to 68% in 1991/92.

Competition

Meanwhile, the new prominence of housing associations, and the financial regime which propelled this, created some internal tensions. A system of competitive bidding for the available grants pitched housing associations into direct competition with their neighbours. This competitiveness manifested not only in seeking to produce lower-cost homes, but in making it more difficult for associations to feel part of a common 'movement' in which the sharing of ideas and mutual support are the major components. This, in turn, may make it harder for housing associations to act collectively in resisting the annual reductions in the levels of their grants, the imposition of unwanted regulations or pressures to take up new roles with which they are uncomfortable. At the same time, in seeking to outbid rival housing associations when seeking Housing Corporation funds, an increasing number are drawing upon their inheritance of assets created over the preceding decades: in cross-subsidising new schemes, so that respectable standards can be achieved at reasonable rents, with lower levels of HAG than requested by their competitors, some associations are 'selling the family silver' and eroding their own financial strength. Funds spent to secure the next project are not available for major repairs, environmental improvements or extra facilities for past schemes. While clearly it would be wasteful for associations to accumulate unnecessarily high levels of reserves, if they denude themselves of resources which they might need later, they weaken the whole sector.

Growth through transfers

During the late 1990s, however, it may not be the expansion of the existing housing associations which will make the biggest difference to the scale on which the 'third sector' operates. At present rates of building, it would take a hundred years for today's housing associations to reach the size of the present local authority sector. The factor that could swing the balance, to the point where the voluntary sector becomes the *second* sector, is likely to be the transfer of council housing into the ownership of newly-created housing organisations. Although it is possible that these would be constituted as local housing companies, rather than as Industrial and Provident Societies, they will fall within the generic title of housing associations because of their not-for-profit status and their separateness from either the private or public sector.

Up to mid 1995, large scale voluntary transfers (LSVTs) were instrumental in moving about 135,000 homes from ownership by local authorities to newly-formed housing associations where most of the staff remained in situ. These arrangements are sometimes opposed because the new organisation is not subject to the same level of democratic accountability. But transfers provide an opportunity for the previous enterprise to be broken into two or more parts, with some competitiveness in achieving better services: the management of each will wish to outshine that in the neighbouring organisations. And these new bodies present an opportunity for greater participation by representatives of tenants in the organisation's management. However, the reason they seem likely to take hold is that, on balance, the financial advantages for all parties are greater than a continuation of the status quo.

While properties remain within council ownership, surpluses from rents get recycled to reduce the government's bill for housing benefit. This advantage to the Treasury is lost if the properties are transferred to an independent organisation. But surplus income can then be used to borrow more and invest in modernising the stock: the government gains because borrowing from private sources, by a non-public body, is outside the definition of 'public spending'. Proceeds from the disposal of the property to a new housing association or local housing company will be used to redeem the local authorities' debt, giving central government a receipt to reduce the PSBR; and many local authorities will end up with a surplus to use for housing (and other) purposes. Even where the sale proceeds are less than the authority's outstanding debt, these arrangements may be able to achieve important financial gains.

The years ahead

Public Expenditure Plans for housing associations show a continuing retreat in the years ahead (1997/98) (see Table 2). Retaining an annual programme of around 50,000 extra homes will only be possible by stretching grants to the point where rents would pass full market levels.

Apart from the huge 'earnings trap' this would create, the government would then be paying unacceptably high levels of housing benefit; this would lead to a swing back to higher grants and more DoE public spending than is currently planned, or to major cuts in the programme.

Table 2 Housing associations' gross investment plans, including use of private finance, in Great Britain £ million

	1986/87	1987/88	1988/89	1989/90	1990/91	1991/92	1992/93	1993/94	1994/95	1995/96	1996/97
England											
Housing Corporation	809	864	881	1,034	1,234	1,703	2,370	1,843	1,533	1,494	1,503
Local authorities	145	156	128	308	193	179	286	393	200	150	125
Private finance	0	0	100	150	175	240	950	800	700	700	700
Total	954	1,020	1,109	1,492	1,602	2,122	3,606	3,036	2,433	2,344	2,328

From *JRF Reveiw of Housing Finance 1994/95*, edited by Steve Wilcox, 1994, page 152
Source: Figures from 'Housing Associations After the Act', and the Housing Corporation
Note: Figures include HAG on deferred interest.

On balance it seems possible to speculate that the growth experienced over the last twenty years will accelerate over the years ahead, regardless of the politics of the party in power. These factors seem likely to maintain the momentum toward a more European-style social housing sector – with a plurality of housing organisations sharing responsibilities, rather than the local authority playing the dominant role:

- *transfers/sales of council housing will gather pace*: the arguments for the break-up of large scale municipal housing operations seem likely to become compelling in an era of shortages of public funds: transfers/sales to new housing associations or local housing companies unlock the opportunity for enhanced spending on improving estates and building some new homes, without affecting adversely the Public Sector Borrowing Requirement. The domino effect of successive areas choosing this option – sometimes propelled by measures such as Compulsory Competitive Tendering or the creation of Tenant Management Organisations – will gradually reach all local authorities;
- *disadvantages of home ownership will stimulate some private renting*: the demand for rented housing will be stimulated by the growth in the number of people with insecure incomes: there is likely to be a reluctance on the part of the building societies and other lenders to grant mortgages to first-time buyers in a more fluid job market. This will combine with the disenchantment – with falling house prices/negative equity/difficulties in selling – experienced by those who bought in the late 1980s. These trends mean homeownership is already less likely for those in their early 20s. So, some revival of private renting can be expected;
- *reductions in tax concessions for owner occupation* will create a more level playing field between renting and owning. Those who are in work and more mobile – usually younger and childless couples or single people – will be prepared to pay market rents for the convenience of easy access/exit, and freedom from maintenance responsibilities, of a rented home. And although government funding for private renting is unlikely to reach significant levels, facilitating the creation of authorised Housing Investment Trusts may stimulate investors by allowing them to pool risks and achieve greater liquidity;
- *nevertheless, investors in private renting* will want to avoid the hassles of direct property acquisition and management: they may wish to use the services of housing associations (or local housing companies resulting from transfers by local authorities). And to avoid segregating richer and poorer tenants, the social housing agencies themselves may want to blur the dividing lines between properties they own (and let to those unable to afford market rents) and those owned by profit making bodies which they manage (and let to middle-income tenants). Private and social rented housing may co-exist, with common management, in the same area/estate;
- *high demand for social housing will remain*: with employment trends indicating not just insecurities for those in work but the likelihood of perhaps 30% of the population of working age being outside of employment, the requirement for social housing – supplying secure homes at subsidised rents – will remain high. If the electorate wishes to avoid 'social exclusion', internal tensions and a divided society, there will be pressure on the politicians to give priority to meeting these needs. Funding through local authorities and through the Hous-

ing Corporation (which might become regionalised in future years) will be essential and may well reach out to a wider role of urban regeneration. And the work of housing associations will have the side effect of creating 'real' jobs in the construction industry;

- *housing management will reinvent itself:* it seems likely that a new mission will emerge for housing professionals who stand between the poorer communities in each city – who make up the residents of social housing estates and often face a range of difficulties in the fields of health, education, crime and employment – and those who allocate resources and set policies for each area (from within central and local government and a range of quangos). It is housing managers who see and hear the views of local people, increasingly through more formalised and more sophisticated ways of involving tenants and community groups in participatory and consultative arrangements. So the housing professionals are likely to become catalysts for change, interpreters of community interests, instruments for capacity building at the community level and agents of change in planning the future of the city. Most of those administering housing programmes are finding themselves involved in 'housing plus': through care in the community, through provision of amenities for residents, as advocates in relation to health needs/education requirements/policing policies, housing managers in social housing are likely to be at the hub of local efforts to strengthen communities and to build up skills and capacity in multiply-deprived neighbourhoods.

Without housing associations, politicians to the right would be dependent upon an owner occupied sector which may have passed the limits of its sustainability, and upon a private rented sector which is reluctant, and unsuited, to take responsibility for housing those who need permanent homes at affordable rents. Without housing associations, politicians to the left would be stuck with the model of council housing which seems unlikely to provide the flexibility, variety and responsiveness demanded by a more discerning consumer; and the public expenditure consequences of reverting to direct local authority provision would mean fewer homes for any given input of public spending.

The outlook may be for a housing associations sector which owns a quarter of the national stock (and may also manage some of the properties in the 'new look' private rented sector). But the future may not always be a comfortable one. Constant financial pressures and high levels of competition can bring insecurity, a loss of confidence and a less pioneering and imaginative approach. The expansion of this sector may achieve some of the sustainability needed for a stable housing future; but this enlarged sector may lack the sense of social significance, solidarity and creativity which characterised many of the struggling housing associations of the past.

CHAPTER 8

Getting the Foundations Right: Housing Organisations and Structures

PETER WILLIAMS

Perhaps for the first time in the history of housing in Britain there has been a period of sustained interest in organisational structures and effectiveness as a key issue in the delivery of housing policy and housing services. Admittedly that focus is almost entirely on management in the rented sector (with most being on the social rented sector) and the housing production sector and most notably house-building remains largely outside of these deliberations (though see the recent outputs from the Rowntree programme on housing production). Despite such omissions, this has been an important development because at last there is a widespread interest in what might be called the 'middle ground', the organisations which sit between policies arrived at by central government and actual social and spatial outcomes on the ground. Organisations are now recognised to be vital 'transmission' mechanisms which can assist, transform or hinder the policy process.

In this chapter the aim is to consider the viability and sustainability of housing organisations and the broad organisational structure of housing in the UK. It is not possible within the space of one chapter to explore all of the issues in exhaustive detail. Therefore the chapter focuses primarily upon questions related to organisational change within local authorities and housing associations and questions of longer term sustainability of the overall structure.

At root the changes which have taken place are a product not of organic change and development or of deeply considered planning and organisation but rather of a complex interaction of economic and social forces allied with a very strong policy direction from central and to a degree local government. The outcomes, like the organisations themselves, vary greatly, not least because all housing organisations operate in different ways and under different circumstances. The pressures for change set in train developments in the shape, style and functioning of housing organisations (see Stewart, 1988; LGMB, 1994). Despite decades of development and change we still have many unresolved questions including the following:

(a) what is an appropriate size and structure for an effective (social rented) housing organisation?
(b) how accountable should it be to its customers and others?

(c) how best can it be managed and regulated?

(d) what is the best way to use the resources of the social rented sector and how can the sector operate most effectively?

(e) how far should issues of quality be traded off against concerns with economy?

(f) how do we balance issues of high cost, reduced subsidy, residualisation and effective communities?

There is nothing inevitable or given about the nature of housing organisations. What we have before us is a product of history, politics, economic and social circumstances and policy. As those factors change so will the organisations.

What we need to consider, however, is whether in broad terms we have the right set of organisations and organisational structures in place to secure the efficient and effective delivery of affordable, secure housing of the right standards and, if not, what changes we would wish to put in place to move us closer to that objective. What this chapter will show is that we have struggled to find the way forward not least because of fundamental disagreements about the organisational framework for housing in the UK, reflecting a complex amalgam of deeply rooted ideological differences, vested interests and inertia. Arriving at a better structure is no easy task though most would agree that without some agreement on organisational roles and structures, Britain will continue to have difficulty in arriving at an adequate and effective long term framework. At present, although arguments have been advanced regarding particular types of organisations (e.g., see Power, 1987 and Clapham, 1989 and 1992) it is clear there is no universal agreement as to the way ahead.

Modes of intervention

A range of housing organisations is involved in 'the delivery' of national housing policy (or at least parts of it). In general terms, central government formulates housing policy and sets the overall social and economic context in which those policies will operate. It does so in consultation with and knowledge of the different organisations, agencies and individuals which actually build, finance, sell, let, manage, repair and maintain homes. It is important here to be clear that the very framework of policy set by central government can be a source of conflict with the organisations which actually provide housing. Indeed as this chapter (and other chapters) will show, the history of the last decade or more of housing policy is one of intense conflict with at least some of these organisations, most notably local authorities.

As already noted, for the most part central government in the UK does not build or manage housing although there have been periods when it has been actively involved (in the 1940s for example). However, there have been and remain agencies (or non-departmental public bodies) strongly influenced by central government which have done so (for example, the North East Housing Association, now Home Housing Association, the Scottish Special Housing Association, now Scottish Homes, the Northern Ireland Housing Executive and the Commission for New Towns. More typically, however, it is local authorities and housing associations which have done so. Both are independent of central government but highly reliant upon it, not least in terms of funding and subsidies.

The most obvious areas of government intervention and control are through these organisations. Land holding, building construction and materials, housing finance, individually owned homes and the private rented sector are typically seen to be outside of this. However, as students of housing history will know, government has been involved (and this continues in the limited compensation sense) in land pricing, purchase and distribution through, for example, the Community Land Act 1975 (of which one remnant remains the Land Authority for Wales), in the building materials and production processes (most notably immediately after the Second World War but also through monopolies and mergers inquiries), in the provision of loan finance for example through the Public Works Loans Board, its own Option Mortgage scheme, local authority mortgages and the regulation and control of mortgage finance in general and building societies in particular. Most recently the government set up the favourable tax regime for the Business Expansion Scheme (through which properties were purchased for renting) and it has now announced a successor regime in the Housing Investment Trusts.

Rent control has been a feature of the UK housing market since 1919. Largely eradicated under successive Conservative governments, it has now returned in related but rather different forms. Central government sets annual guidelines for local authority rents and these are now scheduled to become binding in terms of entitlement for rent rebate subsidy. Equally although government has not set housing association rents, it has controlled the level of funding and thus the degree of dependence on private finance. The revenue stream to service loan financed debt is the rent. While government has been happy to see both local authority and housing association rents rise and thus become more exposed to private sector competition this has had considerable consequences for the housing benefit bill.

The Treasury, the Department of Social Security and now the government in general has become very concerned about a rising benefit bill and is seeking to curb access to and the cost of housing benefit. This has led to proposals to adopt local reference rents and a new government regulated rent increase formula (the so called RPI +/– X factor regime). The latter could introduce rent control in the public sector but through the operation of local markets this will also impact upon the private sector (that impact will be direct if private sector companies bid for housing association grant and thus move into the new rent control regime).

Thus just as we began this century with controls on rents so we seem destined to end it doing the same. Just how best to subsidise rents and yet prevent profit taking still seems to be an unresolved issue. In a different way the same is still true of house prices. In a country where home ownership is the dominant tenure, the movement of house prices is a matter of considerable importance not just to home owners but also to government. Prices affect mortgage costs which in turn impact upon inflation, wage pressures and patterns of savings and expenditure. At the end of the Second World War, the government proposed controlling house prices in order to prevent speculative profit taking derived from the general housing shortage.

Until the 1980s, the government was able to influence the housing market via the building societies and the building societies' cartel arrangements. Building societies were the dominant providers of mortgages and their funds were raised from the retail savings market (see Boléat and Coles, 1987 for a useful review). Interest rates influenced the supply of funds to building societies and this in turn influenced the amount of mortgage credit available. In general terms it was under-supplied through this specialist housing finance circuit even though the system was maintained and favoured by government. In the 1980s this cartel broke down under competitive and government pressures and the specialist circuit was abandoned. The housing finance market was liberalised (e.g., the Building Societies Act, 1986) and became highly competitive. One consequence of this was that the supply of housing finance was easily able to match demand. Indeed such was the capacity to raise money that lenders now had to compete in terms of the cost and terms under which the money was lent. The growth in the supply of funds meant that, given the right circumstances, it would no longer exert a downward pressure on any inflationary tendencies within the housing market.

In the late 1980s, house prices were rising uncontrollably and bringing considerable inflationary pressures to bear within the economy. As a consequence government put up interest rates and began a wider process of reducing government assistance to home ownership (since in part it was the very measures taken to promote home ownership which had built up momentum in the market). The impact of these measures plus a worsening economic environment (not least because interest rates were high) was to drive house prices down and the housing market into a recession from which it has yet to recover.

The government (including the Treasury and the Bank of England) takes the view that house price rises above some modest increase in line with inflation have the capacity to threaten their success in sustaining a low inflation economy. House price rises affect both housing costs (and therefore put a strain on wages) and equity extraction (leading to increased consumer spending). Since the control of inflation stands at the heart of the government's strategy (and for which it and the country as a whole has sacrificed a great deal) it is clear that the 'control' of house prices is itself seen as an important issue. Such 'control' will not be direct but rather through interest rates.

Government influence in and regulation of the housing market therefore remains considerable and has changed over time as policy itself has changed. It would be wrong to suggest government does not intervene directly in the provision of housing. However, over the years the level of direct intervention has fallen and government has sought to establish control and influence via housing subsidies and assistance and through general taxation. Freeing housing or related organisations from direct control has many benefits but it does have the consequence that those organisations might behave in ways which are unwelcome to government, policy, the housing market or the housing system. Thus although housing organisations have been 'freed' in a variety of ways they have in turn become exposed to the disciplines of the market place. This creates its own pressures and opportunities, some of which are unanticipated. These outcomes are explored later in the chapter.

This discussion of 'control' via central government is not intended to promote a view that the direction and management of the housing system is within the gift of government. Indeed this chapter seeks to argue that in some senses it is almost the very opposite. The operation of the housing system is complex and the outcomes it produces are not always predictable. It is striking that generalised models of the housing market have been unable to explain recent developments (Meen, 1995).

Notwithstanding our continuing inability to fully understand and anticipate changes in the housing system it is evident that there are fundamental weaknesses in structures, systems and approaches within the UK housing system and that central government is an important part of the problem.

Having set out some of the broad issues and parameters the chapter now moves to focus upon the more specific arena of housing management. Through this example it is possible to set out the conflicting pressures at the operational level in the housing system and to gain insights into what might be done to correct and change the system.

The process of housing management: change and conflict

The housing management function within the social housing sector provides an excellent example of how the demands and pressures have changed and where there are real tensions between financial viability and long term social sustainability. In many respects the demands are now for a more intensive management service (and for a more varied one) yet all the financial pressures are to reduce costs and in all probability limit the service. In part this also reflects the continuing tension between the property management function, common in the private sector, and the more expansive housing management function in the public sector and, at least until recently, the generally poor understanding and status of the latter.

Background

The housing management function really only developed through the growth of local authority housing provision in the 1920s and 1930s although its origins lie in the private sector in the late nineteenth century (Kemp and Williams, 1991). The landlord function was well established in the nineteenth century not least because most households rented their homes. However, detailed consideration of how that function should be carried out was limited not least in relation to households on low incomes. Partly in response to this, the middle class Victorian reformer Octavia Hill propounded a system of intensive supervision of the tenants and through that giving them greater capacity to pay the rent and improve their own lives. It was a philosophy which was driven by a concern to become active agents of social change, albeit that it did little to tackle the fundamental problem of low incomes. It was a limited success although the Octavia Hill system was copied by a range of housing organisations both in Britain and abroad. Most significantly it led to the creation of the Society of Women Housing Managers (formed from the joining together of a number of womens housing organisations including the Association of Women Housing Workers formed in 1916 (Brion, 1994)).

The Society grew slowly even though local authority housing provision was expanding rapidly through the building of new estates. Britain faced a huge housing shortage in the 1920s and it was through municipal building in the period 1920–1940 (and 1950–1980) that both shortages and improvements in the quality of housing were secured. A small number of authorities and associations adopted the Octavia Hill system but for the most part housing was run by staff based in Town Clerk's and Engineer's Departments. In 1931, the Institute of Housing was formed by a group of predominantly male local authority staff. Unlike the Society (which was restricted to women and had a strong housing and social welfare focus) the Institute was much more property focused in outlook.

The divergence between the two organisations and their approaches is evident in the report of the Housing Management and Housing Associations Sub Committee of the Central Housing Advisory Committee (CHAC) on the *Management of Municipal Housing Estates*. The report was published in 1938 (and reprinted in 1947) and was a specific attempt to assess the merits of employing trained housing managers. The report fully acknowledges that Britain was making good progress in tackling the slums through demolition and the building of new estates but noted that 'in solving one problem other problems are created'. And the report goes on (1947, pp 9 and 10):

> At the beginning those who doubted the wisdom of slum clearance and questioned the advisability of spending huge sums of public money on the provision of up to date homes for the very poor, spoke with pessimism of tenants who would keep 'coals in the bath' and the futility of trying to make a 'silk purse out of a sow's ear'. We know that as a general proposition these dismal prophecies were wrong. Yet waste of both of the houses and of opportunity can and does occur . . . On the business side good management may, therefore, be defined as the application of skill of caring for the commodity, the house, in order that the commodity may retain its value to both landlord and tenant.
>
> But management must include far more than rent collection and the ordering of repairs, for unless some steps are taken so to educate the tenant as to secure his co-operation, the landlord, striving to maintain his property, and the tenant, destroying it by his neglect, will remain warring parties. Hence good management additionally postulates the application of skill in treating the person who is paying for the use of the commodity so that he too may do his share in preserving its value; it is in effect a form of social education and aims at teaching a new inexperienced community to be 'housing minded'.

This was the paternalist thinking of the 1930s. The evidence submitted by the two organisations to the subcommittee were 'largely conflicting'. The Society argued for the integration of business techniques and social services through one person, the Institute took the contrary view. The subcommittee agreed there was a need for the social work function but saw no reason for all staff to have this training.

Over successive decades this debate faded but did not disappear. In the post war period, council housing expanded rapidly through the creation both of new suburban housing estates and, in essence, through the new towns. Since the population for these developments was being drawn from the old inner cores of cities there were major problems of dislocation from jobs and social networks and substantial gaps in the physical and social infrastructure of the new areas they were moving to. Some local authority housing departments and housing associations took on housing welfare officers or housing visitors (now tenancy relations officers). It has, however, always been a limited activity and there has always been tension as to whether this is a housing or social services function. Partly this is a product of what has been needed since in many local authority areas the number of tenants requiring assistance was quite limited.

Different management models were put in place in the UK. The Paisley system, for example, related to housing new tenants by isolating them in a block and only allowing them to move on once they had proved they were 'satisfactory'. Decentralisation became quite widespread in the early post war period and in the CHAC report of 1959 *Councils and their houses* there was a recommendation to extend and develop cost accounting in local authorities and the development of uniform accounts. Perhaps most significantly the report stated:

> tenants today are much more representative of the community as a whole and are, for the most part, independent, reliable citizens who no longer require the support and guidance which was often thought necessary in the past. Local authorities must recognise that this is a major social change which is likely to become more marked in the years ahead: and that this recognition must be given positive effect in their management practice.

In the 1960s and 1970s authorities responded in a variety of ways to these changing circumstances. Efforts were made to streamline services, not least reflecting use of new technology and the new corporate management theory. Estate caretakers were withdrawn to be replaced by 'flying caretakers', estate offices were closed and door to door rent collection withdrawn. In many respects therefore council housing was poorly prepared for the 1980s. Debt was high, much system and non traditional building had taken place in the 1960s/1970s, service levels had been reduced and the circumstances of tenants were changing as both increased demand from poor households and ever tighter targeting made their impact.

Moreover, the size of the enterprise was huge; while only a small number of authorities had stocks of over 100,000 dwellings many authorities would have been the dominant provider of rented housing in the area and no substantial debate or thought seems to have been given to how to manage such 'empires' in the light of changing circumstances nor as to whether further growth was needed, possible or indeed desirable. The absence of a long term plan to create a financially or politically sustainable local authority housing sector meant authorities were poorly placed to defend themselves and the benefits which were to be reaped from having a mature and increasingly debt free stock. While it is certainly incorrect to argue that local authorities had done little to respond to change (e.g., Power, 1987) there was an absence of strategic planning for the long term partly because the debate had always been about numbers and partly as a consequence of having to respond to immediate pressures.

Present context

There is widespread concern that the decline in resources is producing a downward spiral in terms of the sustainability of local authority housing (and the communities that the local authorities provide for). A supply of new dwellings is an important lubricant from both management and tenant points of view since it allows for adjustment and change in relation to family circumstances and management efficiency. With declining resources, pressure from central government, the local community generally and tenants specifically, local authorities have been facing difficult decisions. With the continuing loss of stock via the Right to Buy, with pressure to put rents up (and because of falling subsidy to therefore meet the costs of housing benefits) it has been increasingly attractive for authorities to transfer their housing stock to existing or newly formed housing associations (or private companies). However, this might be seen as a rather chaotic and unplanned dismemberment of a major national asset.

This has been an important factor in the expansion of the housing association sector. This has been a privileged sector in a number of ways because it has been viewed as a better way of delivering social housing services than local authorities (Clapham, 1992). This status has faded in recent years and it is evident now that we are in the midst of what might be termed the 'housing association recession'. However, despite current (and past) difficulties, associations have grown and prospered under the Conservative government. They now provide around 1 million homes, up from around 400,000 in 1979. Setting aside transfer associations which, unsurprisingly, have characteristics similar to local authorities, it is evident that the size of associations and the extent to which their property is located on estates have grown. This reflects the fact that not only have associations had to become more rigorous and targeted in terms of who they house but more and more of their tenants are coming via the local authority nomination route (Page, 1993).

That housing associations have begun to face management problems similar to the local authorities they are meant to replace (and do better than) has itself been a cause for concern. However, added to that has been the real evidence that associations have been less well equipped to cope with large scale operations and a more difficult operational context. This reflects the fact that although they have tended to adopt a generic model of housing management they have until recently remained very centralised and have not always put into place the accessible (and perhaps decentralised) offices, detailed procedures and the specialist staff which might be deemed necessary to deal with the changing scale of their operations and the circumstances surrounding their tenants.

Associations have the difficult task of trying to balance the pressures of becoming or remaining financially strong and viable alongside the concern to stay close to the community and the customer. There are probably some economies of scale to be achieved by being bigger and this combines with a stronger asset position and a greater capacity to raise loans at preferential terms. The variations in the size, levels of activity and viability of housing associations are considerable. Regulation via the Housing Corporation, Housing for Wales and Scottish Homes has ensured that, in broad terms, where problems have arisen they have been dealt with without any significant loss to lenders or major disruption to tenants. However, as the scale, diversity and complexity of the sector continue to grow it may become harder to achieve this. Indeed, it should be borne in mind that some associations have got into considerable difficulties despite the presence of the regulatory bodies.

The arrival of new associations via large scale voluntary transfers of local authority stock has already brought a new dimension. Some of these associations will achieve strong financial positions quickly (by reducing their transfer debt burden much faster than had been anticipated and because of the advantageous transfer sale price) and they will then be well placed to take new and possibly radical steps in the market place. They contrast with many traditional associations where the debt position is worsening. There seems a certain irony that the benefits of a debt free mature stock should ultimately be achieved outside of the local authority sector which gave birth to them.

Regardless of that, increasingly they influence the agendas in the sector and this will put further pressure on traditional associations. Although it is certainly the case that some small associations are and can remain strong and viable, the very weight of regulation and control, market pressures and the changes which are driving the system would suggest that there are considerable challenges ahead of housing associations in general and small associations in particular. The case for group or federated structures, for contracted and shared services and for a series of strategic alliances and even mergers and takeovers seems very strong. Admittedly the latter could pose a major challenge to what might be seen as key features of the housing association sector, i.e., that they are small, local and responsive.

Housing management lies at the heart of the social housing service. Ultimately it is through housing management that the service is delivered. It is therefore crucial to the long term sustainability of a social rented sector that we arrive at efficient, effective and sustainable models of management. The reality at present is that the search continues. For local authorities, the work involved in preparing for both CCT and Care in the Community has been a significant source of stimulus (and frustration) and has encouraged thinking about this, although it is probably too early to draw final conclusions (see for example, Baker et al., 1992 and Scott, 1994). Recently the Labour party has set out proposals for housing quality programmes as an alternative to CCT and the idea of a British quality standard for all social housing landlords. This does suggest that we may now see a move to government specified standards in housing management.

The Scottish Homes programme of personal housing plans and the Scottish Office's housing management plans also give clues here. First there is a requirement for bespoke arrangements tailored to individuals and groups and second there is a need for formalised plans. Housing management has been treated as an unimportant and common sense activity and it is somewhat ironic that it is only now, after seventy years of major social housing provision, that due attention is being given to this activity (Bines et al., 1993).

New agendas, new structures?

Both associations and authorities face immense difficulties in the future, not least because of declining resources and an increasingly disadvantaged client group. There is general agreement that effective housing organisations need to be flexible and adaptable. However, there are a number of changes working their way through the UK housing system which will impact upon such developments, both positively and negatively. These include the following:

Local government reorganisation

Impacting variably on Great Britain, this will have the effect of breaking established links and creating new organisational structures in some authorities. Longer term, these may be helpful not least because they may break or diminish any unhelpful departmental boundaries (and influence thinking more generally) but in the short term they will not assist. One suggested model in the reorganisation process is joint housing and social services departments. There has been relatively little enthusiasm for that arrangement amongst housing staff (LGMB,

1994) although a number of authorities have gone down this route. Although the opportunity has existed to do otherwise, reorganisation is above all else a political process and the outcomes are driven by that rather than by objective service needs. Given the uncertainties regarding the future of local authority housing services, there is perhaps some justification for this even though it does not provide a sound basis for long term planning.

The introduction of compulsory competitive tendering for local authority housing management

This has placed a new emphasis on cost management and on tightly defined housing services (Baker *et al.*, 1992). Welfare elements may be excluded even though there is a strong logic for keeping them (they are excluded from the defined list of functions that have to be put out to tender). For the most part tenders have been won by the in-house teams competing on the basis of both price and quality (Brown and Fraser, 1996). Authorities have found the process of preparing for CCT time consuming and expensive but also quite useful. They would argue they now have a better understanding of their business and a greater capacity to manage it.

However, there must be questions as to how this can be sustained and whether there will be a slow but inevitable incursions by private sector contractors, some of whom are prepared to operate contracts at a loss in order to gain expertise and track records. It is notable that one private contractor, having won a tender at a price significantly below that of the in-house bid, has now withdrawn from other competitions. The view is that the company will absorb the experience of what might be a loss making contract before tendering for work elsewhere. The emergence of the private contractors association and their complaints to the DoE of unfair practices in the tendering process could be seen as part of a softening up process (*Local Government Chronicle*, 19 January 1996 and 10 May 1996).

Another consequence of CCT is that it now prices organisational arrangements. Perhaps for the first time an organisation can see how much a particular arrangement costs, e.g., decentralised offices, and this has raised a series of questions about whether the arrangement in question is the most efficient and effective way of carrying out the function. In time this market price will be used as a benchmark for particular services and will substitute for the more elusive research based evidence.

The challenge of course remains to link price to outcome and to explain differences between organisations. Moreover it must be recognised that the specification process can produce a range of costed outcomes depending upon the assumptions which underpin it. Questions about the use of existing premises, computers and other equipment and the extent to which specific services are *de minimis*, i.e., below the level at which they must be contracted out (£500,000), have an impact upon the tender price (Newbury and King, 1996).

Given the depth of housing management expertise in local authorities (and the absence of such expertise elsewhere except in housing associations and a few private sector companies) it is not surprising that most authorities have been successful when they have mounted in-house bids for the housing management contract (89% of contracts had been won by in house teams as at 1 March 1996). In terms of price and quality they have been very competitive and this has typically meant the cost of the service is now budgeted to fall (ignoring the costs of making the bid and evaluating tenders). In addition, as might be expected, local authorities have become expert at devising and packaging contracts in order to maximise the advantages which might accrue to them legally and fairly (and the upshot has been that around seventy authorities have been able to claim *de minimis* – hardly the outcome sought by the DoE).

CCT has the effect of setting out structures and arrangements for the life of a contract term (variations are possible but at a cost). Where an entire specified housing management service is contracted out to the private sector there is a risk that the authority not only loses the staff and competence to ever regain the contract but it also loses control of the information base. However, it can buy back in any staff that went 'out' with the contract although there may be practical problems to doing this.

Budget restraint and policy changes

The social housing budget has been very exposed to cuts and new controls. This has acted to divert organisations from planning for the longer term and leads them towards a focus on the immediate. Thus although there is a business planning process in place in most housing organisations that is easily overtaken by the need to respond to new 'challenge' funding (i.e., competitions) or new cuts in anticipated income (the possible loss of the Section 54 Corporation Tax Rebate for non charitable housing associations is a case in point). Moreover, the planning horizon involved in both housing investment programme bids and approved development programme bids has been reduced and increasingly 'top sliced' so that funds for centrally initiated projects can be funded. Thus although central government may criticise local government and associations for short termism, in practice this is what its own actions have encouraged.

In the past both local authorities and housing associations have been required to raise rents but given the rising housing benefit bill this has now come to an end. Local authorities are to lose any entitlement to benefit subsidy where rents are above a stated maximum while housing associations may be placed in a 'rent control' regime where increases will be specified by government. Moreover, they are to face private sector competition for housing association grant. The upshot of this and the CCT regime for local authorities is that there will be a substantial and continuing downward pressure on operating costs. This will increase the pressure to consider organisational structures and processes. Recently one Director of Housing has suggested that this will lead to tenant managed organisations because this could have the dual effect of reducing costs and increasing local employment (Cowans, 1996).

Performance based regimes

All of the above place great store on performance. Performance measures, performance indicators, benchmarking, league tables and peer groupings (and most recently credit ratings) have all become familiar features of the social housing landscape in recent years (Walker, 1994; for a useful general discussion see Jackson, 1995). Their use has been backed by sustained research into housing organisations, their efficiency and effectiveness. However, as is evident from this research, we are still a long way from being able to explain why performance varies so greatly. Certainly it is clear that operating context is crucial and in that sense it would be wrong to argue that the success or otherwise of an organisation is simply down to the quality of management or the appropriateness of its organisational form (Kemp, 1995; Murie, 1995). This suggests that while debates about the effectiveness of decentralisation or tenant participation have some real value these measures cannot of themselves totally transform the prospects of an organisation struggling to deliver its service. Equally, success is not totally outside of the control of the organisation.

With the circumstances in and contexts surrounding social housing organisations, the challenges to current organisational form and processes are considerable. Tighter finance and intense competition may threaten staffing levels, organisational arrangements (most notably decentralised offices) and cultures. Generic working will be encouraged as part of a wider move to flexible structures which can adapt to changing workloads and more use will be made of contracted staff and services. If all of this results in greater efficiency and effectiveness within social housing agencies and better use of public expenditure then there may be much to commend it. But as was touched upon earlier, the management product could be eroded and with it the long term viability of the sector since it is through housing management that the value of the asset is maintained and repaid and that consumer demands and needs are met. Moreover as Walsh (1995) so cogently argues;

> The use of the contract has only begun to affect the core of the public service, and when it comes to have its full effect is likely to require fundamental changes in organisation and culture.

Localities and governance

Although the housing plan process has now been in existence for around two decades and the local authority enabling role has become part of the language and thinking of the sector (Goodlad, 1994) it is still the case that the overall organisational structure for the effective spending of public resources and the delivery of well coordinated services leaves much to be desired.

Somewhat belatedly there is now widespread interest in and activity around common waiting lists between housing associations and local authorities (and the so called community lettings approach whereby a wider view of the consequences of a lettings policy is taken on board) and there are limited examples of associations and authorities sharing or purchasing services from each other (e.g., private sector leasing for the homeless, repair and maintenance services). In part this stems from the still limited contact between associations and authorities in terms of any joint planning framework (reflecting not least the incomplete links at central government level). While the funding agencies expect housing associations to have taken account of local housing needs and to have the agreement of local authorities with respect to planned development, it is evident that there are continuing weaknesses in the local needs assessment and housing provision framework. Most recently government itself has recognised this and suggested action might be taken (Department of the Environment, 1996).

Partly these relate to local politics, partly to inadequate information and planning mechanisms. Again Scotland appears to have come closest to resolving this. Scottish Homes has taken on the role of the national housing agency and has built upon the legacy of housing plans developed by the Scottish Office in the 1970s by putting in place a more developed local housing market assessment procedure which it is hoped local authorities will take ownership of. Housing for Wales has put a number of strategic housing agreements in place with local authorities in Wales but these have yet to become universal or a serious part of local planning (Bader, 1996). But it is evident that across the UK it is not that most housing agencies have failed to recognise the importance of the long term but rather that central government has failed to sustain a long term planning framework and has given inadequate encouragement to agencies to consider longer term issues.

The continuing weaknesses in coordination between local authorities, housing associations, the DoE (or equivalent) and the Housing Corporation (or equivalent) is a matter of some concern not least in an era of tighter resources and the need for effective targeting (National Audit Office, 1989). This problem is then much worse if account is taken of the private sector. Although some authorities have managed to develop and sustain local fora to which all providers of housing related services can contribute, it remains difficult to translate this into a firm planning framework. Yet in the emerging housing markets and housing systems of the late 1990s and beyond the balance of demand and supply, need and provision will require very careful management. It is a matter of some relief that the DoE (but not the Welsh or Scottish Offices) is now actively considering future housing requirements although that leaves open the question of how that will be developed regionally and locally.

The debates about housing association governance and in the review of the role of the Housing Corporation (NFHA, 1995; Day et al., 1993)) have raised important questions about the appropriate organisational structure for housing provision. In some respects all the pressures are to enhance control and coordination from the centre. This fits with a model which is seeking to ensure maximum output for the public funds spent. However, how well equipped is the centre, whether DoE, Housing Corporation or some other body, to undertake this role? Would the very nature of a centralised process drive out the very flexibility and adaptability required in the system? There are many who feel it would and that such a process sits uneasily with the independent status of housing associations and local authorities. Ultimately there has to be a creative partnership between the centre and the providers. As the reliance on public funding reduces so the influence of the centre is diminished in some respects. Indeed in an era of private finance there must come a question about whether the housing finance industry should have a stronger influence over the shape and direction of policy.

In addition, a process which is driven from the centre will be sensitive to and reflect the pressures which exist at the centre. Thus in recent years government has been concerned with the control of public expenditure and inflation and with reducing the role of local government. These have dominated above all else and even committed Environment and Housing ministers have found it difficult to break through the straitjacket this has imposed. Housing has not been a major priority as is evidenced by the proportionately higher budget cuts in this area.

It is apparent that both local authorities and associations have shown considerable powers of creativity. It is certainly not the case that policy change is driven only from the centre. Large scale voluntary transfers are one good example of local authority initiatives and the same was true with respect to decentralisation (without the financial resources which followed under PEP and Estate Action), improvement for sale, block renewal and private sector leasing. Being close to the issues and aware of the costs of inaction local housing agencies can often be better placed to take action. The challenge then for central government and related agencies is to assess whether such a programme has merit elsewhere. Sadly in the UK there has been only a limited history of pilot programmes and the encouragement of local variation and adaptation. In an era dominated by a negative stance regarding local housing authorities, it has been convenient to portray them as incompetent. However, it is evident that despite failings, local authorities have taken important initiatives and have a continuing capacity to do so. Moreover they (and local housing associations) can mobilise other local resources and as the system moves ever closer to a plurality of provision this will be crucial.

The future of housing organisations or housing organisations for the future?

As local authorities move further towards an enabling role so the issue of integration with other programmes becomes more central. There are questions of cost efficiency and there are those who would argue that direct intervention is best but pragmatically this is a change which must now be accepted. Despite sound arguments to the contrary, it would seem unlikely that housing will ever again command the share of national resources which would enable local authorities to return to the era of mass provision. All parties accept the role of private finance and see that one key task for government and a good use of government resources is to lever in more private finance.

The renewed concern with wider and more comprehensive housing strategies and a recognition that housing management can also mean both the management of the local housing service and the wider local housing system has meant some authorities have begun to take a much broader and potentially more interventionist stance with respect to their local housing markets. With appropriate checks and balances, this should be encouraged. However, logically this also raises questions about 'competing' housing association and local authority funding structures and planning frameworks. It is clear this must change but the outcome should be one which secures the benefits of plurality of provision alongside cost efficiencies and economies of integration and coordination between sectors and organisations.

Recognising that today's orthodoxies may look equally outdated in years to come it is necessary to think very hard and clearly about the 'models' being used. Participation and decentralisation have been two strongly promoted themes. Neither necessarily tackle the fundamental problems of resources which face both tenants or housing providers and they can (and have) become ends in themselves rather than means to an end. The upshot of this is that they can be 'overpromoted' and in conforming with the latest 'best' practice an organisation may actually commit time and resources which would be better deployed elsewhere. Clearly both decentralisation and tenant participation can provide the means for better communication and they do offer the potential for greater local control. However, they may also do little to enhance the efficiency of the organisation and one frustrating reality is that there would seem to be no universal housing model which guarantees good results in whatever setting. It will be interesting to see how both develop under the tighter cost control regime brought into place by CCT.

The pressure for cost efficiencies and for a willingness to think more radically are now growing. Housing organisations will need to give greater consideration to working collaboratively and to sharing resources, not just with other housing providers or other departments in the same organisation but with any public or private agency which has similar requirements. Central government needs to enable this though it must recognise that it cannot be a universal and required solution.

Organisations also need to maximise their use of IT and to ensure that what they build is to the highest standard for the longer term. It is quite clear that housing management in particular and housing organisations in general have yet to fully exploit developments in information technology. Technology can bring tenants into much closer contact with their organisations and allow access to be enjoyed by a far wider spread of users than those who can get to a decentralised office. Equally much can be done to streamline internal management information and records in ways which can enhance the efficiency of organisations.

The conclusive evidence is that regardless of general context housing organisations can achieve some success if they have determined/capable management, a well trained staff and a sensible organisational structure. However, none of this will transform situations where resources are limited and where the economic and social context is very adverse and it has been shown that context has been the most consistent factor in accounting for management performance (Bines *et al.*, 1993; Kemp, 1994a; Murie, 1995). It is also very evident that some organisations do perform better than others and it is important the system is capable of learning from this. This applies as much to central government as it does to local housing organisations.

Organising from the centre?

There must also be questions about the overall organisational structure of the UK housing system. There is an unresolved tension between the apparent flexibility of a multiplicity of providers and the need to make best use of dwindling public resources. Equally, there is a need to maximise the capacity to adapt to changing circumstances and to local housing situations while at the same time ensuring effective control and use of resources. Looking ahead, it is likely that a Labour government would enhance the role of local authorities but this should not be done in ways which diminish the capacity of all local providers to meet the range of needs.

One of the problems for housing is the range of new issues and new initiatives which are constantly being promoted. This tends to deflect interest from a fundamental reappraisal of the system itself. The last major housing policy review was published in 1977 and the recent White Paper does little to address the mechanisms through which policy is delivered. Local housing companies (LOCOS) and housing investment trusts (HITS) are two new instruments and their emergence will pose further questions about the complexity and efficiency of the overall system (they will also trigger further developments in new vehicles for funding housing). Equally we are now seeing a range of tenant led organisations emerging. The Royal Borough of Kensington and Chelsea has transferred its entire housing stock and staff to a tenant managed organisation and elsewhere, estate transfers are taking place to associations led by tenants. Estate management boards are now widespread.

Although not in the Housing Act, the government still plans to introduce a new system of controlling rents in the 'subsidised' sector (whether public or private) and this in turn will raise issues about assets and viability. In essence the government has overseen a revolution in the operation of the housing system and this process is continuing. But it is being done without a clear consideration of the forces which have been unleashed and the ways these will work out over time. The introduction or enhancement of markets into almost every sphere of the system – whether for private finance, residential mortgages, management contracts and care contracts – has created new dynamics and tensions which are only slowly emerging. The question is will this emerging (and unplanned) framework sit comfortably and positively with the wider and evolving social and economic context? The effective operation of the housing system is crucial to the overall success of the UK as a competitive economy. Only in time will we be able to establish how compatible our evolving housing system is with our fast changing and developing economy.

Finally, there is always the danger that our concern with organisational structure leads to a focus on local arrangements and on single issues. It is no coincidence that the UK has reorganised local government again yet the basic framework of central government remains unchanged. It is not at all clear that local government reorganisation will resolve many of the issues touched upon in this chapter. Yet there is widespread agreement that the current arrangements for delivering housing services are not adequate for today's and tomorrow's needs and the same would be true at central government level in relation to planning and financial control and the co-ordination of central policy guidance.

This was highlighted by the Central Policy Review Staff (CPRS) in 1978 and it remains a key concern today. There is the question too as to whether the debate should simply be about the organisational arrangements for housing. If the overall operating context is so adverse it may be that the agenda should focus not on housing but on employment, health or education. The CPRS commented in its 1975 report *A Joint Framework for Social Policies* (pp 1 and 2):

> Resources are always scarce. Economic constraints and the constraints of the legislative programme limit the speed at which things can be done. There are limits to how fast the institutions both of central and local government can respond to change. Many of the most intractable problems affect more than one department, and involve central government, local authorities and other bodies. There is a serious lack of information about many social problems, and thus no reliable basis for assessing need or the effectiveness of provision. There is no effective mechanism for determining coherent and consistent priorities in the field of social policy generally.
>
> All this suggests that a new and more coherent framework is required for the making and ejection of social policies . . . This is necessary not only for reasons of social justice, but also in the light of the current and prospective economic situation.

The effective coordination and integration of policy is a key concern in the overall structure of housing provision. It is ever more widely recognised that the solutions to many housing problems lie outside of the housing sector itself and that they will require the involvement of a wide range of organisations, both in the public and private sectors.

This of course has implications for central government and for the housing 'quangos' which have been part of the structure of provision since the 1970s. One can denote a tendency within central government to focus on policy and overall resource provision and then to allow lower level agencies to distribute and utilise those resources (this is partly a necessity as staff numbers are reduced in central government). Scottish Homes is now using the subtitle the National Housing Agency and Housing for Wales has developed strategic housing agreements with local authorities. The Housing Corporation has recently indicated its desire to widen its role and to work more closely with local authorities. The Audit Commission has shown an equally strong desire to extend its housing remit to what some would see as the 'quasi' public sector, housing associations.

The recent report of the House of Commons Environment Committee (House of Commons, 1996) and the Government's response (Department of the Environment, 1996) give a clear indication of some of the perceived weaknesses in the current housing system and associated organisational arrangements. These include concerns with the forecasting of housing need, our weak understanding of the process of household formation, sustaining the quality of the housing stock, potential crowding out of private housing investment, the performance of social housing landlords and the tensions between top down regional planning process and local housing need assessment. Indeed on this last point the government comments (paragraph 117):

> there could be merit in commissioning further research to investigate a 'preferred method' for estimating local needs and to consider the merits of the various formulae currently in use. This would help avoid unnecessary disputes between developers and local authorities.

Overall, the government response acknowledges a series of weaknesses in the current system and the case for change in relation to housing need assessment. The remit for the Inquiry was limited so more radical proposals were unlikely. However, there may also be a case for examining a range of organisational changes which might better tune the UK's housing system to the tasks before it. These might include removing all direct social housing provision from local government or alternatively merging housing association and local authority housing activities. In the past arguments have been put forward for the creation of a housing bank which could channel resources into the housing system in a targeted way. It is less evident that the case for this still exists. Yet, although the concern is less now with the overall provision of funds (the market has been able to do this) there are questions about the management of risk. In other countries (e.g. USA and Australia) the government has backed the creation of insurance vehicles which have been able to enhance private provision in certain parts of the market.

While there is not space here to examine the merits of these different ideas the point is simply that we should not assume we have in place the right set of structures to manage the UK's housing system. As this and other chapters in this book make very clear there have been fundamental changes in the housing system. Yet we have largely retained the overall national framework which has been in place for many years. We have more actors and more varied actors at a local level but they sit within a framework which is remarkably unchanged.

The time has surely come for a review. The Nolan Committee has recently taken a fresh look at regulation and accountability in the housing association sector. Now is the time to think again about the overall organisational framework for the UK's housing system and the ways it might be better able to adapt and change to the emerging social and economic patterns of the late 1990s and beyond.

Acknowledgements

I would like to thank Alan Murie for his helpful comments on a draft of this chapter. It should be clear that this chapter has been written by the author in a personal capacity only.

CHAPTER 9

Towards Sustainable Policies for Housing Renewal in the Private Sector

PHILIP LEATHER AND SHEILA MACKINTOSH

Throughout the 1980s, state policies relating to the renewal of the private sector housing stock took a back seat to the major issues of the decade such as the privatisation of public housing. Even in the renewal field itself, attention focused on the public sector through initiatives such as the Priority Estates Projects and Estates Action, rather than on policies to deal with poor condition privately owned housing. Despite the completion of a major review of renewal policy in 1985 (Cmnd 9513, 1985), it was not until 1989 that legislation to revise the policy framework went through Parliament. The new system involved radical changes to the previous approach, which had remained substantially unchanged since its introduction in the early 1970s.

But expectations that housing renewal policy would settle into a smooth period of implementation proved wrong. After only a year of operation the legislation underwent its first official review which resulted in a number of minor changes. But a few months later, before the findings of the first review had been implemented, the government announced a second, more substantial review of policy. The new legislation had created a demand for renovation grant aid which could not realistically be met within current and likely future public spending levels. Local authorities were faced with growing demand for help from those living in dwellings which were unfit for human habitation, but they lacked the resources to meet this demand. After a white paper in 1995, the government introduced measures in the Housing Grants, Construction and Registration Act 1996 to abolish any automatic entitlement to renovation grant aid by making this form of assistance discretionary. Although it is too soon to anticipate the impact of these changes, there is a fear that local authority assistance to private owners with repair and improvement will decline sharply with the removal of the duty to provide help.

It might have been hoped that the abolition of the right to a grant would have been accompanied by measures to boost investment by home owners themselves, but the 1996 Act contained no new ideas. As the legislation passed through Parliament, proposals from the Opposition to give local authorities powers to develop new forms of assistance to owners were consistently refused by the government. If nothing more is done, the future for housing renewal policy is the gradual withering of the grant system to one which provides limited help for those on the lowest incomes to deal only with worst house condition problems. Elsewhere, individual owners will fend for themselves as best they can.

In this chapter, we shall argue for a more positive approach to dealing with the condition of the UK housing stock. The chapter firstly examines the background to the crisis in renewal policy, the operation of the new grant system in the first three years, the nature of the problems which occurred, and the options which are available to government and to local authorities in the short and medium term to get renewal policy back on its feet again. But in our view there is a need for a more fundamental reassessment of where renewal policy is going. The second part of the chapter will argue that what is needed are policies which recognise that Britain has an ageing housing stock and an ageing population. Transferring older houses to individual ownership has not ensured that they will remain in good condition. Effective renewal strategies for the 1990s and beyond will need to recognise that housing decay is not a short-term problem found only in the older housing stock but an ongoing process across the whole housing stock. With limitations on public spending only likely to increase, new ways need to be found to use the resources which are available more effectively while at the same time developing mechanisms to increase the level of private investment by home owners in the repair, improvement and ongoing maintenance of their housing.

The housing renewal crisis

Successive national house condition surveys have shown a continuing problem of poor physical housing conditions, although comparisons over time and between the components of the United Kingdom are difficult because of national differences and changes in definitions and variations in survey methodology. Table 1 shows the extent of unfitness, missing amenities, and urgent disrepair revealed by various surveys covering the constituent parts of the UK. In total, about 1.8 million dwellings are unfit for human habitation or in Scotland below the tolerable standard. As an alternative measure, more than 3.7 million dwellings are in a state of serious disrepair, with urgent repair costs in excess of £1,000, although many of the unfit dwellings would also fall within this category. While there are problems in the local authority and housing association sectors, the majority of houses in poor condition are to be found in the owner-occupied and privately rented sectors. In 1991, some 81% of occupied dwellings in England, Scotland and Northern Ireland with urgent repair costs in excess of £1,000 were privately owned.

Housing renewal policies

We have examined the historical development of housing renewal policies in more detail elsewhere (Leather and Mackintosh, 1992). After a period in the 1950s and 1960s when demolition and rebuilding were the preferred options, the emphasis of public policy in the 1970s and 1980s switched to the provision of grant aid to owner occupiers and private landlords. Substantial sums were invested by local authorities in the improvement of privately owned housing during this period. From April 1981 to March 1992 alone, some £8.3 billion was spent on grants in England (at 1990/91 prices), together with almost £1.0 billion in

Table 1 Housing conditions in Britain, 1991[1]

	Unfit/BTS[2]	Lacking amenities[3]	Urgent repairs over £1,000	Ave cost of urgent repairs
Number of dwellings				
England	1,498,000	205,000	3,511,000	664
Wales	151,200	37,000	not available	not available
Northern Ireland	50,360	19,100	91,900	222
Scotland	95,000	13,000	109,500	899
Percent of dwellings				
England	7.6	1.0	17.8	
Wales	13.4	3.3	not available	
Northern Ireland	8.8	3.3	15.9	
Scotland	4.7	0.6	5.4	

Sources: Department of the Environment (1993); Welsh Office (1994); Northern Ireland Housing Executive (1993); Scottish Homes (1993); EHCS 1991 special tabulation; SHCS 1991 special tabulation.

Notes: 1. Figures for England, Scotland and Northern Ireland are for 1991; figures for Wales are for 1993. Figures for unfitness in Wales are not comparable because they relate to the pre-1989 standard.

2. Figures for Scotland are for dwellings below the tolerable standard, which differs from the fitness standard in various ways, particularly by the exclusion of disrepair.

3. Figures for Wales relate to households, not dwellings.

Wales, £1.6 billion in Scotland, and £0.8 billion in Northern Ireland (Mackintosh and Leather, 1993), a total of almost £12 billion.

But such levels of expenditure are now a thing of the past. While the number of grants provided in England exceeded 200,000 per annum at its peak in 1982–84, the level of activity subsequently fell back to less than 100,000, and dropped even more dramatically after the introduction of the new grant system in 1990. Only 22,000 renovation grants were provided in England and Wales in 1991, and 44,000 in 1992, compared with 114,000 improvement, intermediate or repair grants under the previous system in 1990. At this rate, it will take more than 30 years simply to deal with the backlog of properties identified as unfit in 1991.

Despite its scale, the programme of capital grants to home owners has never been fully evaluated. The main emphasis has been on the effectiveness of area-based renewal through housing action areas (HAAs) or general improvement areas (GIAs) but these initiatives have only accounted for a small proportion of the programme. A recent study by the authors, funded by the Joseph Rowntree Foundation, examined the effectiveness of grant policy, and concluded that there were a number of criticisms which could be levelled (Leather and Mackintosh, 1994a). The main conclusions of the study are discussed in the following section.

The effectiveness of grants

Firstly, the durability of the work which was carried out with grant aid is open to question. It was intended that much of the work would last for 30 years but studies have shown that this was often not the case. One problem was the lack of supervision of the quality of work carried out. The local authorities which administered grant aid were given few powers to ensure that work was carried out properly by competent builders. In most cases, building work was only inspected on completion or when interim payments were required. Local authorities lacked powers to require work to be uncovered to check what had been done, and there is ample anecdotal evidence of poor workmanship and fraudulent practices.

Limitations on the type of work eligible for grant aid also prevented long-lasting solutions in some cases. The initial emphasis of grants was on the provision of amenities. Awareness of the need to deal with disrepair problems did not emerge until the 1980s. Many properties which were provided with amenities during the 1970s remained in a state of considerable disrepair despite the provision of grant aid. On top of this, the limits on the costs of work eligible for grant were not regularly updated to keep pace with building costs so many authorities were forced to cut standards or to omit important items of work if jobs were to go ahead at all. There were not enough resources for the achievement of long-term solutions, and in our view never could be.

Benko (1991) has described experimental arrangements in the Netherlands to require renovation grant recipients to enter into a maintenance agreement but there are no such arrangements in the UK. Local authorities have never had powers to compel grant recipients to undertake any ongoing maintenance of their houses after work was completed, despite the obvious benefits in terms of protecting public investment. In most cases, authorities made little effort even to stimulate voluntary maintenance. Most have regarded subsequent maintenance as being outside their influence. However, there have been some exceptions and interest in such approaches has grown in recent years (Leather and Mackintosh, 1994b). In Birmingham, a network of area caretakers was set up in the 1980s. Their duties included carrying out minor jobs in areas which had been subject to improvement activity. Rochdale, Leicester and a few other local authorities developed local maintenance initiatives, and other authorities prepared booklets for distribution to owners. But these activities were the exception. Not surprisingly, studies of grant policy have shown that second or third grants are being provided for a substantial proportion of properties already improved with grant aid in the past.

Finally, it can be argued that grant policy over the whole post-war period following the introduction of the first grants in 1949 was in itself a deterrent to maintenance investment. The main emphasis of grant provision prior to 1969 was on assistance with the *provision of basic amenities* in properties which had been built without them. *Repair* work was regarded as the responsibility of owners. In 1969, the scope of eligible improvement work was expanded in order to achieve higher standards and a longer life span for improved properties. Although a limited proportion of grant aid could be directed towards associated repair work, the main emphasis remained on improvements. In 1974, it was recognised that low income households could not be expected to meet the often substantial costs of repair in poor condition older houses, so a new repair grant was introduced, although its use did not become widespread until after 1980. By the mid-1980s, authorities such as Birmingham had concluded from their own experience and from the work of housing associations in renovating pre-1919 properties that repairs and improvements to individual properties were more expensive and less effective than the simultaneous renovation of whole blocks. It also became clear that comprehensive repairs to the external envelope of the dwelling were the key to an extended dwelling life. Although this evolution of grant aid was reasonable and perhaps inevitable, it may have encouraged even those owners who could afford to invest, to neglect their properties, as in the long term there was a good chance that grant aid from the state would be forthcoming.

The pattern of grant provision

There were also problems with the targeting of grants. From 1969 onwards, area improvement was a key component of policy, with the aim of stimulating or levering in private investment to build on that made available through grants. But more than 80% of grants went to properties located outside such areas. Only 17% of properties in the worst condition and 12% of properties in unsatisfactory condition in 1981 were included in area-based programmes between 1981 and 1986. Furthermore, the 1986 English house condition survey (Department of the Environment, 1988) showed some disappointing results relating to scattered grant investment over the 1981–86 period. The lack of improvement in conditions occurred because much grant aid had not been directed towards the worst properties. Some 30% of the grants provided had gone to dwellings which in 1981 were found to be in satisfactory condition. Only 14% of grants went to properties which were unfit and in serious disrepair.

It is also clear that improvement grant investment was only a minor element of total expenditure by households on repair and improvement activity, despite the scale of provision. The 1986 English house condition survey revealed that some £13.6 billion was spent by owner occupiers and private landlords on the repair and improvement of dwellings in 1986, of which only about £0.4 billion (3%) was accounted for by grants (Department of the Environment, 1988). Some 59% of this investment was on less essential work such as internal decorations, extensions, central heating, double glazing and porches. But even if this expenditure, much of which is carried out by more affluent owners who are already living in satisfactory conditions, is deducted, the proportion of investment accounted for by grant aid only increases to 7% of the remaining £5.8 billion. It is individual investment decisions made by private owners which determine the overwhelming majority of expenditure on the repair, improvement and maintenance of the older housing stock and hence its overall condition, rather than public investment policies. Changes in housing conditions result from increasing or decreasing investment levels relative to rates of decay and obsolescence. In periods of boom, such as the late 1980s, it is likely that the overall condition of the housing stock improved, as individuals borrowed more or invested their savings or income in building work, encouraged by rising incomes, low interest rates and rising house prices. During the current recession, it is more likely that the level of investment has declined, with the investment decisions of many home owners influenced by the problems some households have experienced with mortgage payments, and by the problem of negative equity where falling house prices have led many recent purchasers to have a mortgage for more than their house is worth.

The uneven spatial pattern of improvement grant investment at local level means that there are some exceptions to this pattern. In a few cities such as Glasgow, Belfast, Birmingham, and Leicester, higher levels of public investment and successful area improvement programmes made the impact of grant activity much greater than in areas where investment was more scattered. But this impact was confined to a small number of cities and often to relatively small areas within those cities. The scope for intensive area renewal was also reduced because of the way in which grant resources were allocated – or rather not allocated – to individual local authorities. Although larger towns and cities have spent more on the provision of improvement than smaller districts, they have generally been unable to achieve as much in terms of relative indicators such as the provision of grants per 100 pre-1919 private sector dwellings. In part this arose as a result of policy decisions by many urban authorities to spend housing capital resources on other activities such as public sector renovation. But the main cause has been the government's capital expenditure allocation policy (including the arrangements for the use of capital receipts) which has rarely isolated an overall sum for investment in the private housing stock and allocated that sum directly to this programme on the basis of need. If this had been done, area improvement programmes in towns and cities might have been better funded and more effective.

In overall terms, it can be concluded that while a great deal of improvement has been achieved through the grant system, much effort has also been wasted through the absence of targeting on those most in need, the failure of government to concentrate resources in the worst areas, and a lack of powers for local authorities to ensure that the work funded by grants was properly carried out. Housing renewal policy in many areas of pre-1919 housing is now based on an entrenched expectation by owners and practitioners that grants will continue to be available. Yet there is little prospect that adequate levels of public resources will be forthcoming.

The new grant system

The main aim of the new grant system introduced in 1990 was to target grant expenditure more effectively on unfit properties and low income households. The mechanism for achieving this aim was a means test to determine eligibility for grant. At the same time, the government decided to make grant aid available as of right for any work required to make dwellings meet the revised standard of fitness, provided that the owner was eligible on income grounds. A fuller description can be found elsewhere (Mackintosh and Leather, 1992a). But this apparently open-ended commitment was modified by the retention of a strict system of overall control on local authority capital expenditure which, by a combination of restrictions and penalties, ensured that the overall level of grant activity was limited.

The crisis

As we have suggested, by mid 1993 the new system was already heading towards serious problems. There were concerns in many areas that the demand for mandatory grant aid would soon outstrip the available resources. This was officially recognised late in 1992, when the government announced the second review. The rate of progress with grant investment was far too slow to make any rapid impact on existing house condition problems, let alone those arising as a result of the ongoing deterioration of the housing stock. In addition the average amount of grant provided rose very sharply. In 1990, the average grant under the old system was approximately £3,500. By the second quarter of 1992, average mandatory renovation grants paid under the new grant system had reached £9,900 in

England and £16,000 in Wales, representing increases of 283% and 478%. Although some of this increase is accounted for by the fact that 100% grants are now being paid, it is also likely that the amount of work being done per property has increased substantially and that more comprehensive solutions (renewing rather than repairing or patching) are being undertaken. It is most unlikely that this is what the government intended. As an interim measure, maximum mandatory grant levels of £50,000, and subsequently £20,000 (£24,000 in Wales) were introduced to try to limit expenditure. What has emerged is a new system which provides a much higher level of support for a greatly reduced number of households with no help at all in prospect for the remainder. Unless more resources are forthcoming, it seems unlikely that the present approach can be sustained.

The pressure on limited resources was compounded by the increasing demand for the new disabled facilities grant, which comes from the same budget. In the second quarter of 1992 these made up 35% of the total number of grants given (excluding minor works grants) and 16% of total grant expenditure. These grants are an essential part of policies to encourage care in the community and demand is likely to gather momentum as rates of home ownership increase amongst older and disabled people and more of these groups remain living at home. The demand for mandatory grants also limited the extent to which discretionary grants such as minor works assistance could be provided. These grants allow older people on means-tested benefits to carry out small repairs and adaptations to improve the safety and comfort of their homes. Such grants are especially useful to enable someone to return home from hospital or to prevent a move into institutional care.

The options

But what are the options for the review? There is little room for manoeuvre. The first option is to provide more funding to enable local authorities to meet a higher proportion of the demand for grants. In 1991/92 local authorities in England spent only £335 million, compared with £840 million in 1985/86 (at 1991/92 prices) and £1.7 billion in 1983/84. A programme of 90,000 renovation grants a year (twice the current level but still representing only 7% of the 1.5 million unfit properties in England in 1991) at an average cost of £10,000 per grant would require public expenditure of well in excess of £1 billion per annum, if other types of grant are also allowed for.

Elsewhere we have attempted to estimate the cost of remedying the backlog of poor housing conditions, using cost estimates from the national house condition surveys (Leather, Mackintosh and Rolfe, 1995). These estimates suggest that the total cost of dealing with the current backlog of disrepair in the UK housing stock is at least £54 billion, of which 83% relates to owner occupied and privately rented housing. These figures represent the minimum sum needed to deal with identified disrepair problems and in practice, the actual costs of work are likely to be higher, perhaps as much as £80 billion. As we have argued above, most investment is undertaken with private funds, but much private investment is cosmetic rather than essential. Even if only half of the investment needed to deal with disrepair comes from public funds, it will take many decades simply to deal with the backlog of problems in the private sector at current rates of progress, to say nothing of future deterioration.

Clearly, these figures bear no relation to current levels of provision. Indeed, public expenditure plans show a *decrease* in the government's contribution to the costs of private sector renovation, as Table 2 shows (Department of the Environment, 1995). For 1993/94, there was a reduction in the amount of specified capital grant (SCG) available although this was portrayed as an increase in resources. This feat was achieved by lowering the rate of SCG provided by the government from 75% to 60% of local authority expenditure. To enable them to find the extra resources, local authorities were given permission to reinvest a higher proportion of capital receipts for a limited period. The table also makes it clear that further cuts in the rate at which SCG is paid will be necessary in 1994/95 simply to keep expenditure at its planned 1992/93 level.

Table 2   Public expenditure on renovation grants (£ million)

	91/92 outturn	92/93 outturn	93/94 outturn	94/95 estimate	95/96 plans	96/97 plans
			£ million			
Specified capital grant for renovation of private housing						
	251.7	335.3	324.4	225.8	219.2	222.6
Amount available for grants assuming subsidy of:						
75%	335.6	447.1	432.5	301.1	286.8	290.5
60%			540.8	376.3	358.5	363.2
50%				451.6	430.2	435.8
33%				684.2	651.8	660.3

Source: Department of the Environment, 1995

Most authorities are already under severe pressure on both the capital and revenue sides and a major boost to grant expenditure borne to such an extent from their own resources is unlikely to materialise. At the end of the 1980s the government was providing subsidy at an effective rate of about 95% on grant spending. Nor do broader prospects look very promising. With the continuing likelihood of a large public sector borrowing requirement, demographic and economic pressures pushing up spending on social security, pensions and health provision, and no signs of a government-led investment boom to revive the economy, it would be very optimistic indeed to expect much priority to be given to the renovation grant programme despite the extent of need revealed by the national house condition surveys.

A second option is to modify or abolish the right to a grant when a property is found to be unfit. It might also be necessary to remove the parallel right to a disabled facilities grant. This would not only require new legislation but would also represent a very obvious abandonment of the government's commitment to dealing with poor housing conditions. Some practitioners have, controversially, suggested a partial relaxation of the right to a grant in areas where local authorities can demonstrate that they have a coherent strategy for dealing with older housing. But this would be very difficult to define and could provide the government with an easy way of shifting the blame for the loss of entitlement to a renovation grant on to those local authorities which declared that they had a renewal strategy. The removal of the mandatory right to a disabled facilities grant would also be in conflict with the expressed aim of increasing care in the community. However, recent press speculation suggests that this may be the government's preferred option.

The third option is for the government to require local authorities to take a narrower view of the fitness standard. This would enable the cost of making a dwelling fit to be substantially reduced, and spread resources more thinly across a far greater number of properties. There is a limit to how far this could be taken, and it is certainly a measure which would meet with almost unanimous opposition from those involved in the provision of grants. But a reduction of average grants to 1990 levels would enable the number of grants to be trebled and thus make it unnecessary to take the politically embarrassing step of abolishing existing rights to grant aid. The disadvantage would be that the long-term impact of grant investment on the housing stock would be greatly reduced. But in all probability the government no longer sees itself as being in the business of long-term investment in private housing anyway.

Low income home ownership

For many people on low incomes living in poor condition properties grant aid is realistically the only source of funds for necessary repairs so a system of grant aid will continue to be required if they are to remain living in reasonable housing conditions in the owner occupied sector. But the review also provides an opportunity to re-examine the broader question of what housing renewal policies are trying to achieve. To do this, we need to understand how radically housing circumstances have changed since rehabilitation policies began in earnest in the late 1960s. The key factor is that the ownership and ultimate responsibility for the repair, improvement and maintenance of almost three-quarters of the housing stock now lie with individuals. For many, perhaps even most, households, repair and maintenance work is not a problem. Those in stable and well-paid employment, those living in newer or newly renovated houses which do not require much investment, and those who can easily move on when conditions start to deteriorate are in the best position.

But there are many for whom investment in housing renewal is more problematic and their numbers are increasing. The growth in the number of old people who enter their later retirement years as home owners has been charted elsewhere (Rolfe, Mackintosh and Leather, 1993). While many people can afford to keep their houses in good condition while they are still in employment, the reduction in income which they experience in retirement makes this much more difficult, often at a time when their dependence upon paid contractors rather than DIY becomes much greater with increasing frailty. Few older people have savings levels which are adequate to provide for long term repair and maintenance costs (Hancock and Weir, 1994) and there is no tradition of investing in long term insurance for such purposes. In the past, shorter life expectancies and moves into residential care might have ensured that houses neglected by older people were sold on for renovation by younger people, but increasing longevity and the impact of community care policies make this less likely.

Other groups likely to experience problems include single parents, especially women, who have been left in owner occupation by relationship breakdown but who are heavily dependent upon income support to meet mortgage costs. The income support system does little to help such households to meet these needs.

The high overall level of home ownership means that most people who become disabled are likely to be owners with responsibility not only for repairing but perhaps also for adapting their houses at a time when incomes are likely to have fallen. Somewhere between a million and a million and a half households have negative equity, and recent work has confirmed the likelihood that this reduces the willingness of those affected to invest in their properties (Forrest, *et al.* 1994). Last, and perhaps numerically most significant, are those who become unemployed, those who are in unstable short-term employment, and those who are in part-time work. Most analyses of future economic prospects in the UK foresee an increase in these types of employment (see for example Ford and Wilcox, 1994). The implications for home ownership of what has been euphemistically labelled the 'flexible housing market' are only just being explored (Maclennan, 1994). Although the main emphasis has been on the problems of mortgage arrears, the longer term implications for repair and maintenance investment are bound to be serious. This evidence points clearly to a growth in the number of home owners who will experience difficulties in keeping their houses in good condition in the future. Few will be mobile, undermining the processes of ownership transfer and renewal investment which have underlain much investment by individual households in the past.

But if it is unrealistic to expect private investment and the normal operation of the housing market to cope with problems of disrepair, and if public spending at the required level is unlikely to materialise, what can be done? It is difficult to be optimistic, but there are some ways forward. The remainder of this chapter discusses the options.

There are two overall elements to public policy in relation to privately owned housing in poor condition which could have an impact on poor housing conditions. The first would be to ensure that the public sector resources which are available are spent in the best way, the way which draws in most private finance, and the way which achieves the greatest impact on the poorest housing conditions. This may mean challenging the view that capital grants, and the present system in particular, are a cost-effective way of using the available resources. The second element of a new renewal policy would be to persuade private owners to nvest more of their own resources in repair, improvement and maintenance, and to ensure that the money they spend is used in ways which have the maximum long-term impact on poor housing conditions. With limited public resources available, it is essential that policies to attract private investment should be more effective than the present, largely token, efforts. This may involve far more intervention in the housing market than under the present system.

Stimulating private investment

There is a variety of ways in which home owners could be persuaded to increase the amount which they invest in the repair of their houses to maximise the long-term impact of this investment on poor housing conditions. In the past housing renewal policy has attempted to focus on older housing in the poorest condition, but a key objective of policy in future should be to adopt a more preventative approach by developing measures which also focus on properties in better condition. There are various measures to stimulate private investment.

Borrowing

As we have shown, private owners fund the bulk of investment in repair, improvement and maintenance from their own resources. Income and savings are the main sources of funding for this work. But if owners are to be persuaded to undertake more substantial amounts of investment, or if those on low incomes, who do not have any savings, are to undertake work, it is essential to develop mechanisms which enable owners to afford to borrow, using the equity tied up in their houses as security. Few houses have repair costs so great that there is no potential to borrow against the value of the property. Such mechanisms could include the following:

- The reintroduction of mortgage interest tax relief (MITR) on loans for certain types of repair, improvement and maintenance. To avoid abuse, lenders could be required to inspect completed work.
- The extension of proposals for a system of mortgage benefit payments to low income households to cover loans for repair, improvement and maintenance.
- Households could be allowed to set expenditure on repair, improvement and maintenance against tax liabilities, including inheritance tax.

But many households do not borrow to carry out repairs because they cannot afford to do so. New mechanisms are therefore needed to reduce or defer the repayment cost of loans.

- Equity-sharing loans, like those proposed by the government in its 1985 Green Paper on housing renewal policy but subsequently dropped, have great potential (Cmnd 9513, 1985). In lieu of repayments, households would assign a share of the value of their house to a lender, probably a local authority. Providing support for a scheme of this kind (and meeting the inevitable losses) could be an alternative use for some of the public sector resources currently used for grants.
- Rolled up interest loans, on which repayments of both capital and interest are deferred, may have some potential in paying for smaller jobs. This is mainly an option for older people as the size of the overall debt can increase rapidly after a few years.
- Department of Social Security help with interest payments on maturity loans for building work for older people on income support could potentially be used more extensively, provided that the practical difficulties in obtaining it, and the general reluctance of older people to borrow, could be overcome.
- Fixed rate or subsidised interest rate loans supported either by public subsidies or from 'ethical' lending sources (where capital is provided by charities or individuals which are willing to accept a lower than market rate of return) could be utilised.

Below market interest rate loans have been used extensively in the USA for the rehabilitation of owner occupied housing. Federal Community Development Block Grant funds can be used for this purpose, and some states have also provided revolving funds to be loaned at low interest rates to encourage home repairs. In some cases, loan repayments can be postponed until a property changes ownership. Similarly, low income home owners in Canada are eligible for subsidised loans to upgrade substandard dwellings through the Residential

Rehabilitation Assistance Programme. Home owners in the US can also, in some circumstances, deduct the interest on home improvement loans from federal income taxes.

The problem is to persuade a reluctant government to intervene to boost the limited demand for renovation loans from low income households. Mortgage interest tax relief on house purchase loans is being progressively withdrawn and it is unlikely that it will be re-introduced for renovation purposes. Proposals for mortgage benefit have also been firmly resisted. The Treasury is seeking to restrict rather than to increase the provision of assistance with loan interest payments to those on income support.

The financial institutions have also failed to take a positive view of lending for renovation purposes, preferring to argue that as long as loans are adequately secured, dwelling conditions are beyond their legitimate area of interest. Yet it could be argued that the overall condition of the dwelling stock is a matter of central concern to lenders, especially when disrepair reaches a scale where whole neighbourhoods begin to decline. One small building society, the Marsden, which operates in and around Pendle in Lancashire, is attempting to take a more active role in housing renewal within the local community. As well as providing financial support to a home improvement agency which it runs as a subsidiary and lending actively to housing associations for renewal or redevelopment projects, the society also acquires vacant properties in the area, renovates them, and sells them on to local buyers with mortgage finance if required. The same society is also active in lending small sums to older people for repairs and improvements, despite the commercial unattractiveness of this type of business in isolation. Detailed knowledge of local housing markets, commitment to the local community, and good relationships with local authorities and other organisations make this approach feasible. But even those societies which no longer have any strong local community base could do far more to encourage and facilitate housing renewal. Interest rates on top-up loans for renovation, for example, are often higher than basic rates, whereas it can be argued that there is a case for lower rates to stimulate essential repair work. There are a number of other ways in which mortgage lenders could contribute more actively to housing renewal policies which are discussed further below.

The demand side problems associated with persuading individuals on low incomes to borrow should also be recognised. Those houses in the poorest condition are generally those where there is the least borrowing potential. Likewise, older people, who often have the most potential to borrow because they have paid off their mortgages, may be the most resistant to doing so. Younger people, who might be willing to take on loans, may be too heavily indebted as a result of house purchase costs. But we believe that, in the longer term, it is inevitable that more people will be forced to turn to borrowing to meet the costs of building work. So long as they can afford to do so, it is better that they should use their accumulated housing wealth in this way rather than saving it to pass on to their heirs.

Insurance or savings schemes

A number of commercial mechanisms have recently been introduced to enable people to insure themselves against the need for future repair and maintenance work, or to save in order to cover these costs. This might be an alternative to borrowing. Such schemes fall into three main categories:

- Comprehensive insurance schemes provide a package of services including an annual survey, internal and external maintenance cover, an emergency repairs service, defects insurance, and security measures for which participants pay an annual fee. Take up of such schemes so far is extremely limited. The initial costs of bringing properties into a good state of repair and the high premiums are a major disincentive.
- Emergency repair services provide cover for a limited range of repairs to items such as central heating, plumbing, drains, roof, locks, windows, and gas or electricity supply on an annual or monthly subscription basis. The costs are much less than those of more comprehensive schemes and take up is greater. Some schemes are operated on a national basis by companies mainly providing car breakdown services. The technology associated with such services and the experience in providing and managing a large network of garages can readily be applied to the operation of an emergency house repair service using a network of vetted builders. At least one major DIY chain is also promoting such a service. More basic services at lower cost which provide only the name of a reliable builder are also being marketed.
- Mechanisms for saving to meet repair costs could also be established. In the mid 1980s a national building society examined the feasibility of an unsecured budget-type savings account (with the facility to overdraw) specifically to cover the costs of building work. Savers were also entitled to free technical advice, an emergency service, and access to a list of recommended builders. On the basis of market research the scheme was not launched, but there is potential for the introduction of such savings accounts particularly if government contributions were available as an inducement.

The take up of emergency repair services has demonstrated that there is a demand for such schemes, but there is little evidence of widespread public interest in more comprehensive maintenance schemes at the present time. In the long term, insurance-based schemes are more likely to appeal to more affluent house-holds than to those on low incomes who could not afford to save or to pay premiums, unless help with the costs is available from the Department of Social Security. As assistance with rent through housing benefit includes provision for repair and maintenance costs, it could be argued that low income home owners should also be provided with help in meeting these costs.

Maintenance funds

A more radical approach would be the establishment of compulsory sinking funds for all privately owned houses to ensure that resources would be available for all necessary building work. A fund, managed by building societies, surveying prac-tices, or local authorities, could be established for each privately owned property when it was next sold. The size of the fund would be set at a level necessary to cover the estimated cost of all work needed over a specified period falling into certain pre-defined categories. These would include essential repairs to ensure that the building was wind and weather proof and structurally stable; work required to meet the fitness standard; and work needed to bring the property up to a specified energy rating. The fund could also be used for work to ensure that older and disabled people are able to remain living independently in comfort and safety in their own homes. We have proposed such a standard of fitness for community care elsewhere (Mackintosh and Leather, 1992b).

The money to establish the fund could come from the seller in the form of a deduction from the proceeds received on the sale of the house. This would act as an incentive to owners to keep their properties in good repair. At the point of each subsequent sale a new estimate would be made of the amount of resources needed to replenish the fund.

A great deal more work is required to develop an option of this kind. This approach is far more interventionist than any existing controls over the rights and duties of private owners, but in the long run it may the only way to ensure that the right type of work is carried out and that the resources are available to meet the costs. Effectively this solution would prevent equity leakage and ensure that money from the sale of properties was reinvested in the repair, improvement and maintenance of the housing stock.

Changes to the housing market, the building regulations, and lending requirements

There are also more long-term changes to the operation of the housing market, the building and planning regulations and the requirements imposed by mortgage lenders which could encourage or require owners to pay more attention to the condition of their houses. The primary need is to increase awareness of future repair and maintenance costs and to enable buyers to negotiate price reductions on this basis. If those buying poor condition properties paid less for them, they would be able to invest more resources in essential repair work. Greater awareness on the part of buyers would also persuade existing owners that it was not worthwhile to neglect repairs. Possible measures include:

- making vendors responsible for latent property defects for a period of time after the sale of the dwelling;
- requiring vendors to provide an independent survey report for the information of buyers;
- extending the coverage of the building regulations to deal with more repair work, and enforcing the regulations more strictly, for example by requiring vendors to produce certificates of compliance at the point of sale;
- requiring all work of specified kinds such as electrical work or gas installation to be carried out by qualified contractors; again this would need to be enforced through the production of certificates at the point of sale;
- persuading mortgage lenders to be more active in raising awareness of potential house condition problems when they are approached to provide loan finance;
- persuading lenders to be more demanding about house conditions when they agree to lend;
- encouraging the establishment and use of warranties or guarantees covering a much wider range of building work, to ensure that home owners are able to get redress for poor workmanship.

Education, information, advice, and practical help to owners

Surveys have shown that there is a substantial lack of awareness of the need for repair, improvement and maintenance investment (see for example Department of the Environment, 1988). There has been some limited progress in recent years in overcoming these problems. A few local authorities have distributed information booklets. In Leicester, the city council has gone further and appointed urban management officers and home maintenance advisers to carry out surveys and provide technical advice, financial advice and access to a list of competent builders in the City's former Housing Action Areas (Leather and Mackintosh, 1994b). The United Kingdom also has a well-established network of home improvement agencies which provide help with the diagnosis of house condition problems, finding reliable builders, organising the finance to pay for work, and supervising the work on site.

But to raise awareness of house condition problems and to encourage more effective repair, improvement and maintenance behaviour a number of other measures are also desirable:

- regular campaigns to educate home owners on both house condition problems and solutions;
- support from government and the private sector for adult education courses on repair and maintenance strategies and techniques;
- free or low priced surveys to advise home owners on what work is required over a specified period;
- extension of the existing home improvement agency network to give comprehensive national coverage.

Past experience suggests that the private sector will not contribute substantial sums to the provision of such services and it is likely that the main burden of funding will fall on central and local government.

Reform of the building industry

The sector of the building industry which deals with small scale repair and maintenance work also poses many problems for those seeking to carry out repairs or improvements. This sector generally has a poor reputation and the fear of experiencing problems can deter home owners from carrying out work. Older people are especially vulnerable to exploitation. If people are to be encouraged to undertake more work to their homes the following reforms are necessary:

- People need to be able to find reliable builders and trades people and to have guarantees that the work carried out will be of a reasonable standard. This requires government involvement in the promotion and backing of guarantee schemes and proper vetting of builders who offer them.
- 'Cowboy' builders should not be able to undercut reputable builders in price terms. Stricter enforcement of health and safety standards and the requirement that only qualified contractors can carry out certain types of work would help to prevent this.

- The government should provide practical support for builders in setting up and running businesses, together with encouragement and financial support for building industry training schemes.

Strategies for public sector investment

The policies described above would aim to increase the amount of private investment in repair, improvement and maintenance. If this occurred, the role of public investment could change significantly in the future. Public expenditure could aim to lever in private investment wherever possible. Grant aid, or other new forms of direct public support, could then be targeted on those cases where there was no real potential for private investment. To take account of local variations, housing authorities could be given powers to provide assistance to home owners with repair, improvement and maintenance in the form which most suited their local needs. Government preferences and priorities could be expressed through decisions on the level of financial resources to be provided to support local initiatives.

We have already discussed several of the most promising options for making more effective use of limited public sector resources. Instead of providing capital grants for renovation, local authorities could provide grant aid towards interest payments in cases where loans had been taken out to cover work required to bring houses up to a minimum standard. The amount of assistance could be linked to an applicant's resources in a similar way to the present grant system. The disadvantage of this approach is that the owner would need to submit to a periodic test of resources. But this could also be seen as an advantage as the amount of help provided could be tailored to reflect changes in the owner's circumstances. The chief advantage, however, is that the amount of work which could be funded from public resources would be much higher than under the present system of capital grants. The precise amount would be dependent on interest rates, loan repayment rates, the average level of support required, and the amount borrowed by home owners, but even under fairly conservative assumptions it could be some two to three times as great as the annual cost to the public sector. A mixture of this approach and the current grant system could provide a limited capital grant together with assistance with loan charges to pay the remaining costs.

A further alternative would be the provision of equity-sharing loans. This would not lead to any increase in the amount of work funded in the short term. But in the longer term, when loans begin to be repaid, there is the potential for recycling receipts to increase the volume of lending. However, it is quite likely that losses would accrue on many properties in poorer condition. If commercial lenders could be persuaded to become involved in equity-sharing loans on older houses, this would also increase the resources available, but it seems unlikely that there would be much interest in this option.

A more radical approach would be to earmark some public resources for particular purposes, for example by limiting grant aid to designated renewal areas, or to other areas designated as priorities within a broader renewal strategy. Resources could also be concentrated on clearance and site preparation in particular areas where the condition of the stock made this the most sensible option.

Conclusions

We have argued in this chapter that the housing renewal policies pursued over the last two decades have in many ways proved unsuccessful and short-term in impact, and that the current set of policies is unsustainable in the present economic climate because of the shortfall of resources in relation to need. We have examined a range of measures which could produce investment both to bring houses up to a reasonable standard and to enable them to remain in good condition. This includes not only repair and improvement but also regular maintenance. The key step in developing sustainable housing renewal policies is to accept that housing decay and disrepair are ongoing processes and that policies to tackle them must produce long-term and affordable solutions.

In the private sector, with which this chapter is concerned, the key problem is that many of those who own, or who are buying, houses simply cannot afford to keep them in good repair. The most significant step to improve their ability to do so would be to increase the sensitivity of house prices to repair costs. If this could be achieved, houses which were more expensive to repair or to maintain would fall in price relative to other dwellings, as people became more aware of the true costs of ownership.

Making owners more aware of the need to prepare to meet repair, improvement and maintenance costs, would change attitudes to borrowing, saving, and other forms of preparation such as insurance schemes. It would become as important to plan to meet housing repair costs in old age as to obtain an adequate pension. Houses would come to be seen as liabilities as well as assets. Owners would be persuaded to see housing equity as a resource for repair and improvement work rather than as a source of wealth to be utilised for consumption purposes or passed on through inheritance. First time buyers would be less willing to pay high prices for houses in poor condition or less able to find lenders to assist them to do so. In inner city areas, there would be a relative decline in purchase prices, releasing money to be used for repair, improvement and maintenance. Many more people would see owning as less desirable than renting.

The problem with such proposals is that they represent a substantial increase in the level of control over or interference in the operation of the housing market, and are certainly unlikely to appeal to a government which has placed great emphasis on the removal of controls. The backlog of disrepair clearly indicates that the market currently fails to facilitate an adequate level of investment in many privately owned properties. Effectively the state currently meets the costs associated with this market failure in a number of ways. The most immediate stems from the impact of poor or dangerous housing conditions on health (Leather, Mackintosh and Rolfe, 1994). Although these costs have not yet been effectively quantified, they are likely to be substantial. With older people far more likely than most other groups to live in poor condition housing, the additional costs of unnecessary residential care for those forced to move by poor housing conditions should also be taken into account. Although declined, the costs of renovation grants themselves remain substantial. Finally, it is important to take into account the potentially large sums required for the acquisition and clearance of those properties which decay beyond economic repair. Unless the state abandons responsibility for dealing with these problems, there will always be broader and longer term costs associated with the neglect of the older housing stock. Seen in this context, the case for controls on the operation of the housing market becomes more attractive.

Many, although not all, of these proposals are a long way from implementation and some may prove to be impractical. The aim of this chapter has been to stimulate debate rather than to provide solutions. But sooner rather than later, there will be a need for a fundamental rethink of renewal policy in which these, or similar initiatives, will play a crucial part. Low-income home owners – older people, single parents, disabled people, the unemployed, those in short term and low paid jobs – cannot readily afford to repair and maintain their houses, and if nothing else this imposes costs on society as a whole which are not easily ignored. Unless we find measures which make it easier for the vast majority of owners who are never likely to receive grant aid to afford to invest in their houses, the prospects of decent housing for those on low incomes are bleak indeed.

CHAPTER 10

Standards, Quality Control and House Building in the UK

BARRY GOODCHILD AND VALERIE KARN

What is the relation between housing quality and sustainability, defined as the achievement of a standard and type of development that will prove durable and popular for the long term and will also minimise any possible impact on the natural environment? Is housing quality always consistent with broader concepts of sustainability? What standards are appropriate for social and private house building? How might quality be promoted and enhanced in each sector? Such are the questions asked in this chapter.

The quality and design of new housing can be examined in two overlapping and complementary ways. It can be examined either in terms of existing and possible rules and regulations or in terms of the development processes and the factors that determine the output of house builders in the private and social sectors. The former approach has the advantage of focusing on the main policy issues, but is essentially static. The latter enables an appreciation of changes in the practices of the main institutional actors, but it begs the question of how public policy should respond. The former is normative and prescriptive. The latter is more descriptive and largely involves the analysis of trends.

The present account comprises a mixture of trend and normative analyses. The account starts with an analysis of recent trends. How have private house building firms adapted to changing patterns of consumer demand in the 1980s and 1990s? How, in the 1980s and 1990s, have the providers of social housing sought to increase the efficiency of production? The account goes on to provide a normative analysis and asks what standards are appropriate both in the light of recent trends and in relation to concepts of 'sustainability' and sustainable development. Sustainability is currently a key concept in discussions of the built environment. However, it is also a very broad concept and requires clarification. The emphasis throughout is on the quality of housing design, as measured by such factors as size, floorplan and amenity standards, rather than either the build quality of the dwellings or their locational and environmental quality.

Trends in private house building

The private house building industry has long been subject to periodic fluctuations in which periods of growth are followed by decline, sometimes sharp and sudden decline. Indeed, a cycle of growth and decline may be inevitable, given the usual dependence of house purchase on long term borrowing and the consequent sensitivity of the market to the level of interest rates. Nevertheless, the character of the building cycles in the 1980s and early 1990s has been distinctive. The periods of decline have been more profound than at any period since private house building restarted after the Second World War. Moreover, the peak of demand in the boom years of the late 1980s was lower than in previous peaks in the 1960s and early 1970s. (See Chart 1, below, derived from successive editions of the *Housing and Construction Statistics*.)

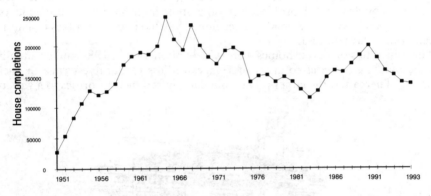

Chart 1   Private house building in Britain, 1951–93

The result, from the viewpoint of the industry, has been a greater volatility of demand and a shorter time-scale in building programmes (Lyall, 1983). The turning point was the depression in house building in the early 1980s. Developers realised that they had to offer new incentives to encourage house purchase. They also realised that they had to open up new markets (Rowden, 1981, pp.6–7). Developers did their best to reduce costs through building smaller dwellings at higher densities on less expensive sites. The dwellings built at this time include, in the form of Barratts Studio Solo, the smallest built in England during this century. At the same time, the developers sought to promote sales through a package of incentives such as carpets, washing machines and fitted kitchens included in the sales price; solicitors fees and moving expenses paid; 100% mortgages for those eligible; and part exchange schemes for those who already owned a house. While most of these incentives were made available throughout the range of new houses, it was the first time buyer who was the main target of sales promotion (Goodchild and Furbey, 1986).

At first, in 1982 and 1983, the new package deals created few problems and proved very attractive to first-time purchasers. The packages provided a free agency service to resolve the complexities and delays of house purchase. This was a particularly attractive feature for an inexperienced young person or couple. Moreover, the inclusion of furnishings and fittings within the sales price avoided the burden of heavy hire purchase repayments. House purchasers were, in effect, given the benefit of long term, low interest housing loans (subsidised through MIRAS – mortgage interest relief) on the purchase of modern fittings and equipment.

However, in many areas of the Midlands and North of England starter homes were not the cheapest on the market and, compared with older houses, they were more expensive per square foot of floorspace. In Sheffield, for example, a modernised pre-1919 terrace house, three times the size of a starter home, could be bought for less. Moreover, when the first-time buyers tried to resell their property, they found the value was less than they supposed. Most new houses possess what estate agents sometimes call a new house premium attached to their initial sales price. In the case of starter homes, the premium was enhanced by the special package of incentives that included consumer durables whose value depreciates rapidly. In addition, local estate agents dealing with resales were, and remain, unable to provide the high profile advertising of the large national house builders. As a result, the owner of a small starter home was likely to face a loss or had to accept long delays on resale.

The difficulties of starter homes were widely publicised in 1984 and eventually led the building societies to grant mortgages on less favourable terms for such property. Thereafter, the larger private builders shifted their priorities to a variety

Figure 1 In Sheffield in the 1980s a modernised pre-1919 terraced house could be bought for less than a new 'starter home', a third of the size.

of middle market and upmarket schemes that were less risky and more profitable. Improvements in design and amenities, notably the provision of utility rooms, ground floor toilets and *en suite* bathrooms, coupled with attention to popular external appearance, have enabled such new homes to compete successfully with larger second-hand homes of similar price.

Figures 2 and 3 Improvements to design and amenities coupled with attention to popular external appearance have enabled new homes to compete successfully with larger second-hand homes of a similar price

A variety of key marketing targets for larger private builders may be identified:

- young, single affluent professionals who want easily maintained property, often in the form of flats, close to city centre amenities;
- young childless couples, with a double income who want a small house or flat of sufficient size to enable both partners to maintain a degree of privacy and autonomy;
- families with young children who want a house with a garden in a quiet safe environment;
- older families who possess at least one adolescent child and have sufficient earning power to purchase a larger house in a more attractive area;
- older families whose children are in the process of moving or have moved away and who want a smaller house or bungalow in a more exclusive area;
- retired households who want a bungalow or other form of ground floor accommodation or perhaps purpose-built sheltered accommodation.

Recent changes have, in some ways, favoured the larger developers. The promotion of starter homes in the early 1980s favoured larger firms at first, as these were better able to organise and finance national and regional advertising campaigns. Likewise, the growth of specialist housing markets has tended to favour larger firms as these are generally better equipped to deal with the complexities that arise in the development of new products. For instance, the provision of city centre flats for young single professionals was pioneered by the larger house builders, notably Barratts and Wimpeys. Likewise, the development of private sheltered housing has been dominated by a few specialist firms, for example McCarthy and Stone.

On the other hand, the subsequent failure of starter homes in the mid 1980s damaged the reputation of the larger builders, notably Barratts, whilst the boom in house building in the mid 1980s encouraged new firms to enter the house building industry. Many small and medium sized firms have shown that they can successfully compete with the larger national developers and they still account for the majority of completions in the private sector. The smaller, more local firms are often better informed about the details of site availability and the policies of the local planning authority; they are prepared to build in depressed areas which the larger developers avoid; in addition, they can attempt to counter the advertising and marketing strategies of the larger builders through offering better value for money and lower costs.

The housing market entered a further period of depression in the early 1990s. The fall in sales in the early 1980s encouraged innovation in marketing strategies and the development of new types of starter home. This later depression has again encouraged some developers to include carpets and household appliances in the sales price and to offer other incentives such as free valuations, part-exchange and discounts for quick purchases. This time it has not led to a widespread revival of the smallest types of starter homes, though small dwelling types remain common in the output of local builders in the South of England and in particular Greater London. In the financial year 1991/ 92, nationally 17% of private sector starts with a price of less than £100,000 were bedsitters or one bedroom dwellings, whilst in Greater London the proportion was 57%. However, these were predominantly flats. The building societies are now more reluctant to grant 100% mortgages or to encourage the expansion of owner-occupation to households with low or insecure incomes. As a result, the market for starter homes in the form of very small houses is more limited.

The scope for marketing as a solution to the problems of the house building industry is, in any case, limited. When the basic problem is the market, not the marketing, the private developers can do little, except increase the efficiency of their operation and hope for better days. They have, as we will see, been offered some sort of life-line by building for housing associations, but this represents a relatively small proportion of their output and is itself vulnerable to public expenditure cuts.

Trends in the development of social housing

The development of social rented housing, including both the local authorities and the housing associations, has long been characterised by a greater separation of design and construction than in the private sector. The government and the social housing agencies have generally specified the standards in advance, sometimes in considerable detail through design briefs and, on occasion, the preparation of a catalogue of standard house types. The scheme has then been put out to tender, with the contractor having little or no say in design. The best known standards are those that derive from the Parker Morris Report, published in 1961 and compulsory for all local authority housing in the period from 1967 to 1981. These comprise a matrix of floorspace standards classified by the type of dwellings (for instance, semi-detached, end terrace, flat and bungalow) and expected occupancy. For a five person mid-terrace, for example, the standard is $85m^2$, plus $4.5m^2$ storage.

The typical separation of design from building was criticised in 1978 in a Department of the Environment report *Value for money in local authority house building programmes*, on the grounds that it reduced the 'buildability' and therefore increased the cost of new housing. Three years later, in 1981, the Department of the Environment introduced new project control procedures that encouraged local authorities to search for the most favourable ratio between cost and expected market value in new house building. In other respects, however, the organisation of local authority house building remained largely unchanged throughout the 1980s, although, as a result of new financial constraints by government, output fell dramatically and overall floorspace standards were reduced (GLC, 1986). (See Chart 2, derived from successive editions of the *Housing and Construction Statistics*.)

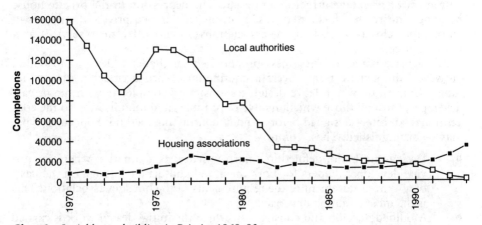

Chart 2   Social house building in Britain, 1969–93

Likewise, up to 1988, development practice in housing associations remained much as before. Eligibility for subsidy was determined by two main considerations. On the one hand, housing associations were required to meet basic design standards laid down by the Housing Corporation (1983) in their *Design and Contract Criteria*, the provisions of which largely reflected the assumptions of good practice in local authority housing design, including the recommendations of Parker Morris. On the other hand, the housing associations had to meet a set of cost norms, classified by the size and height of the dwelling. These varied by region and were updated on a quarterly basis.

The Housing Act 1988 led to more radical change. The Act assumed that housing associations would replace local authorities as the main providers of social housing. It provided the financial framework for a subsequent expansion of housing association new build (Chart 2).

At the same time, the 1988 Act changed the rules under which housing associations finance their operations. Housing associations must now attract an element of private finance to add to a fixed proportion of public subsidy so that 'mixed funding' may go ahead. This 'fixed' proportion has been continually reduced by government since 1988. In addition, housing associations compete with each other for funding approval from the Housing Corporation almost entirely on the basis of the public funding requirement per unit.

The resulting 'blind auction' produces a tendency to bid down costs and standards more than, at face value, the funding arrangements apparently require. In the financial year 1989/ 90, 53% of housing association general needs was built 5% or more below Parker Morris standards (Walentowicz, 1991). By 1991/2, at the time of a study undertaken for the Joseph Rowntree Foundation, the figure had risen to 68%. In addition, in 1991/2, only 9% of housing association properties were built 5% or more above Parker Morris compared with 21% in 1989/90 (Karn and Sheridan, 1994).

Under present financial arrangements, housing associations carry a greater financial risk. The housing association is responsible for any cost over-runs in building. In response, housing associations have used new procurement methods intended to reduce the uncertainty of building contracts through a greater involvement of private contractors in design. The depression in the private house building industry has facilitated this, as it has encouraged private developers to work more closely with housing associations and to offer their services at a reduced price.

The generic name for these new procurement methods is 'design and build'. However, the generic term covers a continuum of procurement methods that ranges from those which leave design responsibility completely with the private developer, through those which involve only a marginal modification to the conventional 'architect-designed before tender' contracting method. Four main types may be distinguished. These comprise:

- Design-and-build, defined in a narrow sense, as a situation where the private developer tenders for both the initial and detailed design on the basis of a written statement of the requirements of the housing association. This is the most common approach.
- Modified develop and construct in which the initial design work is carried out by the housing association, with the remainder undertaken by the contractor after the tender.
- Off-the-shelf schemes in which the housing association buys privately built dwellings after completion, most recently under the Housing Market Initiative.
- Package deals in which, before completion, the housing association is offered the private developers standard dwelling types to be built on land owned by the developer.

For the construction process, there are positive advantages to collaboration between housing associations and private builders. Design and build simplifies the development process with benefits both to the contractor and the housing association as client. This is exactly the argument of the 1978 report *Value for money in local authority house building programmes.* Moreover, for housing associations, the experience is that private sector procurement methods do indeed reduce cost uncertainties in new housing development and that they also have advantages of speed (Olsen, 1991).

For design, the advantages are less clear. Karn and Sheridan (1994) found that the quality of in-house design by housing associations is extremely variable. Collaboration either between different housing associations in local consortia or between housing associations and the private sector may encourage more reflection on the design process and help to reduce the worst examples of poor design. On the other hand, many within housing associations argue that the new procurement methods are leading to a loss of control over the final output and that this, associated with increased financial restrictions, is leading to a loss of quality. The key issue is whether housing associations prepare detailed standards of their requirements and whether, in practice, they keep to these requirements.

The results of the Joseph Rowntree Foundation survey give some, though not unqualified support to the fears of the critics. At the time of the survey, in the financial year 1991/ 92, private sector procurement methods were not as widely used as now. Only about 27% of dwellings were based wholly or in part on private designs. Housing associations that used unmodified private sector designs were the most likely to provide dwellings that fell well below Parker Morris. However, modified private sector designs were little different in their overall space standards from those designed in-house by housing associations.

The new financial regime has had other consequences. It has worked against small housing associations (whether they offer good, imaginative design or not) in favour of larger associations that have the technical resources to manage the risks of housing development and that have sufficient capital resources to retain a land bank and to offer the various sources of private finance more security to cover loans. It has also worked against rehabilitation work whose costs are more difficult to estimate in advance than those of new build. Finally, it has discouraged tenant participation in design, as well as efforts to provide tailor-made housing for specific individuals or communities, as the ethnic minority associations are finding (Karn *et al.*, 1995).

The role of standards in quality control

New build adds only very small numbers of dwellings to the existing stock: from the mid 1970s onwards, only about 1% or less per year in Britain. Nevertheless, the development of a house is an expensive undertaking and is likely to result in a design and a form of construction that cannot be easily changed after completion. It would seem sensible, therefore, for a government to ensure that the dwelling is built to a standard that permits its use for many years ahead. This is the rationale for governments to set standards, used in their normative sense as a statement of some minimum level of adequacy.

Though the general rationale for government intervention in this way is clear enough, the detailed application is more difficult. The continued, long term use of a dwelling depends on many factors: on the durability of materials and stability of construction, on the absence of any threat to the health and safety of the occupants, on the ability of the design to meet the future expectations of consumers for comfort and convenience. Moreover, from the viewpoint of government, the promotion of good standards may conflict with other policy aims. The promotion of standards is, for example, likely to conflict with the aim of building as many dwellings as possible to reduce problems of homelessness or to expand home-ownership.

The relation of housing standards to sustainability

In addition, though this is seldom explicitly recognised, the promotion of quality is not always consistent with policies to protect the natural environment. The conflicts between environmental protection and the promotion of quality are most acute in town planning and the broader environment outside the home, particularly in relation to density of development. For instance, environmentalists often argue that the density of new housing should be raised to reduce the con-sumption of land and to create a pattern of development that is more conducive to public transport. Such arguments ignore the possibility that the search for high densities may result in cramped external layouts and unusual types of dwelling that are unpopular with users (Goodchild, 1994).

Even for the amenity standards in housing, environmental protection raises difficult questions. For example, it is sometimes suggested that domestic heating costs should be cut through a reduction in the habitable floor area of new housing (Nystrom, 1994). Obviously, any such reduction could adversely affect the ability of a dwelling to meet the needs of users, depending on its scale and the type of housing to which it applies.

The conflict between environmental protection and housing quality reflects different interpretations of sustainability. As generally understood in the planning and architectural literature, 'sustainability' implies a long term view of housing and is therefore consistent with the usual rationale for standards. In some ways, sustainability is no more than a restatement of the usual rationale. Sustainability implies that dwellings should be built and designed in a way that avoids health and safety problems, that is durable and that maintains demand for the long term.

At the same time, sustainability raises broader questions about the feasibility of maintaining affluent consumption levels for the future, especially the consump-tion of non-renewable building products (for instance, tropical hardwoods), the consumption of land resources and the consumption of energy resources. Sus-tainability also means 'sustainable development' of a type that minimises possible impacts on the natural environment. Conventional approaches to social policy assume that inequalities in housing, as in other aspects of social life, should be tackled through raising the consumption levels of the poor. Sustainable develop-ment, especially in its more radical interpretations, assumes that housing ine-qualities should also be tackled through measures to reduce the consumption levels of the rich.

A comparison of practice in private and social housing

The application of standards takes a different form according to whether dwell-ings are built by the private sector for sale or by social housing agencies for rent.

In the private sector, the main driving force over design is the market. Design becomes differentiated according to its intended market into a large number of variations, each distinguished by style, the quality of fittings and finishes, the size and number of rooms and the size of the plot.

The dominance of the market in private sector design is, moreover, supported by a long standing reluctance of governments to introduce controls unless very strongly justified. In the private sector, public controls comprise a mixture of the building regulations in respect of health and safety, drainage, sanitary conveniences and thermal insulation and planning controls in respect of those aspects of design that influence neighbouring properties or are relevant to traffic safety or other matters of community interest, such as security and crime prevention.

In addition, in the private sector, control and influence are exercised by the National House Building Council (NHBC), the consumer protection body of the private house-building industry. However, the controls of the NHBC have mostly focused on the quality of construction rather than the quality of design. When they have covered space and layout, the approach has been mostly to provide advice to builders on avoiding the worst. For instance, the NHBCs advice on minimum bedroom sizes takes the form of a more general statement advising builders to demonstrate on the plans that bedroom furniture can be adequately accommodated. A previous set of advice that no room should be described as a bedroom if it were less than 4.5m^2 was dropped in 1994 after the Property Misdescriptions Act came into force.

In contrast, in the development of social housing, the economic rationale is a search for cost minimisation, with housing design being determined by a trade-off between financial constraints and an official perception of what standards are appropriate. Floorspace standards themselves tend to be higher than those in operation at the lowest end of the private market. Even though Parker Morris standards are no longer required they still represent a target which associations would like to achieve.

The difference between the public and private sectors is shown in the results of the Joseph Rowntree study. In the financial year 1991/ 92, private sector properties sold for up to £100,000 had a slightly larger net floor area than those built by housing associations (on average 70m^2 as opposed to 67m^2). What is more important, however, private developers provided a much wider range of sizes. 75% of housing association dwellings had a size between 5% above the Parker Morris minimum and 14.9% below Parker Morris. The equivalent proportion for private housing was 52%. Only 2.9% of housing association dwellings had a size of more than 10% above Parker Morris, whereas the equivalent proportion for the privately built accommodation was 17.7%. There was a pronounced 'bunching of housing association properties up to 10% below Parker Morris.

The scope of public control over housing design is related to the method through which development is financed. Because housing associations and local authorities are subsidised directly by local or central government, the choice of standards is a public issue, capable of resolution only through an explicit policy decision as to what taxpayers and tenants can and should pay. The Housing Corporation, like the Department of the Environment during the era of local authority house building, maintains a system of cost control that prevents housing associations from providing houses that could be criticised as too luxurious.

In contrast, in the private sector, the financial responsibilities of local and central government are less clearly defined. Although tax relief on mortgages may be viewed as a type of subsidy, it is seldom recognised as such by central government. As a result, housing design is more likely to be defined as a private matter to be settled by the consumer and the developer.

Differences in financial responsibility lead to differences in how developers define quality. Social housing developers (and there is no distinction between local authorities and housing associations on this point) generally work within an administrative framework that is well adapted to the achievement of specific standards concerning, say, floorspace or the number of fittings in a kitchen, if this is the intention of government. Moreover, because social housing developers are likely to possess a continuing responsibility for the property after completion, they have an interest in minimising repair and management costs for the long term. This continuing responsibility encourages a concern with specification standards, covering the standards of material, fittings and finishes. It also encourages housing associations to take out longer building insurance cover than private builders. About a third of recent housing associations completions are subject to a 35 year insurance cover offered by a specialist insurance firm, Housing Association Property Mutual, rather than the ten year cover offered by NHBC.

However, social housing agencies have relatively little incentive to promote quality for design features that are either unrelated to long term costs in use or not specified in official guidelines as a precondition for the receipt of public finance. Housing associations build for need. They have relatively little incentive to promote quality as a means of enhancing the attractiveness of their properties to consumers.

Figure 4 Housing associations commonly build terraced houses, without garages or on-plot parking and with more utilitarian, low maintenance exteriors

In contrast, except for down-market schemes, where price is the most important feature, private house builders always have an incentive to improve the attractiveness and marketability of their properties. They have an incentive to improve the so-called 'kerb appeal' and the general attractiveness of the setting of the house. They also have an incentive to meet consumer demand for attractive features for the interior.

Figure 5 Private housebuilders have an incentive to improve the 'kerb appeal' and general attractiveness of the setting of their houses

As a result, private developers have long been more likely to provide semi-detached and detached houses rather than terraces or flats and more likely to provide garages and on-plot parking and larger gardens. In the 1990s, as the Joseph Rowntree study (Karn and Sheridan, 1994) suggests, this pattern continues. In addition, in the 1990s, private house builders have been more likely to provide shower rooms and *en suite*, bathrooms, second WCs in smaller houses (say, with less than five bedspaces), larger kitchens or kitchen diners and weather protection over the front door. The provision of such amenities is linked to the price. However, even those dwellings priced within the Housing Corporation framework of Total Cost Indicators or 30% above had their share of facilities such as separate WCs. In addition, where space standards are restricted, the private sector tends to try to provide a greater appearance of spaciousness by having more open plan layouts, in particular stairs leading out of living rooms.

Housing associations have a social ethos that also distinguishes them from private house builders. This social ethos has, in turn, led to an emphasis on the provision of housing for the disabled, in particular for the users of wheelchairs. Access to housing for people in wheelchairs is prominent in the contents of housing association design briefs. It is also an aspect of the *Scheme Development Standards* of the Housing Corporation.

However, access for wheelchair users is seldom fully achieved in either private or social housing. For example, in the survey undertaken by Karn and Sheridan, only 4% of housing association and 2% of private properties had a 'visitable' entrance that avoided such problems as a raised entrance, inadequate standing area or narrow front door. Only a handful of properties with ground floor entrances (5% of private properties and 3% of housing association properties), were internally negotiable with a wheelchair and none of these also had visitable entrances. About 45% of properties in both sectors had a ground floor WC, but, because of the size of the compartment and the doorway arrangements very few separate WCs were visitable.

In the 1980s and 1990s, the growing use of private sector procurement methods by housing associations has blurred the distinction between the use of standards in social and private housing. The growth of shared ownership schemes and the increased movement of property across tenures (through such initiatives as the Right to Buy council housing, large scale transfers of local authority stock to housing associations and the purchase of private sector housing by housing associations via the Housing Market Initiative) have had a similar effect. However, the distinctive social responsibility of housing associations is still maintained by popular perceptions. For instance, housing associations that have built or improved property for sale have found that buyers still very much hold them responsible for the quality of the property, even though they have no legal responsibility.

The distinctions in financial responsibility, attitudes and social purpose mean that the question of standards has to be discussed separately for social and private house building. In the social housing sector, the question is to define both the standards that are most appropriate and the administrative and financial methods that are most likely to ensure conformity to these standards. In private housing, the question is to determine whether any regulation is necessary beyond that exercised through the building regulations, planning controls or the design controls of the NHBC.

The priorities for social housing

In social housing, debates about standards remain mostly preoccupied with long standing questions about the validity of Parker Morris floorspace standards. Should Parker Morris floorspace standards be permanently abandoned in face of current financial constraints? Or should they be maintained and integrated into a broader conception of design quality?

Cost conscious officials in the Housing Corporation, together with many housing associations, would, no doubt, argue that Parker Morris standards are obsolete, that they have been overtaken by recent financial pressures and that, in any case, they are higher than is typical in the most moderately priced private schemes. The private sector, the sceptics might argue, provides the dominant definition of housing quality in Britain in the 1990s. If the private sector provides houses below Parker Morris standards, housing associations should have no fear of following suit.

The opposing argument has two aspects.

• First, comparisons with the lower floorspace standards used in low priced private housing are inappropriate. Design standards in social housing are conditioned by higher expected levels of occupancy than those in private housing. The first occupiers of the housing association houses in the Joseph Rowntree Study had on average one person more in each household compared to the first occupiers of private housing, as revealed by Forrest and Murie (1993).
• Secondly, Parker Morris standards are not generous. They are similar to earlier standards recommended by the Dudley Report in 1944 and the Tudor Walters Report in 1919. They are consistent with a relatively tight fit between floorspace, human activities and a schedule of furniture requirements. For this reason, Parker Morris standards can, therefore, hardly be described as excessive in comparison with the test of sustainable development. Moreover, even within Parker Morris standards, designers have to take care to use space

efficiently to ensure flexibility in use (*Space in the Home*, MHLG, 1968). For this reason, Parker Morris standards are not easily adapted to the needs of wheelchair users (Goldsmith, 1975).

Floorspace is not the only aspect of housing design. The Institute of Housing and the Royal Institute of British Architects argue in their report, *Homes for the Future* (1983), that design standards should include measures to promote energy conservation and to reduce condensation, as well as measures to safeguard the quality of external spaces. Moreover, the case for a broader approach to design has been confirmed by the results of a survey undertaken in Sheffield in 1982 of tenants living in four estates, designed to different standards (Furbey and Goodchild, 1986). The survey showed that tenants notice even small variations in floorspace and, for this reason, suggested that reductions in floorspace standards below Parker Morris were not justified. On the other hand, if standards were to be improved, other aspects of design than floorspace standards appeared to be more important. From the spontaneous comments of respondents it emerged that the heating systems were, in different estates, both the most liked and the least liked features. The statistical pattern of responses suggested that the appearance of the estate was the most important influence on satisfaction and that, in general, low density, suburban-looking estates were the most popular.

There is a case for further studies of user response to alternative design standards. For example, expectations regarding heating systems may have changed as a result of wider provision of full central heating. However, the importance of appearance and the external environment is confirmed in other more recent surveys, notably the report of the *English House Condition Survey* 1991 (DoE, 1993, p. 128). Moreover, overall appearance is still insufficiently taken into account in new social housing. The Joseph Rowntree study showed that, to achieve higher densities, housing associations tend to build terraced houses with bin stores at the front and grouped or on-street parking.

The main cause of low quality in the housing association sector is a combination of the 'value for money' competition for grant allocations and the failure of the Housing Corporation as funding agency to stipulate any quality floor around which this competition is to take place. When housing associations apply for public grant aid, they have to declare that they are meeting the Housing Corporations *Scheme Development Standards* or if not, the ways in which they deviate from these standards. However, the *Scheme Development Standards* are limited in scope and mostly comprise a series of broad criteria that are open to different interpretation. In practice, quality has hardly been taken into account by the Housing Corporation in the approval of housing association schemes. The relevant criteria are total cost and public sector cost (the level of Housing Association Grant) per unit and per person. Criticisms of the outcomes of this policy of almost total deregulation, notably by Karn and Sheridan (1994), but also from within the housing association movement, seem, however, to be leading to a reconsideration of this approach.

If all housing associations themselves respected a good standard of design, the absence of a quality floor would present few problems. There are moves, supported by the Housing Corporation, DoE, National Federation of Housing (NFH) and the Joseph Rowntree Foundation, for housing associations to work towards a common minimum definition of quality (Derbyshire, 1995). The problem is that the present competitive bidding system discourages any such unified approach. Many housing associations are likely to avoid a commitment to high standards for fear that their bids for funds will be undermined. A further complication is that housing associations are increasingly dependent on part-nerships with private builders to obtain sites and their bargaining power with the house builders involved is relatively weak, in terms of the acceptance of private sector house types. The Housing Corporation has now stated that it may consider design standards in the building process, based on the NFH's Working Party's recommendations, but as the rent levels are also to be subject to greater control, the omens for improved quality are not good. Housing quality is likely to be squeezed between grant rates and rents.

Moreover, it is unlikely that further moves in the direction of private sector procurement will improve quality. Even if private house builders were given grant aid, there would still be no incentive in favour of quality.

There is no evidence that the use of unmodified private sector designs leads to greater efficiencies in housing provision. The prime requirements for efficiency in house construction are simplification and standardisation but savings in this respect can be cancelled out if the homes are not of a suitable size and layout for the occupants. Karn and Sheridan (1994, p. 31) pointed out that under-occupation was likely to be one effect of inappropriately designed properties. Simplification and standardisation may be achieved in any case by modified pri-vate house types or through the standardisation of existing social housing types, much as has been undertaken in Wales by Tai Cymru or by the Northern Ireland Housing Executive.

The absence of a quality floor implies the need for more design guidance, including the provision of design and equipment standards and model floor plans along the lines currently being pursued by the NFH, DoE and Housing Corpora-tion. Such design guidance might indicate precise standards that are unacceptable. Or it might provide some form of financial reward for good quality schemes, based on a points system or quality labelling system such as exists in France, Norway and Switzerland. Or the funding criteria might use a combination of minimum standards and a points system for additional allowances. The *Scheme Development Standards* already refer to the provision of higher cost allowances, without, however, laying down the conditions in which additional financial al-lowances might be justified.

The enforcement of design standards is not straightforward. Design standards, particularly those linked to the external environment, are not always capable of quantification. Moreover, there is a risk that, given financial constraints, social housing developers will give undue emphasis to those mandatory quantifiable aspects of design and ignore the rest. This was certainly the experience of the system of project control in operation during the 1970s. Local authorities main-tained Parker Morris space standards, but used high densities and industrialised construction systems to reduce overall building costs.

The system of project control used in the 1970s was also bureaucratic and slow. The floorplan of each house type had to be checked in advance to determine whether it conformed to Parker Morris standards or to other standards of good practice. The use of broader design standards could lead to even more detailed checking in advance.

Some housing associations would no doubt argue for voluntary compliance based on the use of design guides or a detailed statement of their building requirements. They would argue that the preparation of a design guide should be sufficient guarantee for the maintenance of design standards. Reliance on design guides has the advantage of encouraging a responsible attitude amongst the housing associations. This is vital for the future. Even the most comprehensive statement of standards is not a substitute for the exercise of care in design and construction. Voluntary enforcement has a crucial weakness, however. Housing associations do not always respect the standards included in their design guides and other policy statements.

Another possibility is for the Housing Corporation or for another responsible agency to reserve inspection for completed schemes and to inspect only on a sample of schemes, these being selected either on a random basis or because of a complaint. If the inspection were to find that the housing association had failed to conform to minimum standards, the responsible agency could easily impose an appropriate financial or other sanction. The Housing Corporation already exercises a Scheme Audit. It would be relatively simple to ensure that this Audit had 'teeth', that it involved sanctions against housing associations that failed to provide good quality accommodation.

In practice, some combination of enforcement method might offer the best way forward. For instance, the Housing Corporation might require every housing association to submit a design guide, whilst also undertaking checks before and after completion. Checks before completion might be reserved for schemes that receive additional quality allowances, whilst basic schemes might be checked only after completion. There are a variety of possibilities. The priority is to encourage housing associations to pay more attention to quality.

Priorities for the private sector

In private housing, the developers generally argue against further controls. They maintain that the quality of their housing has never been higher, that a lack of floorspace can be compensated for by a good quality of design and that, in any case, consumers are the best people to choose housing standards. Finally, the builders argue against higher standards because this would reduce their output and would have a particularly damaging impact at a time of economic recession. Of course, many of these arguments receive support from a government committed to deregulation and the expansion of home ownership.

Notwithstanding the objections of the private house builders, it is possible to identify a case for stricter regulation in respect of certain features of housing. Any such additional controls should have specific aims that are clearly related to the promotion of quality. They should be relatively simple to implement and should receive the support of the relevant pressure groups.

One possibility is the incorporation of floorspace controls in the building regulations. To be practical, such controls would either have to be linked to expected occupancy (bedspaces) or would have to specify minimum sizes for habitable rooms. Otherwise, the effect would be to reduce the supply of dwellings for small households. Examples of possible controls exist in other European countries, for example France, Germany and Denmark. Moreover, a requirement for minimum room sizes used to be included in the Scottish Building Regulations until they were dropped in

1985 in response to pressure from English house builders wanting to introduce into the Scottish market standard house-plans with small third bedrooms.

However, floorspace standards are of limited use. In social housing, floorspace controls are linked to an allocation policy that prevents over-crowding. In private housing, in contrast, floorspace controls cannot prevent over-occupation after completion. The only practical way of preventing families from occupying dwellings too small for them is either to provide some form of income support to enable them to buy a more expensive dwelling or to make available acceptable alternative dwellings at a price they can afford. In addition, floorspace controls might reduce flexibility and innovation in internal design.

Instead, there are two main priorities:

- first, the inclusion in the building regulations of a requirement for a draught lobby, this meaning that the front door of a house (and possibly the back door) should not open directly onto the outside from a habitable room;
- secondly, the inclusion in the building regulations and possibly planning controls of a new standard of 'visitability', intended to ensure disabled persons access.

The first priority for a draught lobby is directly related to measures intended to reduce unnecessary heat loss. Moreover, apart from the small increase in floor area and therefore in development cost, a requirement for a draught lobby would encounter few difficulties in its implementation.

The second priority, for disabled persons access, is more complex. Some standard of visitability may be introduced in the next few years as a result of pressure from the disability lobby. The government has been considering a modification to the building regulations. However, as the Joseph Rowntree Study shows, there is a large gap between existing design practice and the full requirements of the visitability standard of wheelchair access. This gap also applies to social housing. The main problem concerns the feasibility of requiring the universal provision of a downstairs WC in small two storey houses, say those of less than 70m², especially a downstairs WC that is designed to accommodate a wheelchair and the provision of wide enough entrance halls.

The visitability standard is not special needs housing. The imposition of standards of visitability would not lessen the need for 'wheelchair' housing or some similar standard intended for permanent occupation by a disabled person. Conversely, these other ambitious standards are too demanding to permit incorporation into the regulatory framework as a universal requirement. It is, nevertheless, possible that planning authorities could negotiate with private developers to provide a proportion of wheelchair housing. *Planning Policy Guidance Note 1: Housing* (DoE, 1992) permits planning authorities to negotiate with developers for social housing provision. However, it prevents the implementation of any policy that requires developers either to achieve specified floorspace standards or to provide a fixed proportion of their output as disabled persons accommodation.

A slightly different priority for private housing concerns the provision of better consumer advice. Private house builders argue that design standards are unnecessary because a purchaser can judge the quality of a dwelling through visiting a show home or an empty property. However, many aspects of quality, for instance thermal and acoustic insulation, are not visible. Consumers require consistent information, presented in such a way as to facilitate judgements about quality.

To an extent, the need for consumer protection has already been met by the Property Misdescriptions Act, 1991. However, this Act mainly protects the consumer against misleading statements, as its name suggests. It does nothing to encourage house builders to provide more guidance to consumers. Indeed, in some ways, the Act discourages house builders from providing consumer information. The less information that is available, the fewer are the grounds for complaint.

A particular form of quality labelling already exists in the form of the National Homes Energy Rating classification of likely heating costs. However, energy rating is seldom used in the advertisements of house builders or given to housing association tenants. In other areas, quality labelling is absent. Moreover, consumers receive little guidance in how to interpret floor plans before construction. In many cases, information is limited to a simple representation of the floor plan and a summary of room dimensions.

The NHBC has issued advice to its members that there is a need for greater detail in the information provided to consumers. Failing voluntary action, the government could require developers to provide information on the energy rating of a home, its overall floorspace and storage space. As part of such measures, developers could also be required, as the NHBC advises, to show the position of furniture in each room.

Conclusions

The standards of recently completed schemes in the housing association sector pose more problems than standards in the private sector. In the private sector, design deficiencies are mostly confined to specific issues, for instance a lack of overall floorspace, a lack of storage space and a lack of disabled persons access. In social housing, in contrast, the concern is that too many housing associations have accepted a generally poor standard of design comprising small terraces without private car-parking and lacking a downstairs WC and other amenities. Such properties are virtually impossible to adapt or expand to meet future expectations. Housing associations face difficult financial constraints. However, they should ask themselves what type of housing they want to be managing in fifty years time and whether recently completed schemes will provide good quality, popular accommodation for the long term.

There are also issues that affect both private and housing association housing. The present Conservative government has repeatedly expressed its belief in deregulation. The private house builders have agreed with this. Yet there are strong pressures that are leading in exactly the opposite direction. The government and many pressure groups have sought to reduce the heating requirements of new housing, as a means of reducing both energy consumption and fuel poverty. In addition, the pressure for disabled persons access is leading towards the imposition of new types of design control covering the provision of level (or nearly level) access at the front, the dimensions of hallways and door entrances and the provision of a downstairs WC. If implemented in full, the achievement of a 'visitability' standard of disabled persons access will amount to a significant change in existing design practices.

The recent experience of low cost housing development in Britain, whether developed by social housing agencies or private builders, enables a reflection on the meaning and validity of concepts of sustainability and sustainable development. These concepts clearly raise broad questions about the consumption of natural resources. Continuing debates about energy consumption in housing provide an example. However, recent trends in low cost housing development also show the importance of social issues in sustainability. Recent trends raises questions about whether design standards are sustainable for households in need, notably for low income households with children, ethnic minority households and households with a disabled person. In addition, and most importantly, recent trends raise questions about whether existing design standards will meet popular preferences for the long term.

Acknowledgements

The authors would like to thank the Joseph Rowntree Foundation for supporting the research by Karn and Sheridan on which this chapter is partly based; and Jennifer Wright for working out a typology of marketing strategies during the course of a project undertaken as part of an HNC in Housing at Sheffield City Polytechnic (as Sheffield Hallam University was then called).

CHAPTER 11

UK Housing Finance: Past Changes, the Present Predicament, and Future Sustainability

ALAN HOLMANS

Financial issues permeate nearly all the chapters in this book, both in analyses of past developments and of present and future problems. This chapter attempts to provide a more general view of the financial aspects of sustainability in housing policy in Britain and to make some suggestions for adapting policy for that purpose in an unfriendly economic environment. It starts by sketching the main features of the history of British housing that have led to the financial predicament in which housing policy finds itself in the mid-1990s. It then attempts to draw some conclusions about possible ways forward, with some suggestions about policy, including restructuring means-tested assistance with housing costs. This is not the place to put forward fully worked out schemes; but a measure of detail is needed in order to make clear what is being proposed and avoid the appearance of a mere wish list.

A central feature of the chapter is the financial consequences thus far and in the future of the policy expressed by successive governments in terms that include a 'separate house for every family that wishes to have one' (1945); 'a decent home for every family at a price within their means' (1971); and most recently (1995) 'a decent home within the reach of every family' (see Holmans (1995b) for references). This aim implies that where necessary public (i.e. tax-financed) funding should be made available to provide access to 'decent' housing. What constitutes 'decent housing' in this context has evolved through custom and practice, embodied from time to time in legislation. On a long view, standards of housing built with subsidy can be seen to have risen along with average standards enjoyed by households that finance their housing from their own funds without aid other than from generally available tax reliefs. A reversal, to force downwards the housing standards of households that depend on subsidy at a time when average standards of housing continued to rise, would not be something to be undertaken lightly. That it might nonetheless be deemed necessary in the name of the financial requirements of 'competitiveness' is a major reason for 'present predicament' being part of the title of this chapter.

One of the major reasons why maintaining the present standard of 'decent' housing for households that cannot afford it unaided has been questioned is the magnitude of the increase in public expenditure generated by the rise in the number of households without the means to afford decent housing from their own funds. The causes of this rise, and its consequences for public expenditure, are an important set of questions to be discussed in the next section of the chapter. The historical record is summarised, along with the other major influences on the growth of private and public expenditure on housing. Chief among them are the growth in the number of separate households, their distribution between tenures, the rise in house prices and costs in real terms, and interest rates.

The second section of the chapter accordingly traces the growth of expenditure on housing from private and public sources as a consequence of numbers of households, their tenure, employment status, incomes, house prices, and interest rates as described in the first section. Three themes are highlighted: the increase in public relative to private expenditure on housing; the changing balance between so-called 'bricks and mortar' subsidies and means-tested 'person' subsidies; and the relationship between the means-tested subsidies and the social security system.

Britain has a two-part system of social security payments, in which scale rates of means-tested assistance are set very low because housing costs are met separately. National Insurance scale rates can therefore be set very low in relation to total living costs including housing, because, if need be, National Insurance pensioners and others can turn to Income Support and get their housing costs paid by that means. If, as is current British practice, assistance with housing costs for households receiving Income Support is counted as public expenditure on housing, the result is to inflate very substantially the British total of public expenditure on housing in comparison with countries that have scale rates of assistance high enough to meet part at least of housing costs and social insurance scales to match. The point is not merely about figures: the two-part system saves very large amounts of money that would otherwise go to home owners with low incomes but without mortgages. Notwithstanding the complaints about how 'burgeoning' expenditure on Housing Benefit is distorting the social security budget, the two-part system is an extremely important part of the explanation of why National Insurance contributions in Britain are much lower in relation to payroll than are social insurance contribution rates in many other European countries. In that respect Housing Benefit makes a major contribution to British 'competitiveness'.

The third and concluding part of the chapter attempts to analyse how changes in housing demand, need, and costs have interacted with forces at work in the national economy and beyond to produce a sense of predicament and impasse; and the problems they pose for sustaining housing standards in the future. Increasing competition in product and labour markets appears likely to constrain the growth of real earnings at the lower end of the distribution to close to nil. It has produced pervasive buyers' markets for labour and other services which oblige employees and earnings, not employers and profits, to bear the costs of instability and change. This is part of the downward flexibility discussed in Duncan Maclennan's chapter. Buyers' markets for many kinds of labour and services have been exploited with increasing vigour, hence the rise of the profits share in the national income and the fall in the share of salaries and wages. Housing is paid for predominantly from wages and salaries, not profits. Another, and up to a point related, set of forces in the economy are high real interest rates and at times unstable interest rates generated by global financial markets in which 'headline' financial quantities are very sensitive. This sensitivity puts a premium on expenditure and financing that can be counted as private and not public even though in real resource terms there is no material difference.

Sustainability of adequate housing in these conditions, which at the time of writing are generally thought likely to persist, has two components: how best to ensure that adequate housing remains within the reach of growing numbers of households in low-paid work or not in work at all; and how best to limit the disruptive effects of labour market and finance market instability on the housing of households that can afford adequate housing from their own funds for much of the time. This is essentially a defensive agenda for housing finance, damage limitation if one wills. That is not, though, an activity to look down on: many a good ship went down through poor damage control and efficient damage control brought many others home to fight another day.

The Influences That Drive Public and Private Expenditure on Housing: the Historical Record

This section of the chapter summarises the historical record for the main 'drivers' of expenditure on housing by households and from public funds: the number of households and their tenure; the course of house prices and rents relative to the general price level and relative to incomes; interest rates; the number of households with non-earning heads or no earning member; and housing standards. A miscellany of sources has to be used, with differing geographical coverage. The United Kingdom is anything but united in housing statistics. In a chapter such as this there is not the space for a full account of sources and methods, but a few words of explanation and warning are inserted where appropriate.

Households and their tenure

The number of separate households and the number of dwellings that they occupy are fundamental influences on expenditure on housing. A sub-division by tenure is extremely important because the housing finance system is tenure-specific, and so is assistance to households with their housing costs. A tenure-neutral system has attractions of principle, and was the centrepiece of the recommendations of the 1985 'Duke of Edinburgh Inquiry' report (National Federation of Housing Associations (1985). This recommendation is discussed in the third section of the chapter; so are the reasons why the second report (Joseph Rowntree Foundation, 1991) modified it. Table 1 shows estimates of the number of households in England and Wales and their tenure, in the absence of immediately available figures for Scotland and Northern Ireland. The tenure of dwellings and households is not identical: a house let in rooms to four households, for example, is one dwelling in the private rented sector with four households renting from a private landlord; and where a household owns a second home as well as a main residence, there is one owner-occupier household but two owner-occupied dwellings. The table starts with 1953 as the first post-war year for which there is the direct evidence (from the Household Expenditure Survey) for an estimate. Housing tenure did not appear in the Census until 1961.

Table 1   Tenure of Households in England and Wales 1953 to 1994
(thousands)

	1953	1961	1971	1981	1994
Owner-occupiers:					
Outright	(2,500)	3,110	3,870	4,620	5,290
With mortgage	(1,850)	3,220	4,570	5,960	8,550
Total	4,350	6,330	8,440	10,580	14,140
Rent from local authority or New Town	2,370	3,430	4,710	5,330	3,890
Rent from housing association			160	400	180
Rent from private landlord	6,870	4,970	3,400	2,030	2,040
Total, all tenures	13,580	14,720	16,700	18,340	20,870
Memo:					
Owner-occupiers with mortgages, LA and HA tenants (*)	4,350	6,800	9,440	11,690	13,550

Note: (*) The figures for 1953 and 1961 are approximate only
Source: 1953 to 1981 from Holmans (1987) Tables V.1 and VI.1; 1994 from Survey of English Housing with an estimate for Wales

Two features of Table 1 require comment in relation to increases in expenditure on housing: the first is the growth of the total of households relative to the adult population; the second is the change in the mix of tenures. In the early 1950s there were 42 separate households per 100 of the adult population (aged 20 and over); in 1994 54 per 100; all would incur expenditure on housing unless they occupied their housing rent-free or were outright owners who spent nothing on upkeep and insurance of their residences. There are three main explanations: a much higher proportion of widows and widowers living as independent households; more separations and divorces; and more single men and women living on their own.

The second feature for comment is the increase in the proportion of households in what may be termed the subsidised tenures, renting from local authorities, new towns, and housing associations; and owner-occupiers with mortgages. Whether owner-occupiers with mortgages could be counted as subsidised as early as 1953 is perhaps arguable; but after the repeal of the income tax charge on the rental value (1963) the tax relief on mortgage interest was clearly in substance a subsidy. One-third of households were in the subsidised tenures in this sense in 1953; in 1994 the proportion was almost two-thirds.

Households with non-earning heads or no earning member

With the increase in households in total that was shown in Table 1 went a substantial increase in the proportion with non-earning heads or no earning member. With the exception of outright owners, and possibly a small number of households in other tenures with substantial investment incomes, households without earners will need assistance to obtain (or keep) adequate housing. The employment status of heads of household (or in 1961 and 1971 chief economic supporters) is shown in Table 2. There are some difficulties of detail owing to having to combine data from different sources with different definitions, which are described in Office of Population Censuses and Surveys (1995), pp 110–11; but the picture derived is reliable enough. The table refers to England, hence the household totals are not the same as in Table 1.

Table 2   Employment Status of Household Heads: England
(thousand)

	1961	1971	1977/78	1993/94
Employed or self-employed full- or part-time	10,470	10,870	10,970	10,980
Unemployed	470	750	580	1,400
Economically inactive, lone parent	500	660	230	520
Economically inactive, other below retiring age			680	1,690
Economically inactive, above retiring age	2,280	3,430	4,270	5,210
Total, all statuses	13,700	15,700	16,700	19,800
Memo:				
Households with non-employed heads	3,250	4,850	5,750	8,800

Source: Office of Population Censuses and Surveys, *Housing in England 1993/4*, Table 9.9

Out of the net increase of some 6 million households between 1961 and 1993, only half a million had heads in paid work. The proportion of households with non-employed heads rose from near 25% in 1961 to 45% in 1993. Rather over one-half of the increase in households with non-earning heads consisted of men and women above retiring age. This was by no means due entirely to ageing of the population. Many more widows and widowers continued to live as independent households, and for longer, which accounted for about half a million of the increase; and many fewer men continued in paid employment beyond age 65. Of the increase in the number of non-earning household heads below retiring age, just over two-and-a-half million, most appears to have been due to the decline in employment opportunities. Non-earning lone parent household heads cannot be distinguished in 1961 and 1971, but could have accounted for at most 400,000 of the increase overall between 1961 and 1993/94. The increase in other economically inactive household heads below retiring age was concentrated between 1977/78 and 1993/94, particularly in the early 1980s. What seems to have happened was large scale formal and informal early retirement during the recession years, which was not reversed when labour demand strengthened.

The households with non-earning heads cannot be divided by tenure until 1977/78. For an analysis by tenure, survey data (mostly from the Family Expenditure Survey) about the number of earners is used (see Table 3). The number of households with no member earning is closely connected with the number with non-employed heads, but is not identical as in multi-adult households someone other than the head can be in paid employment.

There was a very large increase in the proportion of local authority tenant households with no member earning. In part this was the arithmetical effect of

Table 3 Households with No Earning Member (%)

	Local Authority	Owner-occupiers	All tenures
1962	11	17	16
1971	23	19	22
1978	30	19	25
1982	44	21	30
1990	60	24	34
1993	66	29	39

Source: Department of the Environment, *Housing in England Housing Trailers to the 1988 and 1991 Labour Force Surveys* (HMSO 1993) Chapter 9, with 1993 from Family Expenditure Survey

transfers from renting to owning through the Right to Buy, which was taken up primarily by tenants in paid employment; but there was also the effect of tenancies being allocated to tenants in the greatest need, and also the recession of the early 1980s having its most severe impact on local authority tenants. The increase in the number and proportion of local authority tenant households with no earning member was the main driving force behind the steep increase in the number of tenants receiving means tested assistance and hence in the cost of rent rebates discussed in the next section of the chapter. The increase in households without earnings had impacts in other tenures as well: the number of owner-occupiers with part or all of their mortgage interest paid through Supplementary Benefit or Income Support rose sharply, from 134,000 in 1980 to 556,000 in 1993 (Table 10).

Housing costs, prices, and earnings

The total, tenure, and employment status of households discussed above determine the numbers of households with expenditure on housing and the division between private and public expenditure. The next stage is to consider the influences on expenditure per household. The first group is house prices and rents; interest rates are considered subsequently. Long term changes in the price of housing can be measured from rents between about 1870 and 1913; and from house prices since the late 1930s (approximately). Both with rents and with house prices there is a problem about distinguishing between the effects of changes in quality and 'true' price change. From 1968 the house price index used is mis-adjusted but even so does not exclude all quality changes. The point of looking back to before 1914 is to establish that on a long view the faster rise in house prices than the general price level after 1945 was not exceptional, and hence that the 'normal' behaviour of house prices and market rents is that they rise in real terms, taking one year with another. The inter-war years were the exception, explained by developments in public transport which greatly increased the supply of land usable for housing when controls over use of land for housing were generally not strict. For reasons of space, the pre-1914 rent index is not reproduced here. Figures for selected years, and the citation of the original source, are in Holmans (1990), p.123. Between 1874 and 1900 rents were shown to have risen by about 1.1% a year relative to the general price level, of which about 0.3% can reasonably be attributed to quality change, which leaves about 0.8% a year as the 'true' price change, slightly less than the average increase in real income per head.

Index numbers of house prices in selected years are shown in Table 4. From 1968 the index is the Department of the Environment's mix-adjusted index of house prices. For earlier years the index numbers were compiled by the Department of the Environment from information provided by the Inland Revenue Valuation Office (see Holmans (1990) p.112 for a fuller account). The house price index was converted to real terms by reference to the Retail Prices Index (RPI) from 1956 onwards, and the consumers' expenditure deflator for earlier years.

The years in Table 4 were selected to show cycles as well as trends, and so enable long term rates of increase of 'real' house prices to be measured from peak to peak (e.g. 1948 to 1989) or from trough to trough (1958 to 1995). The first gives an increase averaging 2.3% a year, the second 2.6%. These average rates of increase include improvements in average dwelling quality not picked up by the mix adjustment, notably central heating but also double glazing and other forms of better insulation, fitted kitchens, and more recently second bathrooms and shower rooms. Putting a figure on how much of the apparent price increase is explained in this way is problematic, but about 0.5% a year may be suggested as reasonable. That would put the long term trend rate of increase in house prices in real terms at about 2% a year or perhaps slightly less. The increase in average real income was about 2.5% a year. Explanations for the increase in real house prices include a slower increase in productivity in the house building than in the economy as a whole, and limitations to the supply of house building land. Neither seems likely to change in the future in ways that would check the trend increase in the price of housing in real terms.

Table 4 Indexes of House Prices: Selected Years (1970 = 100)

	House Prices	'Real' House Prices
1934/39	12	51
1948	42	93
1954	40	69
1958	43	65
1970	100	100
1973	210	164
1977	276	111
1980	505	140
1982	536	122
1989	1,464	240
1995	1,354	167

The increases in house prices discussed above affect not just the cost of housing to owner-occupiers but also costs of rented housing, including housing for letting by local authorities and housing associations. The price of land for housing is set in the market for owner-occupied housing; and except in a slump in the housing market, the price that housing associations and in the past local authorities have to pay building contractors is determined by what they and their sub-contractors can get from building houses for sale. There are here important reasons why rents and 'bricks and mortar' subsidies rose so much.

Interest rates

Capital costs and interest rates determine mortgage outgoings for owner-occupiers and loan charges for local authorities and housing associations. The increase in house prices and costs just discussed interacted with rising interest rates to drive up mortgage payments and interest charges. Long time series for interest rates, building societies' recommended mortgage rates and then their average rates are shown in Table 5. Rates charged by other lenders are not published in suitable form, so building societies' rates have to represent all lenders. In competitive conditions this is a reasonable assumption; and before the mortgage market became competitive in the 1980s the building societies were the predominant lenders. The rate that borrowers actually pay is the gross rate net of tax relief. Until the £30,000 upper limit began to bite in the mid 1980s, the net rate could readily be calculated for mortgage borrowers not liable to tax at rates above the basic rate. Since then there has been the problem of part of the loan being above the limit and interest on it therefore not being eligible for relief. To bring this to account the calculation of the net rate is made for a loan equal to the average new loan taken by purchasers with building society loan. In the table the 'real' net rate is calculated from the same inflation rates as used for 'real' house prices in Table 4.

Table 5   Mortgage Interest Rates in Selected Years (%)

	Gross	Net	'Real' Net Rate
1957	6.0	4.0	0.4
1966	7.0	4.8	0.9
1970	8.5	5.8	−0.5
1974	11.0	7.4	−8.6
1978	10.2	6.8	−1.5
1980	14.9	10.4	−7.7
1984	11.4	8.0	3.0
1988	11.0	8.5	3.6
1990	15.0	12.3	2.8
1992	10.7	8.8	5.1
1995	7.9	7.1	3.6

From the mid-1950s to the mid-1970s the trend of interest rates, including mortgage rates, was upwards. When monetary policy moved in the direction of expansion, as in 1958–9, 1962–4, and 1970–72 after a period of restraint, interest rates did not go back to their former level. When policy moved in the direction of restraint, ever higher interest rates were needed. At the end of 1979 mortgage rates reached the wholly unprecedented height of 15%. Except for a small number of home owners with very large mortgages 30%, i.e. 4.5 percentage points, was absorbed through tax relief. But when mortgage rates reached 15.4% gross in 1990, tax relief absorbed only 18% (2.8 percentage points) of the gross interest on an average new mortgage. In regions where house prices were higher than average the offset from tax relief was even smaller. The impact of very high mortgage rates was therefore very much greater in the early 1990s than in the early 1980s, especially where house prices were highest. There is here a major reason why the housing market was more depressed in the South of England than in the rest of Britain, and why the general economic recession was more severe there. As will be shown in the next section the mortgage rates in 1990 in conjunction with the volume of house purchase debt generated by the boom of the 1980s produced exceptionally high payments of mortgage interest; and notwithstanding the £30,000 limit, a record total of tax relief.

More and better housing

Improvements to the quality of housing were alluded to in connection with how much of recorded increases in average prices paid for houses and flats reflected quality change rather than 'true' price increases. This is not the only way in which improvements in housing conditions, in the broadest sense, contributed to higher expenditure, private and public, on housing. There was first an increase in the volume of housing, in the sense both of an increase in the stock that was greater than the increase in the number of households and a reduction in the number of households with separate dwellings but short of space; and better physical standards and amenities.

Much expenditure is related to the number of dwellings in the stock to be financed and maintained rather than to the number of households as such. Table 1 above shows how large has been the increase in the number of households; but the increase in the housing stock has been larger still. In 1951 the number of dwellings was some 600,000 smaller than the number of households; by 1991 the number of dwellings was 700,000 greater (figures for England and Wales). The number of households rose by some 7.5 million between the early 1950s and the early 1990s; but the number of dwellings by nearly 9 million.

A great improvement took place in the physical quality of the dwellings. In the early 1950s nearly 60% of dwellings lacked one or more of what had just come to be termed the 'basic amenities' (inside WC, fixed bath or shower, wash hand basin, sink, and hot and cold water supply to the bath, hand basin, and sink) (Department of the Environment (1977) Chapter 1); by the early 1990s the proportion was only 1%. Central heating is not technically one of the basic or standard amenities, but has in practice become standard. In 1960 (the first year for which there is survey information about it) about 5% of dwellings had it (Central Office of Information (1962); in 1991 the proportion was 84% (Department of the Environment, 1993). Modernising older dwellings was very important here. Very few houses were built before 1914 with central heating; but in 1991 nearly three-quarters of the surviving pre-1914 dwellings had it. The capital expenditure to make these improvements contributed to mortgage interest for private owners and to loan charges for public bodies. Installing central heating as standard in new houses and flats had a similar effect.

Public and Private Expenditure on Housing

In this part of the chapter an attempt is made to sketch long term changes in private and public expenditure on housing to provide a context for more recent changes; and then to examine recent changes in more detail, particularly the growth of means-tested assistance with housing costs. In this part also a miscellany of sources has to be used. Some (including total house purchase loan interest in recent years) are from the National Income Blue Book; many of those for earlier years are taken from or depend on Chapter 4 of the 1977 *Housing Policy* Technical Volume; others, especially from 1979 and 1980 onwards, are from government departments' reports collated in the Joseph Rowntree Foundation's *Housing Finance Review 1995/96* (Wilcox, 1995). For some series, notably mortgage interest tax relief, figures for financial years are used as they are readily available. For some of the public expenditures figures for Great Britain have to be used, with Northern Ireland not covered. The error introduced in these ways is not large enough to call into question the inferences drawn from the figures in Table 6, but great care should be exercised in using the figures for any other purposes.

Table 6 gives estimates of private and public current expenditure on housing in selected years since 1950, with tax relief on mortgage interest included as a 'tax expenditure' and hence in substance equivalent to a subsidy. Published official estimates of mortgage interest tax relief go back to 1958/59; before then, extrapolation pro rata to estimated payments of mortgage interest has to be used. The estimates of mortgage interest themselves are uncertain for the earlier years as they depend on extrapolation and interpolation by reference to mortgage debt outstanding and building societies' mortgage interest rates. Totals of rents are taken from the national income accounts and exclude owner-occupiers' imputed rents, and rates. Rents paid through Supplementary Benefit and (before 1967) National Assistance are also only rough estimates made by extrapolation by reference to the number of tenants receiving assistance and average rents. They are put in to complete a picture painted with a broad brush, and are not to be relied on for other purposes. Rent rebates are net of negative subsidy entitlement in 1990 and 1993, that is to say where they are paid from a historic cost surplus in local authority housing revenue account and not Exchequer subsidy, they are not counted as expenditure. This is an extremely important distinction when the changing balance between 'bricks and mortar' subsidy and means-tested 'person' subsidy is being considered.

Owner-occupiers: mortgage interest, tax relief, and payment of mortgage interest through Income Support

The massive increase in expenditure on mortgage interest that Table 6 shows was the result of the growth in the number of owner-occupiers with mortgages (Table 1); the rise in the price of houses in real terms and hence in the size of the loans needed to buy them (Table 4); and mortgage interest rates (Table 5). The increase in the number of owner-occupiers with mortgages produced a continuing increase in mortgage payments, and so did the rise in house prices, given that the amount of mortgage debt is determined by purchases and prices in a run of previous years as well as in the current year. The rise and fall of mortgage interest rates, in contrast, produced increases and reductions in mortgage interest payments that are both large and rapid because so high a proportion of house purchase loan debt is at variable rates of interest. In the early post-war years fixed rate mortgages were fairly common, but in the 1960s and 1970s they virtually died out; they have since reappeared, but are still very much a minority.

Table 6   Current Expenditure on Housing (£million)

	1950	1955	1960	1965	1970	1975	1980	1985	1990	1995
(A) Rent (gross)	299	367	503	813	1,203	2,025	3,841	7,154	10,748	14,639
(B) Maintenance, etc by occupiers	155	225	293	456	718	1,299	2,777	5,217	9,399	11,209
(C) Mortgage interest (gross)	60	109	212	406	915	2,630	6,493	15,627	39,802	27,248
(D) Subsidies to housing revenue accounts	72	99	104	150	280	1,066	2,130	916	1,212	100
(E) *Total current expenditure* = (A) + (B) + (C) + (D)	*586*	*800*	*1,112*	*1,825*	*3,116*	*7,020*	*15,241*	*28,914*	*61,161*	*53,196*
(F) Rents from Supp.Ben, etc. rebates, allowances	60	80	120	200	300	520	1,024	3,177	4,890	8,410
(G) Mortgage interest tax relief [a]	15	35	70	135	300	1,005	2,190	4,750	7,700	4,300
(H) Mortgage interest from Supp. Ben and IS [b]	–	–	–	5	10	30	70	300	550	1,220
(I) *Total public expenditure* = (D) + (F) + (G) + (H)	*147*	*214*	*294*	*490*	*890*	*2,621*	*5,414*	*9,143*	*14,352*	*14,030*
(J) Total current expenditure at constant (1970) prices	1,230	1,340	1,640	2,280	3,120	3,870	4,370	5,920	9,850	7,360
(K) Total public expenditure at constant (1970) prices	310	360	430	610	890	1,440	1,550	1,870	2,310	1,940

Notes: (a) Includes Option Mortgage Subsidy
    (b) 1985 figure interpolated

The increase in payments of mortgage interest took mortgage interest tax relief up with it, augmented from 1967 by Option Mortgage Subsidy which provided the equivalent of tax relief for households with incomes too low to benefit fully from it. In 1983 Option Mortgage subsidy was incorporated into mortgage interest relief at source (MIRAS). As a proportion of gross mortgage interest, tax relief reached its peak (about 38%) in the mid-1970s when the basic rate of income tax was raised to 35% and the starting points for investment income surcharge and higher rates of tax were lowered in cash terms and still more in real terms. The £25,000 limit introduced in 1974 affected only a small proportion of mortgages and a smaller proportion still of total mortgage interest. By the mid-1980s it had fallen to about 30% of total mortgage interest as a result of tax reductions; by the early 1990s it had fallen to only 20%, as a result of further tax reductions and through the £30,000 limit biting hard in the parts of the country where house prices were high. In the period covered by the table the only other restriction on tax relief was the ending in 1991 of relief at the higher rate of tax; the reduction of relief to 20% and then 15% came later. One of the effects of tax relief was to provide partial protection to borrowers against increases in interest rates. As mentioned in the previous section, the protection offered in this way against 15% mortgage rates in 1990 was only about half as great as it was in 1980 when mortgage rates were last raised to 15%.

The other protection for owner-occupiers in the period covered by Table 6 was payment of mortgage interest for households receiving what was successively National Assistance (till 1967), Supplementary Benefit (till 1988) and then Income Support. Assistance in this way with mortgage interest was a side effect of the way in which 'rent' was defined for purposes of a scheme drawn with tenants in mind. The amounts were small until the spread of house purchase on mortgage led to there being more mortgage holders on Supplementary Benefit. Until the 1980s, though, marital breakdown was more common as a cause than unemployment. Its importance grew during the economic recession of the early 1980s when, contrary to common belief, owner-occupiers did not escape unscathed. Assistance with mortgage interest was restricted in 1985, and much more drastically in 1995, when it had come bulk large in public expenditure on housing in the broadest sense. Its development is discussed more fully later in the chapter.

Rents and subsidies: the balance between 'bricks and mortar' and 'person' subsidies

Table 6 shows that in all years a much higher proportion of the cost of rented housing than of owner-occupied housing (including upkeep as well as mortgage payments) was met from public funds; and that from the mid-1970s onwards subsidy payments were a much higher proportion of the costs of rented housing than was tax relief as a proportion of mortgage payments. That would be expected from the incomes of tenants, and the proportions of local authority tenant households with no member earning (Table 3). Distinctions have to be drawn between tenants of local authorities, housing association tenants, and tenants of private landlords. For tenants of private landlords, assistance from public funds is almost entirely from means-tested 'person' subsidies; the only other sources, not discussed further here, are improvement grants paid to landlords and the Business Expansion Scheme tax reliefs. Tenants of housing associations benefit from 'bricks and mortar' subsidy through Housing Association Grant (HAG) and means-tested subsidies; local authority tenants have historically benefited from subsidies credited to housing revenue accounts to hold down rents, and also from means-tested assistance. Local authority tenants have also benefited from the effects of inflation in eroding the real value of debts incurred to finance house building and improvement, such that the rents required to balance housing revenue accounts have been much lower than if a full return on the current value of the assets had to be recovered. Of the three rented sectors, the local authority sector bulks largest in terms of expenditure and numbers of tenants and so may be considered first.

There are three parts to an analysis of expenditure on subsidy for local authority housing and its tenants: general subsidy (i.e. credited to housing revenue accounts); rent rebates to tenants not receiving Income Support and its predecessors; and payment of rent through Income Support. The theme to be studied is the changing balance between general subsidy which holds down rents for all tenants irrespective of their individual circumstances; and assistance that is means tested individually. Only colloquially is the former 'subsidising bricks and mortar'; what it does is subsidise the rents of the people that live there; with tenancies allocated according to need general subsidies are related to need, though not individually.

Table 7 Subsidies to Local Authority Tenants
(£ million or %)

	(A) General (Exchequer and RFC)	(B) Rebates Non SB or IS	(C) All Rebates	(D) (B) as % of (A) + (B)	(E) (C) as Percent of (A) + (C)
1970/71	311	10	. . .	3	. . .
1975/76	1,066	148	. . .	12	. . .
1980/81	2,130	290	841	12	28
1985/86	916	780	2,296	46	71
1990/91	1,425	1,260	3,132	47	69
1993/94	847	1,390	4,273	62	83

Note: In 1990/91 and 1993/94 general Exchequer subsidy is positive entitlements; negatives have been netted from rebates
Sources: 1970/71 and 1975/76 from *Housing Policy Technical Volume*, Table IV.7; other years from Joseph Rowntree Foundation, *Housing Finance Review 1995/96*, especially Tables 62, 68, and 110a. Rebates in 1985/86 and after split between IS and non-IS from number of rebates and average rebates from *Housing and Construction Statistics 1984–1994*, Table 11.3

The changing balance between general and means-tested subsidies for local authority tenants is difficult to measure exactly over a long run of years. Payment of rent through Supplementary Benefit has to be added to 'direct' rebates in 1982/83 and earlier if a comparison is to be made with rent rebates in 1983/84 and later, and the amount can be estimated only approximately. From 1983/84 rebates can be divided into those going to tenants receiving Supplementary Benefit or Income Support and other tenants in terms of gross payments. But in the early 1990s higher rents began to produce housing revenue account surpluses; those that did not continued to receive general subsidy. In Table 7 the figures for 1990/91 and 1993/94 in the 'general' column are the sum of the positive subsidies; the surpluses have been netted off the sum of rebates, and the net rebate total divided between IS and non-IS tenants pro rata to the gross amounts. The sum of general subsidy and rebates paid to tenants not receiving Income Support is a minimum definition of subsidy in the local authority sector, and is approximately what would have been paid if scale rates of Supplementary Benefit had been set high enough for un-rebated rents to be paid from them. The table refers to Great Britain, though for 1970/71 and 1975/76 United Kingdom figures have to be used.

Despite the approximations necessary to produce Table 7, the picture it paints is clear and not in doubt. In the 1980s and early 1990s there was a pronounced shift from general subsidy to means-tested subsidy. To a very substantial extent this happened as a result of policies specifically directed to bringing it about. But before discussing these policies note should be taken of two other causes. One was the higher proportion of new tenants with low incomes and therefore in need of rent rebates irrespective (almost) of the level of rents. The other was the Right to Buy. When houses were sold general subsidy from the Exchequer was reduced, generally pro rata; and interest earned on the sale proceeds helped to balance local authorities' housing revenue accounts as the interest was usually greater in the short run than the rent foregone. In these ways the Right to Buy reduced general subsidy and hence the ratio of general to means tested subsidy, since few if any households exercising the Right to Buy received rent rebates. More important than these reasons for the shift from general to means-tested subsidy, though, was deliberate policy. Before discussing the policy, however, the number of tenants receiving rent rebates must be shown, to complement the financial figures shown in Table 7. The number of tenants receiving rebates has to be shown for England and Wales. Figures are given for 1987 and 1988 to show approximately the effect of the reform of housing benefit that accompanied income support in 1988 (Table 8).

Table 8   Number of Tenants Receiving Rent Rebates: England and Wales 1970 to 1994 (thousand or percent)

	Not Supp. Ben. or IS	Supp. Ben or IS	Total Receiving Rebates	Proportion of All Tenants Receiving Rebates
1970	350	1,023	1,370	30
1975	940	1,103	2,040	41
1980	1,095	1,312	2,410	45
1985	1,330	1,745	3,075	65
1987	1,305	1,705	3,010	65
1988	1,070	1,530	2,600	58
1990	1,050	1,450	2,500	60
1994	960	1,555	2,515	66

Source: Housing and Construction Statistics 1984–94 Table 11.3 and corresponding tables in earlier issues

Between 1980 and 1985, average un-rebated rents doubled in cash terms, and increased by 43% in real terms (relative to the Retail Prices Index); between 1990 and 1994 there was an increase of just over 50% in cash terms, just over 30% in real terms. The sum of general subsidy and rent rebates (Table 7) fell between 1980/81 and 1985/86 by between 20 and 25% in real terms, at a time when the number of tenants not in employment was rising fast during the recession. Between 1990/91 and 1993/94 the sum of general subsidy and rent rebates rose by 1% in real terms; since this was also a time of economic recession, no significant net change in expenditure in real terms must be accounted a success for the policy, that the rent increases did what they were intended to do. The saving was less in 1990/91 to 1993/94 than in 1980/81 to 1985/86 because the proportion of households receiving rebates or Supplementary Benefit in 1980 was much lower than the proportion receiving rebates in 1990. There were still savings of expenditure on subsidy from raising council rents and shifting to means tested assistance in the 1990s, but they were becoming progressively smaller.

Before commenting further, reference must be made to the increase in rent allowances for tenants of housing associations and of private landlords, since both the number of allowances paid and the total cost rose very fast in the early 1990s. Survey information about the number of tenants receiving rent allowances suggests, when compared with the number of allowances being paid, that allowances paid include a considerable number for accommodation occupied on terms other than tenancies in the strict sense. But for convenience they can all be referred to as being allowances for private sector tenants, pending a detailed investigation. Because of the uncertainty about the exact coverage, however, the proportion of tenants receiving rent allowances cannot be calculated for comparison with the proportion of local authority tenants receiving rent rebates (Table 9).

Table 9 Tenants, etc. Receiving Rent Allowances: England and Wales 1970–94 ('000)

	Not Supp. Ben. or IS	Supp. Ben. or IS	Total
1970	—	692	692
1976	190	540	730
1980	215	419	630
1985	420	530	950
1987	480	545	1,030
1988	355	470	830
1990	400	510	910
1994	460	1,040	1,500

Source: Housing and Construction Statistics 1970–1980, Tables 131 and 132; *1975–1985*, Tables 11.2 and 11.3; *1984–1994*, Table 11.3

The increase between 1990 and 1994 in the number of rent allowances paid is very striking. A similar increase is shown by the figures for Great Britain; expenditure on rent allowances in Great Britain rose from £1.76 billion in 1990/91 to £4.17 billion in 1993/94 and £4.91 (estimated) in 1994/95 (Joseph Rowntree Foundation, *Housing Finance Review 1995/96*, Tables 103 and 105). This massive increase in rent allowance expenditure is the main reason for a perception of crisis in 'person' subsidies. Five distinct (and large) elements in the increase in rent allowance expenditure can be discerned: (i) the shift of new provision of social rented housing from local authorities to housing associations; (ii) increases in housing association rents to service loans taken from building societies and banks ('private finance') for part of their capital expenditure; (iii) increases in the number of housing association and private sector tenants receiving Income Support (and therefore rent allowances) as a result of the economic recession; (iv) the increase in private sector rents following the de-regulation of new lettings; and (v) an increase in the number of private rented sector tenants receiving rent allowances over and above what can be explained by the recession.

Of the elements of the increase in rent allowances, (i) is a straight substitution of rent allowances for rent rebates as a consequence of the policy decision to make adding to the social rented stock a housing association function instead of for local authorities. The allowance per claimant is higher than it would have been in the local authority sector owing to the difference in rents. The second element, paying for private finance, is also the outcome of a straight policy choice. The amounts of private finance are large: over £1 billion a year in 1992/93, 1993/94, and 1994/95 (*Housing Finance Review 1995/96*, Table 52). In 1994/95 private finance is estimated to have funded about one-third of housing association capital expenditure. There is here a very large shift from general subsidy (Housing Association Grant) to 'person' subsidy. What exactly has been happening in the private rented sector is far from clear. Beyond doubt, however, is that the number of private rented sector tenants receiving rent allowances rose much more than could be explained by the recession (Holmans, 1996b). The inference is that part of housing need has been met in the private rented sector. Newly arising need has been estimated at an average of 90,000 a year between 1991 and 2001 (Holmans, 1995b), whereas provision has averaged 60,000 a year and is planned to continue at broadly that level. The private rented sector seems likely to have accommodated the others; if so, it has saved the public expenditure cost of 30,000 new dwellings a year, not far short of £1 billion a year. By this indirect route as well as the direct housing association route, 'person' subsidy has been substituted for general subsidy. Obviously both should be looked at together, which however is frequently not done when social security issues are at the head of the agenda.

At the time of writing there is a widely held perception that shifting from general to person subsidies in the interest of 'targeting' can go little if any further. In the first place, the cost of 'person' subsidies has come out much higher than anyone would have thought likely, principally owing to the large and increasing number of households without earners or only with low earners. Attempt to restrain the increase in the cost of 'person' subsidies led to successive steepenings of the 'taper', the rate at which the amount of rent rebate or allowance is reduced as income increases, with consequent concern about the 'poverty trap' caused. This side effect of high rents gets worse as rents rise; but with more and more tenants with low earnings or no earnings, the net saving from more accurate 'targeting' of subsidy declines. By 1995 the net saving in subsidy costs from raising local authority rents had probably ceased to offset the increased expenditure on National Insurance pensions and other benefits indexed by statute or by pledge to the Retail Prices Index, together with the increased payments on indexed Gilt Edged and National Savings Certificates. That effectively has put a stop to increasing council rents in real terms. Housing association rents do not at the time of writing enter the RPI as a separate category; but if housing associations continue to be the providers of new social rented housing and therefore the numbers of their tenants continue to increase fast, it is likely to be only a matter of time. The fixed points for rent policy are considered to be: (a) raising local authority rents in real terms costs money rather than saving it; (b) housing association rents must be accepted at levels high enough to service their loans; and (c) private sector rents must be at levels high enough to maintain at least the present levels of supply. If (c) is not done, then pressures on the social rented sector would rise strongly, with substantial needs for more public capital expenditure, and more private finance serviced out of rents underpinned by rent allowances.

The Future: Problems; Choices, and Some Suggestions for Policy

From this sketch of the evolution of public and private expenditure on housing, five features may be highlighted as particularly relevant to the policy choices to be made in the future:

(i)   The increased number of households with no member earning or with only low earnings has greatly reduced the scope for further net savings in public expenditure from shifting from general to person subsidies.

(ii) For the same reasons, together with instability of income affecting owner-occupation adversely (see (v) below), giving effect to the 'decent home . . . ' objective will require continuing high levels of new provision of social rented housing.

(iii) Holding down the public expenditure capital cost of this provision will require both housing association and private sector rents to be underpinned by rent allowances at levels high enough to attract the necessary amounts of private finance.

(iv) From (ii) and (iii) the 'poverty trap' problems generated by means-tested benefits will be all the more important, particularly if (as widely predicted) the number of low paid jobs increases and people who would otherwise be unemployed or non-employed are put under increased pressure to take them.

(v) Recent numbers of owner-occupiers losing their homes through mortgage possession are far too high to be compatible with the 'decent home . . . ' objective.

Before going on to discuss the implications of these features of the housing policy scene, a short digression is necessary to explain the last, that mortgage possessions at the levels experienced in the 1990s were far too high to be compatible with the 'decent home . . . ' objective. Table 10 shows the number of mortgage possessions; it also shows the number of households with mortgages receiving Supplementary Benefit and Income Support, since payments of interest for these households should have protected them against having their homes taken into possession.

The number of mortgaged properties taken into possession by lenders rose in the first half of the 1980s, when unemployment continued to climb until 1986. Mortgage possessions in the 1990s, however, were on an altogether different scale: from 1990 to the end of 1995 almost 350,000 mortgaged dwellings were taken into possession by lenders and an equivalent number of home owners lost their homes. The scale of forced departures by home owners can be minimised by pointing out that in 1990–95 the average number of possessions each year was only 0.6% of all mortgages outstanding. That implies that the risk of being dispossessed was still very small, only 1 in 170 (approximately). That, though, is a single year risk, whereas households with mortgages are at risk to mortgage default all the time they have their mortgages. From the way in which the proportion of owner-occupiers that have mortgages varies with age, the average length of time that a household has a mortgage appears to be between 30 and 35 years, e.g. from the mid 20s to the early 60s. With a period at risk of 35 years, an annual risk rate of 0.6% would result in a total risk rate over the whole period of 19%, i.e. a risk of losing the home through mortgage possession at some stage of nearly 1 in 5. This is the grim arithmetic of Bomber Command. Such a risk rate does not appear compatible with the 'decent home . . . ' objective. That forced departures ran at this rate notwithstanding the number of owner-occupiers having interest paid through Income Support running at twice the level of a decade earlier is evidence of the limitations to what Income Support could do and hence of the need for something more effective. To provide this is the part of what at the beginning of the chapter was termed the defensive agenda that focuses on owner-occupiers.

Table 10 Mortgage Possessions and Mortgaged Households with Supplementary Benefit or Income Support ('000)

	Possessions	Supp. Ben. or Income Support
1969–73 (average)	3	. . .
1974–78 (average)	4	. . .
1979	3	98
1980	4	134
1981	5	196
1982	7	235
1983	8	242
1984	12	277
1985	19	(*)
1986	24	356
1987	26	334
1988	19	300
1989	15	281
1990	44	310
1991	76	411
1992	69	499
1993	59	556
1994	49	529

Note: (*) Figures not collected owing to strike
Source: Council of Mortgage Lenders, Compendium of Housing Finance Statistics (1995), Table C15; Joseph Rowntree Foundation, *Housing Finance Review 1995–96*, Table 99

In setting out this agenda and considering the possibilities for action on it, the first point to note is that the consensus of opinion is that the British economy will continue to grow in real terms. The rate of growth that is feasible and likely is a matter where views differ; but it is important to note that 2½% a year cumulates to 28% over a decade, and even 2%, about the lowest figure in circulation, cumulates to 22%. With these increases in total real income, there is no genuine sense in which in resource terms 'the country' cannot afford to maintain present housing standards for those with insufficient means to pay for adequate housing while those households with the necessary means and want better housing buy it or rent it. The contrary argument, that the tax rates to finance it would so imperil incentives as to make even 2% a year growth unattainable, lacks credibility.

But apart from the likely increase in total real income, the economic prospect which will condition policies on housing finance is not benign from the point of view of sustaining the 'decent home . . . ' objective. It is generally considered to include a continuation of the shift to profits relative to employment income; and within employment income a widening of the distribution with earnings at the lower end static at best. The prospect also includes unemployment at high levels by pre-1980 standards, and greater instability and insecurity of employment incomes at all levels. The balance of bargaining advantage can be seen to have shifted a long way in the favour of employers, with the result that the costs of uncertainty and change, which must be borne somewhere in the economy, have been shifted to employees and labour income, to the advantage of profits. Most payments of mortgage interest and rents are made from wages and salaries, not from profits. There is ample evidence to show that financial assets are held predominantly by older households, in their fifties and upwards, so that is where the benefits of larger profits will go. The boost to the earnings of life and pension funds form higher profits and share values similarly benefit people long past the stage when they are buying houses. The costs and the benefits of the 1990s-style market economy are distributed very differently: for the most part the costs fall on those that have the greatest difficulties in getting and keeping adequate housing; the benefits go mainly to people that experience no such difficulties.

This prospect defines the context in which housing policy will have to work. The terrain on which it will have to operate includes three prominent features already mentioned: (i) a large and growing number of households with no earning member; (ii) a growing number of households with jobs that pay too little to afford unaided the cost of adequate housing; and (iii) increased risks of serious interruptions of employment incomes that while received are large enough to pay for adequate housing. One of the thrusts of social security policy is to transfer people from (i) to (ii) by exerting pressure on them to take low-paid jobs rather than none. But however successful such policies might be they plainly would not alter the number of households with incomes too low to afford adequate housing without aid.

Instability and insecurity of income are a different problem from chronic low earnings or absence of earnings. Instability matters more for housing than for other goods and services because expenditure on housing can less readily be reduced or postponed. A holiday, for example, can be postponed or a cheaper holiday chosen; purchase of new clothes can be deferred; and cheaper food substituted for dearer in response to a fall in income. But the mortgage interest or the rent must be paid, on peril of losing the home. Because moving to a cheaper house will often mean moving to another district, reducing expenditure on housing is much more disruptive than reducing other forms of expenditure when income falls or rents or mortgage interest rates rise sharply. Support for measures to partially insulate payments for housing from instability of income is therefore not special pleading.

Policies for renting and purchase on mortgage must be looked at separately, because the purposes of the measures discussed are different. Finance for renting has to make 'decent' housing accessible to households whose incomes are too low for extended periods to afford it unaided, either through being in low-paid jobs, or having no jobs at all. For owner-occupiers the purpose is to provide protection against falls in income and possibly as well the vagaries of interest rates for households that could afford house purchase on ordinary terms when they bought their houses. Subsidised house purchase for households with low incomes is not put forward for discussion here, on grounds of risk. A tenure-neutral housing allowance system is not put forward here. The idea has an obvious appeal, hence the support for it in the report of the first 'Duke of Edinburgh' inquiry in 1985. The report of the reconvened inquiry in 1991 supported it in modified form, but with different rent policies. Here the aim is much more limited, to respond to the risk of forced departures from owner-occupation which has loomed a great deal larger since the inquiry did its work.

The policy proposals put forward for discussion as ways of sustaining the 'decent home . . . ' objective have to be outlined in sufficient detail to make clear what is being proposed. But for reasons of space they cannot be described in the

detail that would be appropriate for a Green Paper, let alone consultation papers
on draft regulations.

Reform of rent rebates and allowances

For assistance to tenants, the proposals made here are to leave rent setting arrangements in the three sectors as they stand, and to divide rent rebates and
allowances into two separate schemes, one as a straight supplement to the Income
Support scale rates, the other for tenants not receiving Income Support. In essence
this would bring back the system as enacted into law in 1972, when the Housing
Finance Act provided a mandatory scheme of rent rebates and allowances for
tenants not receiving Supplementary Benefit through being in low-paid employment, having an occupational pension, or having some capital.

The case for leaving rent setting in the local authority and housing association
sectors as now follows from housing association rents being conditioned by the
private finance imperative and increases in local authority rents in real terms
producing a net cost instead of saving. Unification of rent levels in the two parts
of the social rented sector would have to be done (because of the private finance
imperative) by a revenue subsidy to housing associations so that they could
reduce their rents to local authority levels. Its probable cost, net of savings in rent
allowances, would be in the region of £200–250 million. This is not a prohibitive
sum, but in view of other claims on public expenditure is probably best deferred
unless refusal of housing association tenancies by households with paid jobs
produce intolerable stresses. In the private rented sector the requirement is sufficient profitability to obviate a renewed contraction of the sector that would
produce a further large need for social sector tenancies. That implies leaving rents
de-regulated as now.

The case for splitting rent rebates and allowances into two separate schemes as
they were between 1972 and 1982/83 and partially between then and 1988
('standard' and 'certificated' rebates and allowances) has two main parts. The first
is the 'poverty trap' produced by the present taper; the other is the sense of
unfairness on the part of tenants with low incomes but some capital, who see
themselves disadvantaged for having saved. The principal features of rent rebates
and allowances in the original scheme were: (a) the maximum rebate was normally 60% of the rent, so at the margin the tenant paid 40% of any increase; (b)
the taper was 17% of gross income, which together with the basic rate of income
tax and earnings-related National Insurance contributions by employees gave a
combined marginal rate of about 50% (the reason for choosing 17%); and (c) the
means test was of income only. Any income from assets was included in the same
way as income from other sources, but capital as such was not part of the means
test, in contrast to Supplementary Benefit.

This system attracted little controversy. The Housing Policy Review in the
mid-1970s received no representations that challenged it, and made no
recommendation for change. The pressure for unifying rent rebates and allowances
and the rent element of Supplementary Benefit came in the first instance from the
Supplementary Benefits Commission, specifically from its then Chairman, Professor
Donnison. The reason was the 'better off problem', that tenants who could claim
either a rent rebate or allowance or Supplementary Benefit (in practice retirement
pensioners with a small occupational pension or a modest amount of

capital) faced a highly complex calculation to decide which would give them more. The prospect of savings in administrative costs added to the attraction.

To make the cost of a flatter taper than the present 65% (net) manageable, it would have to be combined with a maximum benefit distinctly below the present 100%. Since the Income Support scale rates are intended to provide a minimum income to meet living costs other than housing, a maximum rebate or allowance of less than 100% of the rent would be tolerable only if scale rates were raised. That is the rationale for Hemming and Hills's 'dual taper' scheme (Hills, 1991 pp. 176–9). What is proposed here is more radical, to make the means test a test of income alone, and to compensate have a somewhat steeper taper for investment income and pensions than for employment income. The method suggested to do this is a proportional earnings disregard, that is to say that a specified proportion of earnings, (but not of other kinds of income) would be deducted in calculating reckonable income for purposes of the rebate or allowance.

An example will explain what is being proposed. If a combined income tax, employee's National Insurance contribution, and rent rebate taper of 50% is required, then for a tenant liable to tax at the 24% income tax rate and a 10% National Insurance contribution the rent rebate taper has to be 16% gross equal to 24% of income net of income tax and National Insurance. With a 15% disregard for earnings, then for someone whose income came entirely from employment (or self employment), a taper of 31% of reckonable income would produce the desired figure of 50%. Needless to say this marginal rate is not put forward as sacrosanct, any more than the 60% maximum rebate. The system as set up in 1972 did not include an earnings disregard. The reason for proposing one here is to enhance as much as possible the net gain from entering or re-entering paid employment. The earnings disregard could be a flat sum, e.g. £20 a week in place of the present £10, and a proportion of earnings above this minimum.

Differing combinations of maximum rebate, taper, and earnings disregard could be costed. A taper and earnings disregard equal in combination to 16% of gross income and a 60% maximum rebate would result in rebates or allowances being payable to people with substantial incomes. With a rent of £50 a week, entitlement would not run out until income exceeded around £250 to £300 a week (according to composition of the household). Two ways, not mutually exclusive, can be suggested to avoid this. One would be to raise the minimum rebate or allowance. Setting it at £5 a week would lower by £28 the income at which entitlement to an allowance would run out. More drastic would be setting an income at which entitlement would cease. Clearly this would have to be set high enough not to affect tenants in low-paid work, for whom the scheme would be designed.

From the standpoint of employment incentives, the main disadvantage of re-introducing the 1972 scheme modified only in the ways just discussed would be that coming out of unemployment to take a low-paid job would reduce the maximum rebate or allowance from 100% to 60%, which with a £50 a week rent would take £20 out of the gain from taking a job. One way round this would be to have a supplementary rebate with a steeper taper; another would be to continue the 100% maximum rebate for a limited time.

Among the advantages of a separate scheme for tenants not receiving Income Support would be the prospect of keeping income-related assistance with rents for tenants in low-paid work clear of the stigma of 'the dependency culture' and 'welfare dependency'. Both are highly pejorative terms; their present currency is all the more to be deplored in that for a long time person subsidies were strongly advocated by the free-market Right as giving greater scope for choice by tenants and promoting competition between suppliers of rented housing, as well as saving money by more accurate targeting. If low-paid and unstable jobs are inevitable in the free-market economy, then the need for income-related assistance with rents is simply a fact of life and receipt of such assistance fully legitimate, the more so if minimum wages are ruled out.

For tenants receiving Income Support the present system could be left unchanged provided that the rents for which rebates and allowances are paid are allowed to be high enough to enable housing associations to service their loans and for the private rented sector not to contract and so produce a large additional need for social rented sector tenancies. The second would be hard to formalise; but for housing associations a more formal arrangements could be considered under which housing association rents would all be accepted in full for purposes of rent allowances in return for appropriate undertakings from housing associations. This would recognise that choosing the private finance route for funding social housing should rule out measures that might put security of the loans at risk.

There would admittedly be scope for friction, as happened before between the Supplementary Benefits Commission and local authorities; but it could be made to work, given the will. Administration of the rent element of Income Support could reasonably be handled by local authorities as an agency service for the Department of Social Security, to avoid the upheaval and duplication that would result from DSS taking back this work. There is, though, a need for a clearer sight of how the rent element of Income Support forms part of a larger structure of housing finance, specifically that it underpins private finance for housing associations and through supporting the private rented sector obviates heavy pressure for additional capital expenditure in the social rented sector. Because it is part of this larger structure the rent element of Income Support is not just a part of social security. Adequate recognition of this both in presentation and in policy depends heavily on politics and personalities, notably on Housing Ministers seeing the need to have an effective impact in this area and making sure that they do so.

In the Department of Social Security's published forward look at expenditure on social security, including rent rebates and allowances (Department of Social Security, 1993). The difference between the gross and net cost of rent rebates (owing to housing revenue account surpluses – see page 187 above) was mentioned only in a footnote and all the argument based on expenditure totals that counted rent rebate expenditure gross. If rent rebate expenditure had been counted net the projected increase in social security expenditure would have been sufficiently less to make the conclusion much less dramatic.

Protection for owner-occupiers with mortgages

What is needed for owner-occupiers with mortgages are arrangements that protect households that could afford their mortgages when they originally took them from being forced out either by total or partial loss of income or by disproportionate increases in interest rates. The reason for including the latter is two-fold. The first is the evidence of 1990 (see Table 10) when mortgage possessions jumped sharply even though the economic recession did not begin until the spring of 1990 (dated by unemployment) and then only gradually, but when mortgage rates exceeded 15%. The other is that the protection provided by mortgage interest tax relief has been very severely eroded. The combination of the 15% rate of relief and the £30,000 limit have together cut the proportion of any increase in mortgage interest absorbed by tax relief to well under 10% for many home owners. It is the mortgage possessions in 1990 and the early months of 1991, which can only have been due to interest rates, that are the principal argument. It is true that for any household, the first line of defence against loss of income is its own savings. But, as noted above in connection with who benefits most from higher profits, financial assets are held mainly by older households.

The scheme put forward for consideration is that home owners with qualifying mortgages should be eligible for assistance when as a consequence of a fall in income their mortgage outgoings exceed a defined proportion (for instance 25%) of net income. The amount of the assistance would be a proportion of the excess of interest over the 25% threshold, possibly stepped (e.g. 90% of the first £30,000, and 50% of the rest, up to a ceiling). The assistance could take any of three forms. The first would be the equivalent of an overdraft limit, up to which interest could be deferred without being 'in arrears' in any pejorative sense. Beyond that, interest (in the amounts just defined) would be paid from a Mortgage Assistance Fund, or partly from a Mortgage Assistance Fund and partly from private insurance, written as part of a package containing the three forms of assistance. Provision would also be needed fo deferral of repayments of mortgage principal. With repayment mortgages deferral of the capital element could be part of the 'overdraft'; for endowment policy provision for deferral of premiums in the same circumstances could be built into the policy, for an addition to the premium rate.

A time limit for assistance would be needed, since the purpose of the scheme would be to provide protection against instability of income, not to finance original housing standards indefinitely in the face of a permanent change for the worse. There are various ways in which the time limit could be set, which would take too long to discuss here. To limit the scheme to its intended purpose and to prevent misuse, criteria for original ability to afford the mortgage would be required and effectively administered; so too would a prescribed interest rate for calculating the amount of assistance. Additions to indebtedness through re-mortgaging, further advances, or second mortgages would have to be excluded, apart (possibly) for a few special purposes like adapting the home to cope with disability. Ensuring that these conditions were observed would be the responsibility of lenders, who could conveniently administer the assistance as agents for the Mortgage Assistance Fund. The 'qualifying lenders' provisions of the Option Mortgage scheme would provide a precedent here. Exclusion of interest generated by re-mortgages and further advances has proved feasible for MIRAS and so should present no additional problem for the scheme proposed here.

A scheme for 'qualifying lenders' who issue 'qualifying mortgages' of which the terms were agreed with the Mortgage Assistance Fund would resemble the *prêts conventionnés* scheme in France, but on a much larger scale. How far the costs incurred by lenders in operating it could fairly be regarded as offset by the much reduced risk of arrears and bad debts and how far they would have to be recompensed would be for negotiation. So would any costs of portability of assistance between lenders in the event of re-mortgaging.

A key issue would be financing, which would also govern the transition provisions for mortgages issued before the scheme came into operation. One way would be to finance the Mortgage Assistance Fund from an Exchequer contribution equal to the cost of mortgage interest tax relief plus Income Support payments of mortgage interest, minus the cost of continuing to pay them to existing mortgage holders who chose to continue them. They would be offered a choice between making their mortgages qualifying mortgages and in consequence giving up entitlement to mortgage interest tax relief and the right to claim payment of mortgage interest if they received income support; or staying outside the qualifying mortgage scheme with a reserved right to tax relief and to payment of mortgage interest through Income Support. With new mortgages there would not be this choice. The other potential source of financing would be an insurance premium added to the monthly mortgage payment. If this route were followed it would be necessary to give a choice of not paying the premium and staying outside the scheme; but opt-out mortgages would not get either tax relief or Income Support. Whether the likely cost of the scheme would be high enough to require premiums as well as the equivalent of tax relief and Income Support would require calculations that are beyond the scope of this chapter. The intention, though, is that comprehensive protection against instability of income should be provided at no greater cost to the Exchequer than the present support for owner-occupiers.

The intention would be to include as well a degree of protection against steep increases in interest rates. Because owner-occupiers with mortgages originally took them at an array of different rates, basing assistance on how much higher the present rate was compared with the original rate would seem impractical. If the increase was from a low rate to only a fairly low rate, assistance would not seem necessary. The basis suggested is that assistance would be made available if the increase in interest rates took the payment above a threshold calculated as a percentage of the income when the mortgage was taken out, either straight or indexed. The assistance would be a proportion of interest above the threshold, perhaps 40 or 50%. Costings would be required to ascertain whether the likely cost could also be met from within the equivalent of tax relief and Income Support or whether an insurance premium would be necessary. If a premium was necessary a question would arise as to whether to make protection against interest rate increases an optional extra. It would be more attractive, obviously, to borrowers whose mortgage was large in relation to income at the time it was taken.

The proposals both for owner-occupiers and for tenants are essentially defensive, to sustain access to adequate housing in adverse conditions. For home owners what is proposed are arrangements which would provide protection against being forced out of home ownership, by means of pooling risks at no net cost (compared with measures as they stand in 1996), to public funds. Transition provisions apart, home owners would be paying for their protection by giving up what remains of tax relief on mortgage itnerest. For tenants the purpose is different, to sustain access to decent housing for households for which low-paid jobs are all that are to be had, in ways that have the minimum adverse effect on employment and work incentives. Such policies would sustain an improvement in average standards of housing. Present standards would be protected for those who do least well from the economy, while the gainers are able to afford better housing from their own funds.

The alternative would be to deliberately allow the housing standards of those who do least well from the economy to deteriorate at a time when average standards were rising. That would be the reality on the ground of households being 'asked' (in reality required) to 'take more responsibility for their housing'.

CHAPTER 12

Future Directions?

RAY FORREST AND PETER WILLIAMS

The general themes to emerge from the preceding chapters are of policies which are often anachronisms, of resources misapplied and squandered, of unsustainable commitments and of blanket solutions inflexibly and inappropriately pursued. Any assessment of a portfolio of housing policies would no doubt produce similar critiques. A similar collection of essays written thirty or so years ago would have been preoccupied with the need to transcend more fully the old era of private landlordism. Comparable sets of essays written at the conclusion of either of the two World Wars would have given more dramatic presentations of a changing world and the role of housing within it. It is all too easy to be mesmerised by the present and to see it as a unique and profound configuration of events and processes which requires a new and dramatic response.

Home ownership

If there is one identifiable break with the past as regards housing policy debates, it is perhaps in the recognition that home ownership is no longer a simple uncomplicated panacea for past mistakes. Previously, home ownership was the site of solutions and problems were elsewhere, typically in the rental sectors. The policy goal was relatively straightforward and can be summarised as the pursuit of a range of policies to enable as many people as possible to become individual home owners. For at least the last two decades this has been the explicit policy objective and it has been the underlying theme for much longer. As we approached the end of the century it seemed that the dream of the property owning democracy was within reach. Politicians and policy analysts talked of levels of home ownership of 80% and beyond.

And, of course, this is still possible. What has been recognised, however, is that as housing tenures expand they inevitably change their nature. Different cohorts enter under different circumstances. It is not a simple extrapolation of trends. It is an easy mistake to confuse the characteristics of a tenure with the characteristics of the population within it. So as we approach the end of the century in Britain we are contemplating some basic housing policy questions which provide an interesting contrast with the turn of the century. We have a dominant but diverse tenure, home ownership, which has replaced private landlordism. But private landlordism has come in out of the cold. For so long written off as a residual tenure form with no future, the need for some sustained and strategic revival attracts a strong degree of bipartisan support. And council housing which has been of enormous importance in the transformation of living conditions for most of this century can be viewed as having performed a pivotal role in the transition from one form of market dominance in housing to another. Just as in the early 1900s, we are once again involved in fundamental debate about the legitimate and sustainable role of state intervention in the housing market.

The marked changes which have occurred in housing provision in the post war period are self evident, as is their acceleration in the last fifteen years. And the changing tone of policymakers, politicians, housing market institutions and academic analysts is also explicit and pervasive. There is a broad consensus that we need to review and revise our attitudes towards home ownership and explore more hybrid and flexible forms of housing provision. It is felt we need to have a more balanced portfolio of housing choices to accommodate greater diversity and uncertainty. Consumers need to unlearn the dominant message of the last two or more decades, as Bootle (1996) and others have been suggesting. Thus dwellings are for living in rather than being investment goods. Home ownership is a tenure to be sustained not unrelentingly expanded.

Wider social change

But are these housing policy debates part and parcel of more fundamental social changes? Social scientists are prone to exaggerate the scale and depth of change of the present as signifying a qualitative break from the past. But there is a reasonably consistent message from the theoretical and applied literature in this area. There may be disagreement about the pace and scale of change and the terminology and key concepts may be endlessly debated but there is a shared view that technological advances and globalisation are transforming national economies. The political, economic and social forces which have shaped the post Second World War world are now argued to be in a state of transition to an uncertain future.

Amin (1994) refers to:

Terms such as 'structural crisis', 'transformation' and 'transition' [which] have become common descriptors of the present, while new epithets such as 'post-Fordist', 'post-industrial', 'post-modern', 'fifth Kondratiev' and 'post-collective' have been coined by the academic prophets of our times to describe the emerging new age of capitalism. (p.1).

The symbiotic and virtuous relationship between indigenous mass consumption and mass production has been broken and the social cement of the Keynesian welfare state is being eroded. In this context, societies become more fragmented and polarised. There is a higher degree of horizontal integration linking privileged enclaves of power and control across nation states while new social divisions emerge within nations.

The new social order is one in which those with the educational capital necessary to compete in the 'informational' age (see Castells, 1991) pull away from the less skilled and the unemployed and economically inactive. There is a shrinking core of those in secure employment and an expansion of the self employed, casualised and those surplus to the labour market. Hutton (1996) has recently popularised these developments in terms of a 40–30–30 society. And Reich's (1991) influential study of the changing US labour market in the new global economy highlights the growing penalties for the less well educated and the increasing relative wealth of the minority of symbolic analysts – the manipulators of signs and symbols in an age dominated by the exercise of knowledge and trade in information.

Some of these ideas can be no more than suggestive of a direction of change and tend to be rooted in more exotic examples drawn from major US world cities such as New York and Los Angeles. Nevertheless, there is now substantial evidence of a growth of income inequality in Britain during the 1980s (see, for example, Jenkins and Cowell, 1994) and clear evidence of a decline of secure, full time jobs. Wadsworth (1995b) summarises the situation as follows:

> The British labour market seems to be increasingly polarised into primary and secondary sectors. The secondary sector is characterised by higher labour turn-over amongst the least skilled, young and old and those in atypical employ-ment. For those at the margins, employment in the nineties has become far more unstable and the penalties attached to job loss, in terms of durations out of work and the wage penalty on return have risen. Hence the labour market has become far riskier. (p.11)

The message is clear enough. Fundamental structural changes are occurring in the nature of employment. The evolving post industrial or informational econ-omy requires different skills and will have a different balance between the secure and insecure, the core and periphery, the low paid and higher paid. The housing markets which have evolved, however, grew out of a period in which jobs were more secure, wages relatively stable and where work was spread more evenly across the population – and where full time work was associated typically with a male breadwinner. There was an assumption of reducing income and social ine-qualities and a progressive spread of middle class lifestyles. The advantages of the minority would become the norm for the majority. The idea of a property owning democracy was a pivotal element of this view of the future. Relatively uniform housing options either in the form of mortgaged home ownership or council housing were on offer to a populace whose living standards were underwritten by the universal safety net of the Keynesian welfare state. In contemporary terminol-ogy, Fordist housing options served a Fordist era.

Internationalisation of policy

There are other changes bearing down on the domestic housing market. National economies are now more open and vulnerable to global economic forces. And where housing markets are dominated by individual home ownership these forces now impact more directly and more immediately on individual households. These forces may be in the form of job loss or reduced earnings or in terms of higher costs of borrowing or more stringent borrowing criteria. To a considerable extent landlordism, public or private, acts as a buffer between broader economic change and individual household circumstances by spreading costs over a greater number of people and typically for a longer period of time. Indeed, municipal landlordism remains the primary safety net for those households excluded from other forms of housing provision. And sustained and planned investment in the physical fabric of the housing stock becomes much more anarchic and uneven where the bulk of that activity depends on the varying fortunes of individual households in a less certain economic environment.

The management and organisation of housing provision itself becomes subject to the internationalising forces we see in other spheres of economic activity. The dominant political, ideological and fiscal pressures to shrink and circumscribe further the activities of the state combine with new organisational forms associated with technological advance to offer new possibilities for the way in which housing is delivered and managed at the national or sub national level. These new forms may enable governments to act more flexibly to accommodate a greater variety of housing needs, cultural diversity and a higher degree of economic uncertainty. A recognition that sustainable housing policies require a move away from uniform and blanket solutions may fit with a situation where the state in its various guises operates as an intelligent consumer rather than direct provider.

Dunleavy (1994) has provocatively outlined a variety of scenarios for the future of public service provision in the context of increased globalisation and advances in information technology. One possible future described by Dunleavy is where public sector provision becomes increasingly dominated by large transnational corporations offering highly specialist and niche skills and service packages. Why should public services be immune from the processes transforming the industrial and commercial worlds? Successful organisations now concentrate on their core competences to be 'best in the world' in a particular niche market. As Dunleavy comments (ibid, p52)

> As large corporations progressively develop and refine their capabilities in current or new implementation areas (for example, fields like information systems management, or criminal justice services) they will often be able to acquire extra focus in depth, to make large capital investments, and to reap economies of scale by producing standardized service packages across many different localities, regions or countries.

From this perspective, functions such as rent collection, repair and maintenance packages and a variety of other aspects of housing management and provision could be provided by major private sector organisations operating transnationally. Specific housing services would be delivered in much the same way as hamburgers – a basic standard package but flexibly adapted to local conditions. This is a logical and not inconceivable extension of processes of decentralisation, privatisation and radical outsourcing of government functions which is already well under way. Flexible specialisation and a further withering away of state functions and direct controls is therefore an essential part of the context of a discussion of what could constitute sustainable housing policies.

The need to reassess policy intervention in the housing sphere is not only a reflection of economic transformations, demographic shifts, environmental concerns and new social divisions and inequalities. Bound up with those changes, particularly with regard to information technology, is the possibility of new organisational forms which permit greater flexibility and more rapid adaptation to changing circumstances. In other words, the rise of the so-called informational mode of development is at the heart of the social and economic changes to which housing policy must now adapt. But new technology also offers the scope for new forms of organisation, control and delivery which may be better able to cater for a less certain economic environment and a world in which multiculturalism and other dimensions of difference are more explicitly recognised and accepted.

Hoggett (1994) has, however, begun to explore the changes in the technology of control suggesting that it is 'remote' rather than devolved control which may be superseding the old bureaucratic forms. Moreover, he suggests that the sustaining of the social fabric and social order has shifted from forms of inclusionary to exclusionary control.

There are clearly contradictory processes at work here. There are strong standardising and homogenising tendencies but also greater recognition of the need for flexibility and greater technical ability to adapt rapidly and deliver variety. There are strong tendencies towards monopoly, oligopoly and big organisations but also towards decentralisation, localisation and diversified agencies. The management of housing, forms of delivery and the range of choices available will remain pivotal elements in the quality of life for the majority of the population. Housing policy must adapt to a more rapid and unpredictable pace of change. In this context there will be inevitable tensions between the different dimensions of sustainability in housing policy, between, for example, narrow economic imperatives and broader environmental concerns. And policies which may appear eminently sensible in terms of economic efficiency and public expenditure may in the longer term prove more expensive in relation to the resulting strains on the social fabric.

In the UK context one cannot ignore the impact of the European Union even though, to date, it has no housing powers or housing policy. Through its involvement in social and economic policy European legislation and approaches are steadily bearing down upon UK housing policy and practice in both the public and private sectors. Very obvious examples of this relate to the level of public expenditure (under the rules for convergence) consumer legislation, employment law (Transfer of Undertakings Protection of Employment (TUPE)), contract tendering arrangements but we are beginning to see much more. Consumer legislation may influence the sale and structuring of mortgages, provision for the homeless, competition from companies and organisations based in continental Europe as well as the move to a single currency and much more (for useful reviews see Stephens, 1995 and Murie, 1996).

New contexts, new challenges for housing

In more open and deregulated economies, domestic policy has been increasingly influenced by external factors. Inflation is perhaps one of the best examples of the external context becoming a key driving force in UK housing policy and housing markets during the last twenty years or more. Inflation has been both a negative and a positive factor in the housing system. On the positive side it has ensured rising capital values and income streams. This has allowed households and organisations to generate surpluses which have fed housing market (or other market) activity. More specifically, it has generally acted to reduce risk. Borrowers, be they home buyers or landlords and lenders, have seen asset values rise and loan to value ratios fall.

In the last sixteen years, with a government committed to seeing rents reflect market values, this has meant that rents have risen too. Government, lenders and providers have therefore not had to cope with falling values (at least in nominal terms) and this has aided capital receipts and borrowing capacity (and reduced some of the pressure for increased subsidy or grant aid). More recently with low general inflation and falling property values individuals and organisations have had to reassess strategies and government is now faced by a range of situations where the call is for greater assistance to overcome the consequences.

Looking to the future, governments in Europe and elsewhere will be striving to reduce expenditure and bring interest rates down as part of a competitive strategy for the country concerned. As is evident from the above these strategies spill over directly into the housing sector and they bear down upon housing policy and housing organisations. In many respects the UK housing policies and the housing system were 'rescued' by high inflation. It was one major factor in driving up house prices (through wage inflation) and it made lending much easier. With a high demand for home ownership it was easier to enter into and succeed with policies such as the Right to Buy and to run down the provision of social housing. Now with low price inflation, the Right to Buy and home ownership more generally look less attractive (at least for a period) and the pressure is to ensure that there are other and adequate forms of housing provision capable of taking up the slack created by the home ownership recession.

That of course is much less easy not least because of the need for increased subsidy. Although home owners receive subsidy this is done via the taxation system. Until recently this allowed government to argue there was no subsidy at all, rather it was income tax foregone. It is significant that this argument is no longer advanced. Indeed central to the debates about cutting back mortgage interest tax relief has been the argument that the subsidy was too generous and poorly targeted.

Sustainability – prospect or mirage?

Each of the authors in this volume recognises the limitations of current policy and the real complexities of securing more effective and sustainable housing policies. But as Maclennan forcefully argued in 1994;

> Too much of the UK housing policy expenditure is wasted on national ideological priorities and, at the local scale, in allocating cash to deal with the symptoms rather than causes.

There are much neglected connections between housing and a range of other social and economic factors, whether at national or local levels, and we need to engineer new mechanisms for tackling these much deeper seated and more complex issues. Moreover, it is evident that we need to use a range of mechanisms and resources to take this forward. These views are echoed in the introduction to this volume. Decades of housing policy have not produced the outcomes needed. They may have ameliorated what was there but it is clear from all the chapters that first, much remains to be done, and second, the mechanisms and procedures we have in place are inadequate to the demands which have to be placed upon them.

After a careful analysis of long term trends in the system, Whitehead highlights the decline in housing investment, the growth of private ownership and the increased emphasis upon affordability all within a context of a shift from viewing housing as a social good to one produced and allocated via the market. This then led to important questions about the inadequacies of the UK housing system and the sustainability of the current levels of home ownership. But in conclusion she returns to the distribution of income and the adequacy of income related benefits as a fundamental starting point for a functioning system.

Maclennan takes up some of these themes in his detailed analysis of the UK housing market. He sets out the interactions between housing and the economy and the ways the UK housing market is adapting to fundamental changes in the economy and government assistance, albeit without any substantial modification of housing supply. He argues against any short term palliatives for this transitional market but sets out a range of suggestions about how to restructure policy related to the private housing market. One of these, the suggestion that the Treasury should publish estimates of house price trends, was echoed in the recent Select Committee Report on the 1995 Budget. Others include assistance with loan insurance costs for low income buyers and a re-targeting of assistance via MIRAS for this group but he actually favours encouragement to private renting as a way of slowing entry to home ownership. Overall his concern is with the efficiency of the housing system and the ways this can be improved by better information, lower costs and improved supply mechanisms. Above all he argues against 'quick fixes' and for the need to create a long term sustainable system.

Mark Boléat, the former Director General of the Council of Mortgage Lenders and a long time housing analyst, sets out the extent of change in the UK housing system and examines the case for an expanded rented sector competing with home ownership although he remains very uncertain as to the extent to which any expansion of renting will attract institutional investment. He notes that housing remains a relatively unimportant issue politically and that certain trends such as reductions in HAG and housing benefit should continue. In his view the current structure of housing tenure and the market is 'almost certainly' sustainable but the increased risk must be managed. Overall, he would see the less inflationary market of the 1990s and beyond as far healthier than that of the 1970s and 1980s and in that sense it is more sustainable.

The position of the private rented sector has assumed some significance in debates about the way ahead. The evolution of and the prospects for the private rented sector are examined by Peter Kemp. His brief review of the situation since the 1930s reveals the extent to which both Conservative and Labour governments collaborated in the decline of the sector. This then leads to the conclusion that its decline and its current standing and status related not just to explicit policy for this tenure but for all housing tenures, and wider issues of taxation, social security and macro-economic management. He predicts that the sector is unlikely to grow or diminish substantially and that its future rests strongly on cross-party agreement. As he astutely observes this may only be possible if 'there is similar agreement on the role of social housing'.

Alan Murie's chapter, 'Beyond State Housing', notes that Britain has been unusual in the extent to which it has entrusted the non profit sector to local government. He goes on to examine the way that provision or its functions have been eroded in a variety of ways. The sector has changed substantially as a result of wider social processes and 'the inevitability of that change means that no part of the housing system can insulate itself and reproduce successful formulae from the past'.

He continues (page 3):

> the key questions for a sound and sustainable housing policy relate to the capacity to adjust to change and sustain progress in relation to the condition of the housing stock and the opportunities of households with different resources . . . the key questions are not about reproducing or defending council housing but do relate to conditions and relationships which council housing has been at least partly successful in modifying.

Murie traces the changing role of council housing and the narrowing of the social profile of its tenants and its wider social base of support through the 1970s and onwards despite DoE reluctance to accept this. As a consequence council housing in the 1990s has very different characteristics than at other stages in its history, with a continued erosion of its role in breaking the link between poor housing and poverty. He considers that the changes which have taken place have altered the sector permanently and there can be no reversion to a 'golden age'. But, with continued concern regarding tenants rights and improvements in housing management and a recognition of strength of the underlying asset base, he argues there are substantial possibilities. This may mean local government moving further down the enabling path but this might simply be the best way of changing roles to meet continuing needs.

One of the main challenges to the local authority role comes from housing associations. In his chapter, Richard Best traces the growth of housing associations, from the 'margins to the mainstream'. He recognises the growing tensions around and within the housing associations 'movement'. Funding restrictions and competition are eroding the collective spirit of the movement and pushing associations towards growth by merger and 'takeover' from the local authority sector. He foresees a continuing levelling of the playing field between tenures, a high demand for private and social renting and a substantial strengthening of the role of housing management. Without housing associations the options for both Conservative and Labour are limited (basically more home ownership or more council housing) and this middle ground is seen as providing the potential for further progress. But as Best recognises the future may not be very comfortable. Moreover while its expansion may assist the overall sustainability of the housing system, the housing associations themselves may 'lack the sense of social significance, solidarity and creativity' which characterised the past.

While there has been a continuous struggle over tenure and providers in the last twenty years, the issue of private sector renewal and improvement has been marginalised in the same period. Indeed, Phil Leather and Sheila Mackintosh describe the policies as 'unsuccessful and short term' and 'unsustainable' because of the gulf between resources and needs. Their chapter provides a brief overview of the problems and then focuses upon a range of solutions, arguing that the key step in 'developing sustainable housing renewal policies is to accept that housing decay and disrepair are ongoing processes'. If house prices were more sensitive to repair costs there would be clearer market signals and this would encourage greater planning and action on the part of householders. They suggest that in the absence of substantial changes to policy which move closer to encouraging or coercing households to act then the alternative in the longer term is that the State will be faced with greater costs.

The question of manageability, effectiveness and sustainability are the themes taken up by Peter Williams but in relation to the organisational and institutional framework of the UK housing system. His starting point is that regardless of policy, it is through the organisational and institutional structure it is made real (whether as intended or not) and delivered. He briefly examines the overall structures in place related to the creation and delivery of policy and then goes on to consider local authorities and housing associations in general and housing management in particular. The forces bearing down on the structures and processes involved include CCT, local government reorganisation and competition. He asks the question: what are the appropriate organisational forms for the creation and delivery of sustainable housing policies? Given that housing has inherently 'local' characteristics there are complex issues to resolve about how to secure that sensitivity to local issues while at the same time securing wider efficiencies and effectiveness. Questions too must be asked about the organisation of housing policy at a regional and national level. Are the current divisions of labour effective? He argues that unless we give equivalent consideration to the mechanism for the creation and delivery of policies and services we run the risk of simply repeating the mistakes of the past.

This of course raises the questions of standards. At one level, what are deemed 'good' or 'bad' standards can be subjective. However, as Barry Goodchild and Valerie Karn argue, the setting and maintenance of adequate building standards to secure housing which is sustainable over the long term is a matter of crucial significance, albeit it is perhaps the easiest matter to ignore in the short term (especially if it has public expenditure consequences). The authors examine trends in the private sector and point towards the problems of package deals (i.e., property plus a range of white goods etc) at the bottom of the market which lose value very quickly. They describe the changes in the standard and procurement in the social housing sector, not least under the private finance regime introduced in 1988. The authors examine the incentives or otherwise to provide housing which seeks to promote sustainability (e.g., energy efficiency, adaptability). Goodchild and Karn conclude by asking what type of housing will be required in fifty years time and how the current fall in standards can be reconciled with the growing regulatory pressure for improved energy and accessibility standards.

Alan Holmans examines the financial consequences of past, current and future housing policy. Central to his concerns is the question of the number of households who cannot afford decent housing without some form of assistance and the interactions between housing assistance and social security. This has the effect of keeping total housing expenditure relatively low, low income home owners in poverty and supports the competitiveness of the economy in comparison to other countries. He then develops arguments about the interactions between housing demand and supply and wages and interest rates. As he concludes he sets out a 'defensive agenda for housing finance', one in which his primary concern is to limit the damage which the system might cause. This is an important chapter because without the right underpinning and whatever the housing system intended, unless the right financial structures are in place, needs will never produce effective demand or supply.

Change

What all of these contributions reveal is the considerable degree of change which has taken place in the UK over the last four decades. They also give a clear sense of the complexity of the systems in which these changes have taken place and the continuing failure of policy to create within the UK, the flexible and adaptable housing system which is required. Can we now do better? None of the authors argues there is a single best solution and all would agree there is much we still do not know about the UK's housing system. Better understanding and better information (especially with respect to the longer term) might have contributed to better policy, though as Alan Holmans has made very clear, governments do not come to power with agendas waiting to be filled through the work of researchers and policy analysts.

What then are the current political agendas and how might the contributions in this volume contribute to their evolution and development? Perhaps most obviously they reinforce the substantial consensus about the valid and valuable role of all existing tenures and providers. All would recognise the value of, for example, private renting and the role of local authorities in housing provision. Equally all would recognise that in the final analysis, it is the task of government to produce policy and that policy will be the product of the democratic and political process. As a consequence policy will always be in the making.

What the contributions in this volume try to do above all else is to set out at least some (but not all) of the big housing issues which the political process should absorb and which governments must tackle. Issues of costs, quality, a diversity of provision, interactions with wider social and economic policy and the organisational framework are considered in some detail. While there is no explicit coverage of homelessness, special needs or community care, rising issues throughout the 1980s, all contributors would recognise their significance. Perhaps inevitably most contributors return to the question of resources and the role of government subsidies. There has been a fundamental shift in housing subsidy, away from property based subsidy (and the Department of the Environment or equivalent) and towards people based subsidy (and the Department of Social Security). Most would agree the shift has been too pronounced and that other costs have been generated which potentially challenge the savings which have been secured.

In many respects a concern with balance is common to many of the contributions. Political agendas perhaps inevitably drive policy to extremes. What is different about the late 1990s compared to say the 1970s is the diversity of provision and providers. As Goodlad (1994) reminds us, a description of the institutional framework in the 1970s of the housing world was dominated by the concerns of central and local government, new towns and building societies. In the 1990s, new towns would largely cease to be part of the agenda and instead we would be talking about housing associations, housing action trusts, housing investment trusts, local housing companies, banks, central lenders to name but a few. We now have a national housing agency in Scotland, Scottish Homes, and both the Housing Corporation and to a lesser degree Housing for Wales are playing ever stronger strategic roles. Given that a central argument in the book is flexibility and the capacity to respond to local circumstances this new multiplicity of providers can be seen as both a strength and a weakness. Taking account of this new situation will be crucial to the success of policy in the years to come. Partnerships, coordination and collaboration will be essential parts of policy and practice.

A second major change flows from the shift away from housing subsidies and towards market prices and market competition. Competitive forces have been unleashed in the housing system which are still working their way through it. The potential for variation between organisations becomes ever more sharply revealed when they operate as businesses. Equally it is important not to overstate the capacity of such organisations. The UK will not be able to operate a subsidy free housing system and at the same time secure adequate affordable housing for all.

This raises a further factor which will be of crucial significance. Holmans (1991) noted that government failed to fully appreciate the changes in household circumstances which had taken place in the 1970s and on. The same is potentially true in the late 1990s and beyond. There has been a widening gap between the majority of the population who are relatively well off and the poor. As we move into the next century this may be further exacerbated by the rising housing inheritance effect.

This 'maturation' effect also increasingly applies to the housing association sector. It has grown through the application of public subsidy (just as the local authority sector had done in the period 1950 to 1980) and as debt declines relative to asset values the potential to take advantage of that position grows. Kemeny (1995) argues strongly that the UK should move alongside some other European countries to exploit this maturation effect and to move towards a unitary and unified rental sector. There are strong grounds for supporting this view, not least because of its potential to break subsidy dependence.

A housing system with less assistance, higher real costs, more reliance upon private finance, more movement and adjustment to housing circumstances and greater competition will result in all providers and consumers facing greater risks. This raises the question of whether we might see growing use of insurance or other techniques to reduce those risks. These might include derivatives to reduce the impact of interest rate changes, insurance against the loss of jobs or sickness or the loss of a contract. The creation of a US style government backed financier, insurer and facilitator has much to commend it. An intermediary which can intervene in the market, take risks individuals or agencies might be unable or unwilling to take themselves and which can then be packaged up and passed back to the market has many attractions. There can be no doubt that such a vehicle might enhance the potential to draw in private finance. Regardless of specific housing policies (and governments) private finance has to become an ever more important component of the UK housing system. While this should lead to enhanced resources it must be recognised that borrowing has a cost even though it is spread over the longer term. We should not pretend that it produces a cost free policy and it is essential that policy is constantly examined with respect for associated costs, benefits and alternatives. To maintain maximum effectiveness, a flexible housing system must be closely monitored.

If we are moving to a looser and more *laissez faire* system, where organisations and individuals have the capacity and opportunity to react to changing circumstances and needs in ways which are neither driven solely by or set out through central government policy, then we might expect the structure and content of policy itself to change. In the past, policy has often consisted of targets explicit and implicit and the general approach has been one which has sought to constrain agencies to produce ordained outcomes. The evidence of the past twenty years or more is of the creative ability of organisations such as local authorities, housing associations and lenders. Central government policy should reflect and support such abilities. Central government itself should move further towards an enabling role, supporting and sustaining rather than directing and controlling. This might also suggest that the UK undertakes more 'experiments' in the form of pilot schemes where good ideas can be tested and evaluated in practice. Under such a model we do not have to abandon the past in order to embrace the future. We can much more effectively manage any required transition.

To move to an effective enabling role whether at central or local government is also to presume an adequate housing planning and investment system and a proper system for monitoring and regulation. At present the UK has neither although it is moving in that direction. Local housing investment plans are still very varied in quality reflecting both differing local competencies but also the fact that 'good' plans have not appeared to have any clear relationship to resource allocation. While it is right to distinguish plans from bids and for any local authority to be required to really think through what it is doing and how the local system is operating before any bid can be justified, the absence of any really positive stance by government to this process has been a great weakness. That must change and bottom up planning for housing must become just as important as DoE plan priorities and public expenditure bids to the Treasury.

This of course implies a shift of power and a stronger partnership approach. Neither will be easily achieved but it is difficult to see how we might create the more flexible and adaptable housing system required without going down this route. If this book contributes in any way to moving first debate and then policy and practice down this path it must be deemed a success. The evidence from the contributions here which have sought to look back over our housing histories and forward to our housing futures is that there are lessons to be learned and opportunities to apply them. A housing system which learns from its past and adapts to a future which is both riskier and more uncertain is one which will bring the UK closer to its goal of a well and securely housed population.

REFERENCES

Amin, A (1994) *Post-Fordism: A Reader*, Blackwell, Oxford.

Bader, (1996) Working in Harmony, *Welsh Housing Quarterly*, 22, pp 9–10.

Baker, C (1976) Housing Associations, *Estates Gazette*, p 52.

Baker, R *et al.* (1992) *The Scope for Competitive Tendering in Housing Management*, HMSO, London.

Ball, M (1983) *Housing Policy and Economic Power*, Methuen, London.

Banting, K (1979) *Poverty, Politics and Policy*, Macmillan, London.

Barnett, M J (1969) *The Politics of Legislation*, Weidenfeld and Nicolson, London.

Bassett, K and Short, J (1980) *Housing and Residential Structure*, Routledge and Kegan Paul, London.

Benko, A (1991) *Home Maintenance Insurance Scheme: the Dutch Experience*, Anchor Housing Trust, Oxford.

Best, R (1991) *Housing Association 1890–1990* in S G Lowe and D J Hughes, eds, *A New Century of Social Housing*, Leicester University Press, Leicester.

Best, Richard; Kemp, Peter; Coleman, David; Merret, Stephen; Crook, Tony (1992) *The Future of Private Renting; Consensus and Action*, Joseph Rowntree Foundation, York.

Boléat, M and Coles, A (1987) *The Mortgage Market: theory and practice of Housing Finance*, Allen and Unwin, London.

Boléat, M and Taylor, B (1993) *Housing in Britain*, Council of Mortgage Lenders, London.

Bines, W *et al.* (1993) *Managing Social Housing*, HMSO, London.

Bootle, R (1996) *The Death of Inflation, surviving and thriving in the zero era*, Nicholas Brealey, London.

Bover, G, Muellbauer, J and Murphy, A (1988) *Housing, Wages and UK Labour Markets*, Discussion Paper 268, Centre for Economic Policy Research, London.

Brion, M (1994) *Women in the Housing Service*, Routledge, London.

Brown, J and Fraser, R (1996) First round win for housing DSOs *Local Government Chronicle*, CCT Focus 2, 19 April.

Castells, M (1991) *The Informational City*, Blackwell, Oxford.

Central Office of Information (1962) *Housing in England and Wales in 1960*, HMSO, London.

Central Policy Review Staff, CPRS (1975) *A Joint Framework for Social Policies*, HMSO, London.

Central Policy Review Staff (1978) *Housing and Social Policies; Some Interactions*, HMSO, London.

CHAC (1947) *The Management of Municipal Housing Estates*, HMSO, London.

CHAC (1959) *Councils and their Houses*, HMSO, London.

Chaplin, R, Martin, S, Yang, J H and Whitehead, C (1994) *Affordability: Definitions, Measures and Implications for Lenders*, Discussion Paper No 45, Department of Land Economy, Cambridge.

Clapham, D (1989) *Goodbye Council Housing?* The Fabian Society, Unwin Paperbacks, London.

Clapham, D (1992) The effectiveness of housing management, *Social Policy and Administration*, Vol. 26, no 3, pp 209–225.

Cmnd 9513 (1985) *Home Improvement – a New Approach*, HMSO, London

Coles, A and Taylor, B (1993), Trends in Tenure Preference, *Housing Finance*, No 19, August.

Cope, H (1990) *Housing Association Policy and Company Practice*, Macmillan, London, p 174.

Cowans, D (1996) Social Housing Management for the 21st Century, Paper to the Demography Symposium, Housing Corporation, Liverpool.

Crook, A D H (1986) Privatisation of housing and the impact of the Conservative Government's initiatives on low cost home ownership and private renting between 1979 and 1984 in England and Wales Part 4: Private renting, *Environment and Planning A*, Vol. 18.

Crook, A D H, Kemp, P A, Anderson, I and Bowman, S (1991) *Tax Incentives and the Revival of Private Renting*, Cloister Press, New York.

Crook, A D H, Kemp, P A and Hughes, J (1995) *The Supply of Privately Rented Homes*, Joseph Rowntree Foundation, York.

Cullingworth, J B (1965) *English Housing Trends*, Bell, London.

Cullingworth, J B (1979) *Essays on Housing Policy*, George, Allen and Unwin, London.

Day, P et al. (1993) *Home Rules; Regulation and Accountability in Social Housing*, Rowntree Foundation, York.

Department of the Environment (1971) *Housing Associations*, HMSO, London, p 121.

Department of Environment (1977a) *Housing Policy: A Consultative Document*, Cmnd 6851, HMSO, London.

Department of Environment (1977b) *Housing Policy: Technical Volume Part 1*, HMSO, London.

Department of Environment Development Management Group (1978) *Value for money in local authority house building programmes*, DoE, London.

Department of the Environment (1987) *Housing: the Government's Proposals*, HMSO, London.

Department of the Environment (1988) *English House Condition Survey 1986*, HMSO, London.

Department of the Environment (1992) *Planning Policy Guidance: Housing*, PPG3 (revised), DoE, London.

Department of the Environment (1993) *The English House Condition Survey 1991*, HMSO, London.

Department of the Environment (1994) *Access to Local Authority and Housing Association Tenancies. A Consultation Paper*, DoE, London.

Department of the Environment (1995a) *Annual Report 1995*, HMSO, London.

Department of the Environment (1995b) *Projections of Households in England to 2016*, HMSO, London.

Department of the Environment (1995c) *Project Specification: Feasibility Study of an Economic Model of the Future Demand for Social Housing in England*, DoE, London.

Department of the Environment (1996) *Housing Need*, The Government's response to the Second Report from the House of Commons Select Committee on the Environment Session 1995–96, HMSO, London.

Department of Social Security (1992) *Households Below Average Income: A Statistical Analysis 1979–1988/89*, HMSO, London.

Department of Social Security (1993) *The Future of Social Security*, HMSO, London.

Derbyshire, B (1995) Beginning a quality debate, *Housing*, March, p 16.

Dieleman, F M (1994) Social rented housing, valuable asset or unsustainable burden?, *Urban Studies*, Vol. 31, No 3, pp 447–463.

Dieleman, F M and Jobse, R B (1991) Multi-family households in the social rental sector and the changing Dutch housing market, *Housing Studies*, 6, pp 193–206.

Dieleman, F M and van Engelsdorp Gastelaars, R E (1992) Housing and physical planning. In: F M Dieleman and S Musterd (eds), *The Randstad: a Research and Policy Laboratory*, pp 65–95, Kluwer, Dordrecht/Boston/London.

Doling, J and Davies, M (1984) *The Public Control of Privately Rented Housing*, Gower, Aldershot.

Donnison, D V, Cockburn, C and Corlett, T (1961) *Housing Since the Rent Act*, Codicote Press, Welwyn Garden City.

Donnison, D V (1967) *The Government of Housing*, Penguin, Harmondsworth.

Dorling, D and Cornford, J (1995) Who has negative equity? How house price falls in Britain have hit different groups of home buyers, *Housing Studies*, Vol. 10.

Douetil, D (1994) The interrelationship between the mortgage and insurance industries in the UK, *Housing Policy Debate*, Vol. 5 Issue 3.

Down, D, Holmans, A E and Small, H (1994) Trends in the size of the private rented sector in England, *Housing Finance*, May.

Dunleavy, P (1989) Paradoxes of an ungrounded statism, in F G Castles (ed) *The Comparative History of Public Policy*, Polity Press, Cambridge.

Dunleavy, P (1994) Globalisation of Public Service Provision: Can Government be 'Best in World'? *Public Policy and Administration*, Vol. 9, No 2.

English, J (1979) Access and Deprivation in Local Authority Housing, in C Jones (ed), *Urban Deprivation and the Inner City*, Croom Helm, London.

Ermisch, J (ed) (1990) *Housing in the National Economy: A Review of the Evidence*, Housing Studies.

Ford, J and Wilcox, S (1994) *Affordable housing, low incomes, and the flexible housing market*, NFHA Report 22, National Federation of Housing Associations, London.

Ford, J and Kempson, E (1995) No Way Out, *Roof*, July and August 1995, pp 30–33.

Forrest, R, Kennett, P and Leather, P with Gordon, D (1994) *Homeowners in Negative Equity*, SAUS Publications, Bristol.

Forrest, R and Murie, A (1988) *Selling the Welfare State*, Routledge, London.

Forrest, R and Murie, A (1990) *Residualisation and Council Housing: A Statistical Update*, SAUS, University of Bristol, Bristol.

Forrest, R and Murie, A (1993) *New Homes for Home Owners: A Study of Vacancy Chains in Southern England*, HMSO, London.

Forrest, R and Murie, A (1994a) *The Resale of Former Council Homes*, HMSO, London.

Forrest, R and Murie, A (1994b) Home ownership in recession, *Housing Studies*, Vol. 9.

Francis Committee (1971) *Report of the Committee on the Rent Acts*, HMSO, London.

Furbey, R and Goodchild, B (1986) *Housing in Use*, Sheffield City Polytechnic, Sheffield.

Gibb, K (1994) *Labour Market Flexibility and Housing in Britain*, CHRUS Occasional Paper No 5, University of Glasgow, Glasgow.

Glass, N (1994) Housing and the Economy (Harry Simpson Memorial Lecture), Joseph Rowntree Foundation, York.

Goldsmith, S (1975) *Wheelchair Housing*, HDD Occasional Paper 2/75, London, Department of the Environment, Housing Development Directorate: reprinted from *The Architects' Journal*, 26 June.

Goodchild, B and Furbey, R (1986) Standards in housing design: a review of the main changes since the Parker Morris report (1961), *Land Development Studies*, Vol. 3, pp 79–99.

Goodchild, B (1994) Housing design, urban form and sustainable development, *The Town Planning Review*, Vol. 65, No. 2.

Goodlad, R (1994) Calling a spade a spade: researching the politics of housing, seminar paper, Centre for Housing Research and Urban Studies, University of Glasgow, Glasgow.

Greater London Council (1986) *Housing Standards – A Survey of New Build Local Authority Housing in London 1981–4*, GLC, London.

Gregg, P and Machin, S (1994) *Is the UK rise in inequality different?*, pp 93–125, in *The UK Labour Market*, Barrell, R (ed), Cambridge University Press, Cambridge.

Hamnett, C and Randolph, B (1988) *Cities, Housing and Profits*, Hutchinson, London.

Hancock, K (1993) Can Pay, Won't Pay or Economic Principles of Affordability, *Urban Studies*, Vol. 30, No. 3.

Hancock, R and Weir, P (1994) *More Ways than Means: A Guide to Pensioners' Incomes in Great Britain During the 1980s*, Age Concern Institute of Gerontology, London.

House of Commons *Official Report* (Hansard), 27 March 1961, col 971 and following.

Harloe, M (1985) *Private Rented Housing in the United States and Europe*, Croom Helm, London.

Harloe, M (1989) *Social Housing and the Social Question: Early Housing Reform and its Legacy* (Mimeo).

Henderson, J and Karn, V (1987) *Race, Class and State Housing*, Gower, Aldershot.

Hills, J (1991) *Unravelling Housing Finance*, Oxford, Clarendon Press.

Hindess, B (1987) *Freedom, Equality, and the Market*, Tavistock Publications, London.

HMSO (1995) *Our Future Homes*, HMSO, London.

Hoggett, P (1994) The modernisation of the UK welfare state in Burrows, R and Loader, B (eds), *Towards a Post-Fordist Welfare State*, Routledge, London.

Holmans, A E (1961) *United States Fiscal Policy 1945–59: its contribution to economic stability*, Oxford University Press.

Holmans, A E (1970) A forecast of effective demand for housing in Great Britain in the nineteen seventies, *Social Trends*, No 1.

Holmans, A E (1987) *Housing Policy in Britain: A History*, Croom Helm, London.

Holmans, A E (1990) *House Prices: Changes Through Time at National and Sub-National Level*, Department of the Environment, London.

Holmans, A E *Estimates of Housing Equity Withdrawal by Owner-occupiers in the United Kingdom 1970 to 1990*, Department of the Envionment, London.

Holmans, A E (1991) The 1977 National Housing Policy Review in Retrospect, *Housing Studies*, Vol. 6, No. 3, pp 206–219.

Holmans, A E (1993) The Changing Employment Circumstances of Council Tenants, in Department of the Environment, *Housing in England*, HMSO, London.

Holmans, A E with M Frosztega (1994), *House Property and Inheritance in the UK*, HMSO, London.

Holmans, A E (1995a), Where have all the First-time Buyers Gone? *Housing Finance*, February.

Holmans, A E (1995b) *Housing Demand and Need in England, 1991 to 2011*. Joseph Rowntree Foundation, York.

Holmans, A E (1996a) *Housing Need and Demand in Wales, 1991–2011*, Joseph Rowntree Foundation, York.

Holmans, A E (1996b) Meeting Housing need in the private rented sector, in Wilcox, S (ed.) *Housing Review 1996/97*, Joseph Rowntree Foundation, York.

House of Commons (1981a) *Council House Sales*, Second Report of the Environment Committee, Session 1980–81; Vol. 11, Minutes of Evidence, (HC 366-II; HC 535 i-xi (1979–80), HMSO, London.

House of Commons (1981b) *DOE's Housing Policies*, Third Report of the Environment Committee, Session 1980–81, HC 383, HMSO, London.

House of Commons (1982) *The Private Rented Sector*, First Report of the Environment Committee, Session 1981–82, HC 40, HMSO, London.

House of Commons (1993) *Inquiry into the Housing Corporation*, Environment Committee, HMSO, London.

House of Commons Environment Committee (1995) Department of the Environment Memorandum on Provision for Social Housing, First Special Report, HC 442, HMSO, London.

House of Commons (1996) *Housing Need*, Volumes 1 and 2, Second Report of the Environment Committee, Session 1995–96, HMSO, London.

Housing Corporation (1983) *Design and Contract Criteria*, The Housing Corporation, London.

Howe, G (1965) The waiting list society, in *The Conservative Opportunity*, Batsford, London.

Howe, G and Jones, C (1956) *Houses to Let*, Conservative Political Centre, London.

Hulchanski, D (1995), The Concept of Housing Affordability, *Housing Studies*, Vol. 10, No. 4, pp 471–492.

Hutton, W (1996) *The State We're In*, Vintage Books, London.

Institute of Housing and Royal Institute of British Architects (1983) *Homes for the Future*, RIBA/CIoH, London.

Jackson, P (ed) (1995) *Measures for Success in the Public Sector*, A Public Finance Foundation Reader, CIPFA, London.

Jenkins, S P and Cowell, F A (1994) Dwarfs and giants in the 1980s: trends in the UK income distribution, *Fiscal Studies*, 15,1, 99–118.

Jobse, R B and Musterd, S (1993) Population Change in Residential Environments in the Metropolitan Areas of Amsterdam, Rotterdam and The Hague, *Tijdschrift voor Economische en Sociale Geografie*, Vol. 84, No. 4, pp 304–312.

Jones, P (1985) *National Federation of Housing Associations 1935–1985; The Jubilee Album*, NFHA, p 62.

Joseph Rowntree Foundation (1991) *Inquiry into British Housing Second Report*, Joseph Rowntree Foundation, York.

Joseph Rowntree Foundation (1994a) *Housing Finance Review 1994/95*, Joseph Rowntree Foundation, p 13.

Joseph Rowntree Foundation (1994b) *Inquiry into Planning for Housing*, Joseph Rowntree Foundation, York.

Karn, V and Sheridan, L (1994) *New Homes in the 1990s*, in University of Manchester, Manchester and the Joseph Rowntree Foundation, York.

Karn, V, La Tourelle, D, Symes, M and Todd, M (1995) Housing Design and Management for Ethnic Minorities: do housing associations meet their needs? School of Social Policy and School of Architecture, University of Manchester.

Kemeny, J (1981) *The Myth of Home Ownership*, Routledge, London.

Kemeny, J (1993) The significance of Swedish rental policy: cost renting: command economy versus the social market in comparative perspective, *Housing Studies*, Vol. 8, No. 1, pp 3–16.

Kemeny, J (1995) *From Public Housing to the Social Market*, Routledge, London.

Kemp, P A (1984) The transformation of the urban housing market in Britain c1885 to 1939, D. Phil thesis, University of Sussex: Brighton.

Kemp, P A (1988) The impact of the assured tenancy scheme, 1980–1986, in P A Kemp (ed.) *The Private Provision of Rented Housing*, Avebury, Aldershot.

Kemp, P A (1990) Deregulation, markets and the 1988 Housing Act, *Social Policy and Administration*, Vol. 24.

Kemp, P A (1991) From solution to problem? Council housing and the development of national housing policy, in S G Lowe and D J Hughes (eds) *A New Century of Social Housing*, Leicester University Press, Leicester.

Kemp, P A (1992) Housing, in D Marsh and R A W Rhodes (eds) *Implementing Thatcherite Policies: Audit of an Era*, Open University Press, Buckingham.

Kemp, P A (1993) Rebuilding the Private Rented Sector? in P Malpass and R Means (eds) *Implementing Housing Policy*, Open University Press, Buckingham.

Kemp, P (1994a) Researching housing management performance, paper presented to the Housing Studies Association Conference, York.

Kemp, P A (1994b) Housing allowances and the fiscal crisis of the welfare state, *Housing Studies*, Vol. 9.

Kemp, P and Williams, P (1991) Housing management: an historical perspective, in Lowe, S and Hughes, D (eds) *A New Century of Social Housing*, Leicester University Press, Leicester.

Kleinman, M P and Whitehead, C (1988) British housing since 1979: has the system changed? *Housing Studies*, Vol. 3, No. 1.

Kleinman, M P and Whitehead, C (1996) *The Private Rented Sector*, London National Federation of Housing Associations.

Kleinman, M P, Morrison, N and Whitehead, C (1994) Forecasting housing demand and housing needs, *Development and Planning 1994*, Granta Editions, Cambridge.

Lansley, S (1979) *Housing and Public Policy*, Croom Helm, London.

Lea, M (1994) Efficiency and stability of housing market systems, *Housing Policy Debate*, Vol. 5, Issue 3.

Leather, P and Mackintosh, S (1992) *Maintaining home ownership: the agency approach*, Longman/Institute of Housing, London.

Leather, P and Mackintosh, S (1993) Neighbourhood housing renewal, in R Hambleton and M Taylor (eds) *People in Cities: A Transatlantic Policy Exchange*, SAUS Publications, Bristol.

Leather, P and Mackintosh, S (1994a) *The Future of Housing Renewal Policy*, SAUS Publications, Bristol.

Leather, P and Mackintosh, S, (eds) (1994b) *Encouraging housing maintenance in the private sector*, Occasional Paper 41, SAUS Publications, Bristol.

Leather, P, Mackintosh, S and Rolfe, S (1994) *Papering over the cracks: housing conditions and the nation's health*, National Housing Forum, London.

Linneman, P and Gyurko, J (1995) *The Changing Role of Age and Ageing on Home-Ownership*, Wharton Real Estate Centre (mimeo).

Local Government Chronicle (1996) Contractors draw battle line on CCT, 19 January; CCT Clampdown to follow May Elections, 4 April; Bids built on weak foundations, 10 May.

Local Government Management Board (1994) Just good freinds? Managing housing and social services together, LGMB, Luton.

London Research Centre (1991) *Housing Needs and Supply in London: The Next Five Years*, LRC, London.

Lyall, S (1983) Beneath the housing boom, *Building*, 24 June.

Mackintosh, S and Leather, P (1992a) *Home improvement under the new regime*, Occasional Paper 38, SAUS Publications, Bristol.

Mackintosh, S and Leather, P (1992b) *Staying Put Revisited*, Anchor Housing Trust, Oxford.

Mackintosh, S and Leather, P (1993) *Renovation file: a profile of housing conditions and housing renewal policies in the United Kingdom*, Anchor Housing Trust, Oxford.

Maclennan, D (1994) *A Competitive UK Economy: The Challenges for Housing Policy*, Joseph Rowntree Foundation, York.

Maclennan, D (1994) *Housing Policy for a Competitive Economy*, Joseph Rowntree Foundation, York.

Maclennan, D (1995a) *The changing labour market and the housing system*, Employment Policy Institute Conference, The 30–30–40 Society, London.

Maclennan, D (1995b) Two Cheers and Assorted Heckles: the DoE and Housing Policy, 1970–1995, 25th Anniversary of the DoE, DoE, London.

Maclennan, D *et al.* (1989) *The Nature and Effectiveness of Housing Management in England*, HMSO, London.

Maclennan, D and Tu, Yong (1995a) *A Survivor Model of Mortgages and Equity Withdrawal*, CHRUS (mimeo), University of Glasgow, Glasgow.

Maclennan, D and Tu, Yong (1995b) *Household Consumption and Housing Market Change: Micro-economic Evidence*, CHRUS (mimeo), University of Glasgow, Glasgow.

Maclennan, D and Williams, R (eds) (1990) *Affordable Housing in Britain and America*, Joseph Rowntree Foundation, York.

Maclennan, D, More, A and Gibb, K (1991) *Paying for Britain's Housing*, Joseph Rowntree Foundation, York.

Malpass, P (1990) *Reshaping Housing Policy*, Routledge, London.

Malpass, P and Murie, A (1994) *Housing Policy and Practice*, 4th edition, Macmillan, Basingstoke.

Malpezzi, S and Maclennan, D (1994) Estimating housing supply elasticities: constrasting the UK and the USA, Paper presented at the ENHR Conference, Glasgow.

McCrone, G and Stephens, M (1995) *Housing Policy in Britain and Europe*, UCL Press, London.

McQuail, P (1995) *A View from the Bridge*, Department of the Environment, London.

Meen, G (1994a) *Impact of Higher Rents*, Housing Research Findings No 109, Joseph Rowntree Foundation, York.

Meen, G (1994b) *Changes in the Relationships between Housing and the Rest of the Economy*, Findings No 122, York, Joseph Rowntree Foundation, York.

Meen, G (1995) Is housing good for the economy? *Housing Studies*, 10, pp 405–424.

Merrett, S (1979) *State Housing in Britain*, Routledge and Kegan Paul, London.

Merrett, S and Gray, F (1982) *Owner Occupation in Britain*, Routledge and Kegan Paul, London.

Miles, D (1992) Housing markets, consumption and financial liberalisation in the major economies, *European Economic Review*.

Miles, D (1994) *Housing Financial Markets and the Wider Economy*, Wiley, Chichester.

Milner-Holland Committee (1965) *Report of the Committee on Housing in Greater London*, HMSO, London.

Minford, P and Riley, J (1994) *The UK Labour Market: micro rigidities and macro obstructions*, pp 258–272, in R Barrell (ed.) *The UK Labour Market*, Cambridge University Press, Cambridge.

Ministry of Housing and Local Government (1953) *Housing: the Next Steps*, HMSO, London.

Ministry of Housing and Local Government (1961) *Homes for Today and Tomorrow*, HMSO, London.

Ministry of Housing and Local Government (1965) *The Housing Programme 1965 to 1970*, HMSO, London.

Ministry of Housing and Local Government (1968: reprinted 1970) *Space in the home*, HMSO, London.

Morton, J (1989) *The First Twenty Years*, the Housing Corporation, London, p 53.

Muellbauer, J (1990) *The Housing Market and the UK Economy: Problems and Opportunities*, in Ermisch (ed.) op cit., pp 48–71.

Muellbauer, J and Murphy, A (1994) *Regional Housing Markets and Consumption*, Project Report to the Joseph Rowntree Foundation, York.

Murie, A (1974) *Household Movement and Housing Choice*, CURS, University of Birmingham, Birmingham.

Murie, A (1976) *The Sale of Council Houses*, CURS, University of Birmingham, Birmingham.

Murie, A (1983) *Housing Inequality and Deprivation*, Heinemann, London.

Murie, A (1985) Housing, in M Loughlin, D Gelfand and K Young (eds) *Half a Century of Municipal Decline?*, Allen and Unwin, London, pp 187–201.

Murie, A (1993) Restructuring housing markets and housing access, *Social Policy Review 5*, Social Policy Association.

Murie, A (1994) *Cities and Housing after the Welfare State*, AME, University of Amsterdam, Amsterdam.

Murie, A (1995) Researching housing management: causes, context and questions, Housing Studies Association Conference.

Murie, A, Niner, P and Watson, C (1976) *Housing Policy and the Housing System*, Allen and Unwin, London.

Murie, A and Wang, Y P (1993) *The Sale of Public Sector Housing in Scotland 1979–91*, School of Planning and Housing, Edinburgh College of Art/Heriot-Watt University, Edinburgh.

Musterd, S and Ostendorf, W (1992) Affluence, access to jobs, and ethnicity in the Dutch welfare state: the case of Amsterdam, paper given to IGU Population Geography Symposium, Los Angeles.

Musterd, S and Ostendorf, W (1993a) Dynamics of the Amsterdam urban region in the eighties, Paper presented at the Conference on Migration and Urbanisation, Umea, Sweden.

Musterd, S and Ostendorf, W (1993b) *Ethnicity and the Dutch Welfare State; the Case of Amsterdam* (mimeo).

National Audit Office (1989) *Department of the Environment: Housing Needs and Allocations*, HMSO, London.

National Federation of Housing Associations (various) *Annual Reports 1976, 1977*, NFHA, London.

National Federation of Housing Associations (1985) *Inquiry into British Housing*, NFHA, London.

National Federation of Housing Associations (1987) *Rents, Risks, Rights*, NFHA, London.

National Housing Forum (1989) *Housing Needs in the 1990s*, National Housing Forum, London.

National Federation of Housing Associations (1995).

Nevitt, A A (1966) *Housing, Taxation and Subsidies*, Nelson, London.

Newbury, J and King, A (1996) Managing Housing Contracts; a good practice guide, CIH, Coventry.

Northern Ireland Housing Executive (1993) *Northern Ireland house condition survey 1991*, NIHE, Belfast.

Nystrom, L (1994) *Housing in Sweden: Half a century of promotion and control and environmental challenges for the next*, paper presented at a conference of The European Network of Housing Research, Technical University of Delft in the Netherlands, 10–12 March.

Office of Population Censuses and Surveys (1995) *Housing in England 1993/94*, HMSO, London.

Olsen, A M (1991) Trends in Housing Association Development; a study of procurement methods and funding constraints following the Housing Act, 1988, a dissertation submitted in part fulfilment of the degree of BA. (Hons) Housing Studies at Sheffield City Polytechnic, Sheffield.

Ostendorf, W (1992) Ecological constraints and the spatial policies of municipalities in the Amsterdam Urban Region, in van der Wusten H (ed.) *The Urban
Political Arena*, Netherlands Geographical Studies 140, University of Amsterdam, Amsterdam.

Page, D (1993) *Building for Communities*, Joseph Rowntree Foundation, York.

Page, D (1994) *Developing Communities*, Joseph Rowntree Foundation, York.

Parker Morris Report (see Ministry of Housing and Local Government, 1961).

Parliamentary Debates 1945–6, *Hansard*, Vol. 414, col 1222.

Phillips, D (1985) *What Price Equality?*, GLC, London.

Piven, F (1986) Cities, housing and the rise of 'hyper-capitalist' regimes, paper
presented to the City Renewal Through Partnership conference, Glasgow.

Pooley, C (ed.) (1993) *Housing Strategy in Europe 1880–1930*, Leicester University Press, Leicester.

Power, A (1987) *Property before People: The Management of Twentieth Century
Council Housing*, Allen and Unwin, London.

Prescott-Clarke, P, Clemens, S and Park, A (1994) *Routes into Local Authority
Housing*, HMSO, London.

Prescott-Clarke, P, Allan, P and Morrissey, C (1988) *Queuing for Housing: A
Study of Council Housing Waiting Lists*, HMSO, London.

Reich, R (1991) *The Work of Nations*, Simon and Schuster, London.

Ridley Committee (1945) *Report of the Inter-Departmental Committee on Rent
Control*, HMSO, London.

Ridley, N (1988) Speech to Institute of Housing Conference, 17 August, DoE
news release, London.

Rolfe, S, Mackintosh, S and Leather, P (1993) *Age File 93*, Anchor Housing
Trust, Oxford.

Rowden, I (1981) How's this for starters, *Building Design*, May 29, No. 547.

Samuel R *et al.* (1962) But nothing happens, *New Left Review*, Nos 13–14,
January–April.

Scott (1994) Housing Management – Key Questions, paper to seminar Housing
Policy and Research Priorities, Centre for Housing Research and Urban Studies, University of Glasgow. 22–24 March 1994.

Scottish Homes (1993) *Scottish house condition survey 1991: survey report*,
Scottish Homes, Edinburgh.

Simpson, A (1981) *Stacking the Decks*, Nottingham and District CRC,
Nottingham.

Special Risk Services (1995) *Mortgage Insurance News*, No. 9.

Stafford, B and Doling, J (1981) *Rent Control and Rent Regulation in England
and Wales 1915–1980*, Occasional Paper No. 2, Centre for Urban and Regional Studies, University of Birmingham, Birmingham.

Stephens, M (1995) *Monetary Policy and House Price Volatility in Western
Europe*, University of Glasgow, Glasgow (mimeo).

Stewart, J (1988) *A New Management for Housing Departments*, LGMB, Luton.

Tims, M (1968) *An Historical Survey of Selected Housing Associations*, Joseph
Rowntree Memorial Trust, York.

Van Amersfoort, H (1992) Ethnic residential patterns in a welfare state: lessons
from Amsterdam, 1970–1990, *New Community*, 18(3) 439–456.

Waddilove, L (1954) *One Man's Vision*, Allen and Unwin, London.

Waddilove, L (1962) *Housing Associations*, PEP, London.

Wadsworth, J (1995a) The changing labour market. Paper presented at the Employment Policy Institute Conference, The 30–30–40 Society, London.

Wadsworth, J (1995b) Mind the gaps? An overview of the changing structure of the UK labour market, paper presented at seminar on Economic Flexibility and Housing, University of Glasgow, September 5–7.

Walentowicz, P (1991) Housing Standards: a survey of space and design standards on new Housing Association projects, NFHA, London.

Walker, R (1994) Putting performance measurement into context: classifying social housing organisations, *Policy and Politics*, Vol. 22, No. 3, pp 191–202.

Walsh, K (1995) *Public Services and Market Mechanisms; Competition, Contracting and the New Public Management*, Macmillan, London.

Welsh Office (1994) *1993 Welsh House Condition Survey*, Welsh Office, Cardiff.

Westaway, P (1994) *The Macro-Economic Implications of Equity Withdrawal Project*, Report to the Joseph Rowntree Foundation, York.

Whitehead, C (1977) Where have all the dwellings gone?, *CES Review*, No 1.

Whitehead, C (1979) Why owner-occupation? *CES Review*. No. 6.

Whitehead, C (1989) Rental housing: radical restructuring, *Public Money*, Spring.

Whitehead, C (1991) From need to affordability: an analysis of UK housing objectives, *Urban Studies* Vol. 28, No. 6.

Whitehead, C (1993) Privatising housing: an assessment of UK experience, *Housing Policy Debate* Vol. 14, No. 1.

Whitehead, C (ed) (1994) *Towards a Viable Private Rented Sector*, LSE Housing, London.

Whitehead, C and Kleinman, M (1986) *Private Rented Housing in the 1980s and 1990s*, Granta Publications, Cambridge.

Whitehead, C and Kleinman, M (1989a) The private rented sector and the Housing Act 1988, in M Brenton and C Ungerson (eds) *Social Policy Review 1988–9*, Longman, Harlow.

Whitehead, C and Kleinman, M (1989b) Demand for new housebuilding 1986–2001, *Development and Planning 1989*, Granta Publications, Cambridge.

Whitehead, C and Kleinman, M (1992) *A Review of Housing Needs Assessments*, The Housing Corporation, London.

Wicks, M (1973) *Rented Housing and Social Ownership*, Fabian Tract 421, Fabian Society, London.

Wilcox, S (1993) *Higher Rents and Work Disincentives*, Joseph Rowntree Foundation Housing Research Findings, 93, Rowntree Foundation, York.

Wilcox, S (1995) *Housing Finance Review 1995/96*, Joseph Rowntree Foundation, York.

Wilcox, S, Bramley, G, Ferguson, A, Perry, J, Woods, C (1993) *Local Housing Companies; New Opportunities for Council Housing*, Joseph Rowntree Foundation, York.

Williams, P (1978) Gentrification in Islington, *Transactions of the Institute of British Geographers*, New Series, Vol. 3.

Willmott, P and Murie, A (1988) *Polarisation and Social Housing*, Policy Studies Institute, London.

Index